Resource Strategies *of* Wild Plants

Resource Strategies
of Wild Plants

Joseph M. Craine

PRINCETON UNIVERSITY PRESS

PRINCETON AND OXFORD

Library of Congress Cataloging-in-Publication Data

Craine, Joseph M., 1973–
    Resource strategies of wild plants / Joseph M. Craine.
        p. cm.
    Includes bibliographical references and index.
    ISBN 978-0-691-13911-1 (hardcover) — ISBN 978-0-691-13912-8 (pbk.)
    1. Plant ecology. I. Title.
    QK901.C76 2009
    581.7—dc22

                                                    2008034503

British Library Cataloging-in-Publication Data is available

This book has been composed in Sabon

press.princeton.edu

10 9 8 7 6 5 4 3 2 1

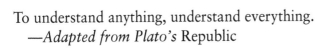

To understand anything, understand everything.
  —*Adapted from Plato's* Republic

I'm like the Platte River—a mile wide and two inches deep.
  —*Dave Wedin*

There is still a lot of good ecology to be done with a shovel.
  —*Terry Chapin*

Contents

Preface

APPROXIMATELY a quarter million terrestrial plants cover the face of Earth today, bequeathed to us by hundreds of millions of years of evolution. To those who try to understand the diversity of life on Earth, a quarter million can seem like a large number, especially in comparison with the numbers of other organisms. For every species of mammal, bird, and reptile on Earth, there are ten species of plants. Over a lifetime, some ornithologically obsessed individuals may just approach having seen every bird in the world. There are only about 10,000 extant bird species. If encountering a new plant species were just as taxing as encountering a new bird, it would take 25 florally obsessed lifetimes to approach having seen all the plants in the world. If it takes 40 years of birding to complete a life list, it would take a millennium to check off all the plants.

Other comparisons can make a quarter million species seem less overwhelming to a botanist. There are almost four times as many species of insects as there are plant species. This doesn't make a quarter million smaller, but it does make a botanist glad to be studying plants and not insects. With a global population of six billion people, there are more than 25 people for every species of plant. Although a botanist could enlist the world's population in botanizing or could take comfort in thinking things could be worse as an entomologist, it has long been the goal of botanists to make the diversity of plant life more manageable for just one person. If the diversity of plants could be collapsed to a few major categories, understanding the diversity of the world's flora would be a less daunting task.

Few topics are as fundamental to research in ecology as categorizing plants and understanding the major axes of variation that define the modern flora. Plant invasions, the responses of ecosystems to global change factors such as elevated carbon dioxide levels and increased temperature, the consequences for plant diversity, plant responses to altered ecosystems, conservation questions such as how to maintain rare and endangered species, and trophic questions such as what regulates herbivore biomass all require a strong foundational understanding of the basic strategies of plants that allow them to grow and reproduce successfully.

Plant strategies also hold a pivotal position at the interface between ecology and evolution. The global research community has invested enormous effort in reconstructing the tree of life. In the not too distant future, the phylogenetic relationships among organisms will largely be reconstructed. Research attention is then expected to turn to identifying the factors that underlie the patterns of radiations observed in the tree.

The fundamental approach to plant strategies adopted in this book reflects two key tenets that define the scientific endeavor. First, there is a strong centrifugal force to scientific progress that leads researchers to ask questions at the frontier of knowledge. Although this centrifugal force focuses research on frontiers (and hopefully not on fringes), working at the edge of knowledge needs to be coupled with a clear grounding in fundamentals. Concentrating on the frontier between ignorance and knowledge would be a perfect approach to science if the first pass through a question led to perfect understanding. Unfortunately, few issues are resolved quickly, and we must continue to take a fresh look at old questions, armed with new knowledge and interpretations. It can be a lot of work to reorganize existing ideas, but no endeavor is more important.

Second, the conduct of scientific investigation requires choosing among competing hypotheses. The scientific method is often held to involve erecting a hypothesis and attempting to falsify it. This approach is a distortion, for there are always alternative hypotheses to explain a given pattern. This book does not put forward one hypothesis about an aspect of plant strategies and recruit support for that idea. Instead, competing hypotheses are presented and then evaluated to see which one better explains observed patterns. In some cases the available evidence favors one hypothesis over another. In other cases we have to live with the uncertainty of not being able to choose among competing hypotheses. This does not mean that all are equally acceptable, only that more work is required.

What follows is an attempt to reorganize parts of scientific understanding centered on a few fundamental questions that have defined the disciplines of ecology and evolutionary biology for more than 150 years. In the course of this attempt, many competing hypotheses are presented and efforts are made to resolve them, if possible. In many ways, it is an endeavor that is better suited to Victorian halls of study than to modern biology departments with their rigorous specialization. The fundamental questions addressed here regarding plant strategies, however, have always been and will always be the ones that define disciplines. And every quarter century the modern pace can slow for a few days and we can step back from the frontiers on which we toil to revisit the roots, if not the very earth, from which current questions grew.

OVERVIEW

The first section of this book, comprising chapters 1 and 2, frames the overarching question of the role of resource availability in structuring natural selection and plant adaptations. Chapter 1 reviews theories of plant strategies and some of the ways in which ecologists have classified plants in the past. Chapter 2 reviews the research of three ecologists that serves as the foundation for the current synthesis. The next section, chapters 3 to 5, sets the stage for understanding major plant strategies by reviewing how resources are supplied to plants, the causes of stress and disturbance in ecosystems, and the mechanisms by which plants compete for the resources. The third section, chapters 6 to 10, lays out the three major plant strategies associated with variation in nutrient supply and disturbance, as well as basic strategies for low water availability and low atmospheric CO_2. Of note, the approach I use in describing the strategies of plants is to categorically define the endpoints of what is certainly a large, multifactorial continuum of strategies used by the world's flora. Chapter 11 provides a broad overview of the selective pressures that have shaped Earth's current flora. I recapitulate the ways in which resource availability and disturbance structure assemblages and the evolutionary responses of plants. I then show how these revised theories of plant strategies can help answer modern ecological questions, such as the effects of global change factors on vegetation and the mechanisms by which plants coexist.

In sum, this book is a synthesis of argument rather than data. With data syntheses, generally all the data that have been collected on a research question are used. With argument syntheses, not all pertinent arguments can be economically incorporated into the synthesis. Instead, key questions, arguments, and research findings are invoked to restructure paradigms. For this reason, not all the research and criticism on the relevant topics has been included here.

Acknowledgments

THIS BOOK originated in a seminar I participated in as an undergraduate at Ohio State University with Ralph Boerner, Peter Curtis, and Allison Snow, comparing the ideas of Philip Grime and David Tilman. Since then, I have had the good fortune of learning from incredible people. Much of the material in this book I learned directly from Terry Chapin, Dave Wedin, Peter Reich, Bill Lee, and William Bond, who have generously shared their knowledge.

Years ago, Dave Tilman and Phil Grime were kind enough to discuss their work with me, which helped lay a solid foundation for understanding the ecology of plants. In writing the book, I benefited greatly from discussions with many other people and am grateful to them for sharing their ideas, in particular David Ackerly on the water relations of plants, Anurag Agrawal on plant defenses, Niels Anten on resource competition, Matt Ayres on defense and herbivory, John Battles on light competition and self-thinning, Dana Blumenthal on plant invasions, Rob Brooker on relative importance, J. C. Cahill on plant competition, Charlie Canham on light dynamics in forests, Lissy Coley on plant defenses, Ed Cushing on plants and their ecology, Mike Cramer on plant ecophysiology, Joe Fargione on plant competition and invasions, Paul Fine on plant defenses, Rachel Gallery on the growth of plants at low light, Uwe Hacke on water relations, Loretta Johnson on ecogenomics, Rick Lindroth on defenses and growth under low CO_2 concentrations, Angela Moles on shade tolerance, David Peart on shade tolerance, Wayne Polley on the growth of plants at low CO_2, Loorens Poorter on understory dynamics, Paco Pugnaire on plant strategies and water relations, Jim Reynolds on water availability to plants, Mark Ritchie on herbivory and defense, Lawren Sack on the growth of plants at low light, Josh Schimel on nitrogen cycling, Susan Schwinning on competition and growth at low water availability, Stephen Simpson on grasshopper feeding, and Ian Wright on plant trait relationships. Matt Ayres, Paul Fine, Paco Pugnaire, and Ross Virginia read all or part of the book in manuscript and provided excellent comments. I am grateful to Peter Ryser for images of root cross sections. Finally, Kendra McLauchlan has long been a great partner and colleague with whom to keep exploring over the next hill.

Abbreviations

ABA	abscisic acid
A_{max}	maximum rate of photosynthesis
ANOVA	analysis of variance
ANPP	aboveground net primary productivity
C_{min}	minimum concentration
BCM	Bloom, Chapin, and Mooney
CAM	crassulacean acid metabolism
K_m	half-saturation constant
LAI	leaf area index
LCP	leaf-level light compensation point
LCP_{wp}	whole-plant light compensation point
LMA	leaf mass area
LUE	light use efficiency
LUE_{acq}	light use efficiency of acquired light
MAP	mean annual precipitation
LWR	leaf weight ratio
NPP	net primary productivity
NUE	nutrient use efficiency
NUE_{acq}	nutrient use efficiency of acquired nutrients
$R*$	minimum concentration of nutrients in a solution at which a population can sustain itself
RCI	relative competitive index
RII	relative interaction intensity
RGR	relative growth rate
RGR_{max}	maximum relative growth rate
RWR	root weight ratio
SLA	specific leaf area
SRL	specific root length
WUE	water use efficiency
V_{max}	maximum uptake rate

Resource Strategies *of* Wild Plants

CHAPTER 1

The Basis for Plant Strategies

By BEST ESTIMATES, the past 325 million years of evolution have left us with approximately 250,000 species of seed-producing plants in the world today (Thorne 1992). The number of extant seed plants can be considered either large or small, depending on the context and one's perspective. The question of concern in this book, however, is not the overall number per se but the patterns of one of the most important evolutionary radiations in the history of Earth, and the forces that drove the radiation in those patterns.

The quarter million plant species on Earth today occupy an immensely diverse set of environmental conditions. Some plants have evolved to endure air temperatures as low as −80 °C and others to exist in soil temperatures as high as 70 °C. Plants may grow to 100 m for light and send their roots as deep as 60 m for water (Schulze et al. 1998). Plants grow in soils devoid of oxygen and in soils with levels of heavy metals that cause most plants to curl up and die. Somehow, the quarter million plant species are able to grow and reproduce even as they fend off attacks from everything from viruses to weevils to rhinoceroses.

Although processes such as vicariance and drift are responsible for some of the differences among plant species, it is natural selection that has shaped much of the modern flora. With natural selection, differences in the characteristics of the individuals lead to differential reproductive success in the face of environmental factors that can restrict growth. For example, a plant with the potential to develop deep roots would have had an advantage over a plant with shallow roots in a dry environment where water was present at depth. Deep roots allow greater water acquisition, which in turn leads to greater acquisition of other resources and eventually greater production of seeds. In a Malthusian world, not all individuals survive. Over long time scales, it is the characteristics of individuals that separate the survival of the fit from the death of the rest.

ASSESSING NATURAL SELECTION

The continued generation of novel characteristics and differential reproduction mediated by a plant's traits and the environment progressively shape lineages. A trait is a heritable characteristic of a plant. Some traits are directly important in the reproduction of plants (reproductive trait), such as flower color or seed size. Other traits are important for the vegetative growth of plants (functional or resource traits), such as types of light-acquiring pigments in a leaf or the depth to which plants can produce roots. Violle et al. (2007, p. 882) define functional traits as "morpho-physio-phenological traits which impact fitness indirectly via their effects on growth, reproduction, and survival." This definition seems to cover what aspects of plants are considered traits and what makes them functional. Other traits can be heritable but have no known importance in the vegetative growth or reproduction of plants. These are considered nonfunctional traits, and although they are often useful for understanding past environments or reconstructing phylogenetic relationships, they are not of interest here. Both reproductive and vegetative traits can be *quantitative* if variation in the trait among plants is discrete. For example, flowers can be yellow or red, stems can have thorns or not. Traits can also be *qualitative* if they vary continuously among plants, such as the intensity of a given color in a flower or the length of thorns on plants' stems.

Natural selection operates to change the frequency of genes in a population and, over long time scales, works in concert with processes such as mutation that generate new genes. Any given plant today might have on the order of 50,000 coding genes (Tuskan et al. 2006). Many of these genes are common to all life, while a smaller subset is common to the quarter million seed plants. It is this subset of genes that separates plants from other organisms. How many of these genes are unique to all plants and how many are responsible for the floral diversity of the world are questions without good answers. The genomes of different plant species are only just beginning to be compared. For example, a comparison of the genomes of *Arabidopsis thaliana* and *Populus nigra* revealed approximately 2,300 genes that were unique to *Arabidopsis* and approximately 5,200 that were unique to *Populus* (Tuskan et al. 2006). From analyzing the genomes of just these two species, a comparison of the effects of natural selection on different species could involve the products of tens of thousands of genes. Although how many traits and which traits are analyzed are both important, whether those traits are the product of ten genes or 10,000 genes has little bearing on the approach to understanding plant traits.

Uniformitarian Principles for Natural Selection

Characterizing the natural selection that produced the modern flora relies on uniformitarian principles. The processes that shaped the modern world are assumed to have shaped past worlds. Although the relative importance of different factors is not assumed to have remained constant, physical laws, whether those governing the diffusion of nutrients in soil solutions or those behind the tension that arises in a water column as leaves are placed farther from the ground, have been constant throughout the evolutionary history of any species. It is also assumed that plants' struggle for existence has been shaped by a small number of major selective agents throughout their evolutionary history. Put simply, there are only so many basic reasons why plants die before reproducing.

Although it would seem straightforward to assess the contemporary manifestations of natural selection, understanding the growth and reproduction of plants in the modern world remains a challenge. Growth is the process by which plants accumulate resources from the environment and then use those resources to generate structures. Vegetative growth is defined as the construction of novel structures associated with the acquisition of resources. Reproduction is the production of structures that are associated not with the acquisition of resources but with the production of new individuals. Vegetative reproduction would seem to sit squarely between the two, but it is more akin to vegetative growth than to sexual reproduction. Along these lines, some traits directly affect both growth and reproduction, such as the production of stems that hold up flowers and leaves.

Much of this book focuses on forging a better understanding of natural selection by characterizing the growth of plants in environments of limited resource availability. At the outset, it should be noted that the details of how plants acquire and allocate scarce resources such as nutrients and reduced carbon are still being learned. For example, when Charles Darwin planted seedlings in his Down House lawn, he observed that many soon perished. Yet Darwin was unable to discern whether seedlings died as a result of acquiring too little water or because neighboring plants reduced nutrient availability below some minimum threshold required to persist. Even the observation that some of the seedlings' leaves were consumed by garden snails does not answer whether this would have happened had more resources been available to the plants. Would a better defended plant have been able to resist herbivory and survive to produce the next generation of weeds in Darwin's lawn? Did competition among the seedlings for scarce resources cause the seedling to be more susceptible to the herbivore?

Observing death is far removed from understanding the proximal and distal reasons why plants die. Even if the modern relationships between the characteristics of plants and the probability that agents kill some plants could be quantified perfectly, this perfect knowledge would be insufficient to characterize the mechanisms that produced the modern flora, for two main reasons. First, modern selective agents act on the product of past selection. The factors that mold plants today might not be the same as the factors that molded them in the past. Two plant species may exist side by side in a given habitat with minimum effect on each other, but their minimal interaction comes as a result of competition between their ancestors (Connell 1980). Second, some selective agents no longer exist today, and the relative importance of the ones that remain is different from what it was in the past. An observer of the modern world standing beneath an osage orange tree (*Maclura pomifera*) might have difficulty deducing the benefit of producing the cannonball-size fruits that litter the ground. Unlike 12,000 years ago, mastodons no longer pass under these trees to collect the fallen fruit. Although uniformitarianism is an important component of understanding the processes that produced the modern flora, it has its limits.

Characterizing Natural Selection from the Patterns Left Behind

If the forces of natural selection that shaped the modern flora cannot be characterized solely from an analysis of modern species and environments, what hope is there to better characterize past natural selection? For an analogy, imagine attempting to deduce that continental-scale glaciers thousands of meters thick once covered much of North America by watching snow fall on a winter's day. One could inquire into the consequences of more snow falling than melting for a few thousand years. Yet it would be hard to start from first principles while staring out a window and arrive at an ice sheet like the one that covers Greenland. Could one eventually imagine enough ice covering North America to depress the continental crust into the mantle? Would one arrive at the idea that the mass of the ice caused it to flow like molasses, carving out valleys and depositing ridges of ground-up rock hundreds of meters high at its terminus?

As the example of the Ice Age glaciers suggests, characterizing natural selection requires constraining uniformitarian principles with the patterns the processes left behind. For the continental glaciers, the processes involved in snow accumulation and the observed movement of smaller glaciers are used to interpret the moraines, drumlin fields, and kettle lakes that the glaciers left behind during previous glacial cycles. For natural selection, the modern ecology of plants must be observed, but also the analogs of glacial features.

Just as glaciers pushed boulders well beyond the source bedrock, natural selection has pushed the traits of species outward. The patterns that natural selection left behind are the traits encoded in the genomes of different species. As such, the 100-m trunks of redwood and eucalyptus should be as informative of past processes as a 100-m ridge of till lying across the landscape. Although individual traits are compared among species at a time, natural selection operates on hundreds of traits over time, as evidenced by the analysis of the genomes of *Arabidopsis* and *Populus*. Even though the focus broadens to include a diverse number of traits, it is instructive to consider how to compare individual traits among species before moving on to more complicated analyses of multiple traits.

FROM SINGLE TRAITS TO MULTITRAIT STRATEGIES

In 1837, Darwin presented John Gould with birds he had collected from the Galápagos Islands (Quammen 2006). On first examination, these birds were as different as the blackbirds, "gross-beaks," and finches of England, but Gould soon informed Darwin that they were all finches. The large ground finch (*Geospiza magnirostris*) had a large beak and the warbler finch (*Certhidea olivacea*) had a small beak. Likely all the finches were derived from a common ancestor and had radiated to fill different niches on the islands. Although Darwin never mentions the finches in the *Origin of Species*, the diversity of beak morphology among the finch species became a fundamental lesson for Darwin in his theory of evolution by natural selection. Even though the finch beaks represent a set of tightly connected traits (shape, depth, length, attached muscles), Darwin's finches are an excellent example of the radiation of what can be considered an individual trait.

In contrast to the focus on changes in individual traits, the overwhelming pattern left behind by natural selection is one of coordinated changes in multiple traits. Although the beaks of the finches are foundational examples of adaptive radiation of individual traits, the finches have evolved strategies that exceed a single trait. A key principle to remember in examining the traits of plants is that natural selection does not operate on individual traits. Natural selection is a result of the differential reproductive success of individuals. Natural selection by and large operates on whole organisms, and reproductive success depends on more than a single trait. These unique sets of traits, shaped by natural selection, are considered to represent strategies for successfully growing and reproducing in a given environment. Or, to frame the situation in the negative, trait sets are strategies for not dying before reproducing.

Philip Grime has defined strategies as "groupings of similar or analogous genetic characteristics which recur widely among species or populations and cause them to exhibit similarities in ecology" (Grime 2001, p. xix). This definition is not a bad start, but there are important questions to address regarding whether the trait sets need to have evolved multiple times to be considered a strategy. Moreover, the phrase "similarities in ecology" is vague. For example, most tropical plants die in a similar manner when exposed to freezing temperatures, but disruption of cell membranes and xylem cavitation are not part of a strategy. The definition of strategy must reflect (1) the importance of multiple traits over single traits, (2) the patterns of traits emerging as a result of natural selection, and (3) the identification of trait sets with successful growth in a given environment or set of environmental conditions. Therefore, a better definition of a plant strategy is *a set of interlinked adaptations that arose as a consequence of natural selection and that promotes growth and successful reproduction in a given environment.*

To illustrate the transition from assessing traits to strategies, it is informative to revisit Darwin's finches. In the 170 years since Darwin first collected them, more has been learned about other aspects of finches that allows beaks to be examined in a broader array of traits of the whole organism as shaped by natural selection. For example, for some finches, changes in beak morphology have been linked to changes in foot morphology (Grant and Weiner 1999). There is no necessary genetic linkage among these traits; rather, the linkages are likely a result of natural selection at the whole-organism level selecting for both altered beak and foot morphology. Ground finches scratch the soil in search of seeds. To go with their large beaks, which are used to crush large seeds, they have a longer hallux (hind toe and claw) than other finches.

Differences in beaks have also been linked to changes in internal organs, a logical conjunction when we consider the ecology of the species. For example, vegetarian finches eat low-quality leaves and buds. To access these foods, they have a large beak that operates like gripping pliers. These food types are low in available energy, and the internal organs of vegetarian finches have also changed to reflect the low-energy diet. To go with the large beak, the finches have also undergone selection for larger gizzards that grind the material better, allowing more energy to be extracted. And they have smaller hearts, most likely associated with the lower metabolic rate common in animals that feed on low-energy foods, such as sloths and koala.

The goal in understanding plants is similar to the analysis for the finches: to understand the patterns of differences in multiple, ecologically significant traits among plant species. Natural selection is not limited to a single level of organization but acts on plant biochemistry, the structure of tissues, the organization of tissues into organs, and the effects of plants on their environment.

Natural selection has shaped a broad array of plant traits, and a multilevel approach has a history as long as ecology. For example, Eugenius Warming in his 1909 book, *The Oecology of Plants*, described the adaptations of plants to dry conditions. Even a hundred years ago, his analysis covered chemical compounds such as the group of pigments known as anthocyanins, specialized cells such as epidermal hairs, tissues such as the leaf palisade, the morphology of entire leaves, and the arrangement of leaves in a canopy. As evidenced by Warming's analysis, mere survival and reproduction in a given environment are complicated endeavors. Plants must acquire a multitude of resources while resisting or responding to a variety of agents of disturbance and stress. If plant species have been selected to differentially succeed under different environmental conditions, then natural selection likely has coordinated the adaptations of roots, leaves, and support structures so that individual plants can successfully acquire and allocate limiting resources to successfully grow and reproduce in that environment, given the typical patterns of resource availability in that environment and other factors that reduce growth.

Broadly, traits can be divided into those that are important for the vegetative growth of plants and those that are associated with reproduction. It is true that resources must be allocated for an individual to reproduce, and understanding the resource strategies of plants cannot be divorced from understanding reproduction. For example, approximately 10% of the nitrogen that pine trees acquire during a year can be allocated to pollen production alone (Lee and Booth 2003). The reproductive traits of plants can determine patterns of resource acquisition. For example, the resources stored in a large seed are important because they allow some plants to project their leaves through litter and past other plants to access sunlight.

Although the growth and reproductive traits go hand in hand when one considers individual survival and evolution of the species, in 1909 Warming drew a distinction between reproductive and resource strategies:

> The vegetative shoot adapts itself to the conditions prevailing in regard to its nutrition; but the flower follows other laws, other aims, and particularly adopts very diverse methods of pollination. In the morphology and anatomy of the vegetative shoot are reflected the climatic and assimilating conditions; whereas floral structure is scarcely or not at all influenced by climate, but preserves the impress of phyletic origin under very different conditions of life. (Warming 1909, p. 4)

Reproduction is assuredly a critical phase in the life cycle of plants and under strong natural selection. In this book, however, I shall contribute to the long history of separation by focusing on vegetative traits. Trait sets and associated strategies for using resources are a complex enough subject to warrant an exclusive treatment. Eventually, vegetative strategies and regeneration strategies should be examined together (Grime 1979, 2001), as there is evidence they are not completely orthogonal (Lambrecht and Dawson 2007).

QUANTIFYING PLANT TRAITS AND STRATEGIES

In beginning to assess plant strategies, it is important to consider why different strategies exist at all. Why isn't there just one set of traits that allows one plant to dominate the entire world? This is a well-worn line of questioning (MacArthur and Wilson 1967; Tilman 1988). The simple answer is that traits that lead to success in one environment do not lead to success in another environment. There are trade-offs among traits such that the presence of a trait favorable in one environment precludes having a different trait that might be favorable in a different environment. The traits that allow a tree to grow tall might preclude it from growing well in other environments, such as a closely grazed grassland. If this is so, why are there not plants with the ability to be short or tall, depending on the environment? Even if a given plant had the potential to generate any combination of traits, it is a stochastic world. Perfect adjustment requires perfect knowledge of the future, and death can come swiftly, with little opportunity to adjust. There are also likely costs to certain degrees or types of plasticity that favor less plastic species. Although plasticity of traits is important to plant strategies, one should look elsewhere for worldviews centered on the plasticity of traits (e.g., Grubb 1998).

Quantifying Plant Traits

To identify the strategies of plants, the traits of different species must be compared. Much as with Darwin's finches, traits are measured for a set of species and then compared across species. It is not easy to quantify many of the traits of species. The genetic basis of traits is independent of the environment in which the traits are assessed, but many traits vary with environmental conditions. The maximum height of a tree is likely to be greater when it is well watered than when it is insufficiently watered. Insofar as environmental conditions can affect the expression of traits, it is not straightforward to ascertain under what conditions the height of different trees can be meaningfully measured. To understand the role of tree height in strategies for ecosystems where water is plentiful, it might be appropriate to measure the height of well-watered trees. Alternatively, measuring the height of poorly watered trees might better advance an understanding of strategies in ecosystems where water is scarce. Plants also alter their environments in ways that preclude a clean separation of the influence of genes and environment when comparing species. Species that differ in water usage, for example, make it difficult to determine whether there are inherent interspecies trait differences or whether one species dries out the soil more than another, causing it to respond to water stress.

Quantifying Plant Strategies

If we put to one side the question of what set of environmental conditions plants should be grown in to assess their traits, the process of quantifying plant strategies is more than compiling lists of traits. As Grime (1993) detailed, quantifying plant strategies is an iterative process that bounces back and forth between assessment of traits and assessment of performance in different environments. Differences in environments can occur as a result of natural contrasts or through manipulation, while the traits that are assessed come from theoretical or conceptual models of the relationship between traits and performance in an environment.

A typical progression of research might be to first identify differences in the relative abundance of species along a natural environmental contrast, followed by the generation of competing hypotheses about the mechanisms that lead to differences in performance. Key traits are then assessed for the target plant species and their ability to predict abundance along the environmental contrast is tested, the researcher working within the initial model of plant function in the environment. This approach often leaves us with competing hypotheses, for reasons detailed in this book. As examples, traits are not easy to measure, and genes and environment cannot always be separated completely. There are also competing hypotheses about what factors structure assemblages in different environments, and it is not always clear what traits should be tested in determining a plant's strategy.

RANKING STRATEGIES

Let us assume for now that it is simple to compile a number of traits for a number of species. Each species has its own unique set of traits, but does that mean that each species has its own strategy? How are general strategies identified? When faced with as many unique combinations of traits as there are species, how does one progress from individual examples to broad patterns? In part, this is a statistical question, but statistical approaches rely on concepts of how to compare and aggregate sets of traits. If we assume for now that strategies can be generalized, a more pressing question arises. How are strategies ranked in importance, and how can minor and major strategies be separated?

Considering Phylogeny When Ranking Strategies

In beginning to examine plant strategies, unless one considers all strategies to be equally important, some separation of the importance of different strategies is essential. One approach to ranking strategies is to base the importance of a strategy on the phylogenetic relationships of species. For example, the most basic separations of strategies might have arisen first, with later divergences representing a progressive refinement of the basic strategies. In this case, the most basal divergences of taxa might relate to basal divergences in strategies. For example, angiosperms diverged from gymnosperms approximately 140 million years ago. Might not the differences between angiosperms and gymnosperms represent two basic strategies?

Unfortunately, the phylogenetic tree of plants does not necessarily reconstruct divergence of resource strategies. Processes that are associated with divergence can be independent of resource strategies. For example, lineages can become reproductively isolated from one another without any change in the fundamental resource strategy. Much of radiation could be due to novel reproductive strategies, and not directly related to resource strategies. For example, although angiosperms and gymnosperms differ in how xylem tracheids are connected, angiosperms can also be separated from gymnosperms by the process of double fertilization in producing seeds. As opposed to more ancient lineages of dicotyledonous plants, eudicots—roses and asters—are characterized by triaperturate pollen (Soltis and Soltis 2003), which likely has little effect on resource strategies but is also likely be strongly conserved. Lineages can also differ in certain traits, but the trait divergence does not necessarily have to represent a fundamentally new strategy. For example, the sister taxon of all angiosperms, *Illicium*, the star anise tree, does not appear to exhibit a clearly recognizable difference in basic resource strategies relative to those of all other angiosperms. Although species of the genus have some unique organic compounds in their leaves and fruits, any differences in other traits are not obvious, and there is no evidence that the unique compounds form part of a major strategy, at least in the modern world.

Alternatively, the relative importance of strategies might best be assessed not by examining the oldest divergences but by counting the number of times that a given strategy has arisen or the number of species that possess the strategy. A strategy that evolved once might be important, but one that evolved multiple times is likely to be more important. A strategy held by just one species is probably less important than one held by thousands. For example, the C_4 photosynthetic pathway has arisen more than 45 times, and more than 7,000 species are known to have the C_4 photosynthetic pathway (Sage 2004). However, ranking strategies in this manner has its own problems. Although a given trait set evolving multiple times seems like good circumstantial evidence of the importance of a strategy, it is not a perfect quantitative metric of importance. A given strategy might entail changes in multiple genes, with odds being low that the changes happened twice, and the strategy probably evolved just once. That a strategy evolved just once is a poor reason to consider it less important. Similarly, a given trait held by a large number of species might reflect the presence of another factor that has affected the speciation rate, and its appearance in multiple species does not mean that the strategy is more important than one associated with fewer species.

Considering Modern Ecology When Ranking Strategies

It is useful to understand when a strategy first arose, how many times it arose, and how many species hold the strategy currently. Phylogeny alone is insufficient to assess the relative importance of strategies. Strategies are by definition approaches to successful growth and reproduction in the face of ecological forces that render other approaches less successful. Assessing that a given trait set forms part of a strategy requires understanding the contribution of the trait set to ecological performance. Similarly, assessing the relative importance of different strategies requires assessing ecological performance. Unfortunately, assessing the relative importance of strategies cannot be separated from making arbitrary choices about the importance of different environments.

Assessing the relative importance of strategies would entail determining the relative importance of different environmental factors in natural selection. The unfit have many reasons for failing to survive. Some individuals might have been unable to acquire resources that were in short supply and ended up with too little light, water, nutrients, or carbon to reproduce. Others might not have been able to withstand the presence of herbivores or disease agents. Some plants perish as a result of extreme heat or cold, soil flooding or drought, fire or wind. Can the relative importance of these environmental factors in determining the abundance and distribution of species be ranked in advance as a way of erecting parallel strategies?

To some degree, ecological factors *can* be ranked. For example, a few species have adapted to a high soil availability of heavy metals, such as zinc or magnesium. These habitats are relatively rare but common enough that some species are adapted to grow on them. Yet it is not hard to argue that strategies for dealing with a high availability of heavy metals are less important than strategies for dealing with low water availability, which occurs more frequently in space and time. This raises a further question: should the relative importance of a strategy be scaled by the surface area over which it is important?

Even if the relative importance of different environmental factors on the modern planet could be ranked, this ranking would not necessarily correspond to the evolutionary history of plants, for it would identify modern strategies but might miss evolutionarily important ones. For example, ancient environments were generally warmer and wetter than today's environments, with higher CO_2 availability and lower nitrogen availability. Atmospheric CO_2 was generally two to five times higher for most of the past 300 million years than during the Pleistocene era (the past 1.8 million years) (see chapter 10). Likewise, the N_2-fixing symbiosis of legumes evolved only relatively recently (about 60 MYA) (Sprent 2007). With high CO_2 concentrations and the lack of N_2 fixation from legumes, ancient environments might have had lower nitrogen availability than modern environments. Deserts and extensive dry habitats were largely absent for most of the evolutionary history of plants and did not arise until continental uplift of mountain regions such as the Himalayas and American cordillera cut off moisture to vast areas, and decreased global temperatures reduced evaporation from oceans. Our cold, dry world of relatively low CO_2 levels and high nitrogen availability is likely much different from the worlds in which most of the modern flora evolved.

The Need for Arbitrary Elevation of Strategies

At this point, there seems to be no pure path to assessing the relative importance of strategies. Relying on phylogeny alone does not allow assessment of whether a particular set of traits is or was ecologically important. Furthermore, this approach is subject to the limited resolution of phylogenetic relationships among plant species. Relying on ecological gradients to guide rankings forces arbitrary assessments of the relative importance of different ecological gradients, including environments for which no modern analog might exist. Putting phylogeny and ecology together might improve the situation, but this approach does not eliminate their individual deficiencies.

At this point, arbitrary decisions on the rankings of factors are necessary. For resources, it is important to develop the strategies associated with growing successfully in environments where there is low availability of each of the major plant resources: nutrients (mainly nitrogen and phosphorus), light, water, and CO_2. Most of the discussion on strategies for low resource availability is concerned with nutrients and light. Less is known about strategies that have arisen as a consequence of low water availability or low CO_2, making it difficult to delineate the strategies associated with these environments. In addition to the strategies associated with low availability of specific resources, strategies associated with environments with high water, nutrient, and light availability are also important to include, and these environments occur only when plants have recently been damaged severely. For the reasons stated above, it is unhelpful to rank strategies associated with each resource, even though they may be important strategies. This book pays more attention to nutrients and light than to water or CO_2 for the simple reason that strategies associated with low availability of light and nutrients are better understood than strategies associated with low availability of water and CO_2.

With the resources of interest for analyzing strategies selected and the basic comparative approach outlined in this chapter, the next chapter reviews the foundations of plant strategy theory and the approaches that have been taken to understanding resource strategies, before moving on to the specific components of strategies. Some of the history of research on plant strategies is reviewed first, including the work of three modern ecologists that have contributed the most to understanding plant strategies. Some of the key components that form the foundation of the strategies are identified, and the competing hypotheses that need to be addressed as part of this process are introduced and evaluated.

SYNTHESIS

A first step in characterizing the major patterns of natural selection that generated the current flora of a quarter million species of seed plants entails comparing the traits of species and the characteristics of different habitats, and assessing how plants grow in different environments. Traits are defined as heritable characteristics of plants. Most of the analyses of natural selection have focused on individual traits, such as the beaks of Darwin's finches. Natural selection, however, operates at the level of the organism and coordinates multiple traits at many levels of organization. Darwin's finches differed in more than just their beaks.

Plant strategies are sets of traits that lead to successful growth and reproduction in a particular environment. More formally, strategies may be defined as a set of interlinked adaptations that arose as a consequence of natural selection and that promote growth and successful reproduction in a given environment. Strategies are assessed by examining the patterns of traits among species and assessing the relationship between sets of traits and plant performance in different environments. The traits associated with plant resource strategies are important for the vegetative growth of individual plants and determine the acquisition, allocation, and loss of resources that support successful growth under a particular set of environmental conditions. These traits range from the biochemistry of cells to tissue construction to plant effects on the abiotic environment. Reproductive strategies are not necessarily independent of resource strategies, but are not covered here.

Although phylogenetic issues should be considered when assessing the relative importance of plant strategies, phylogenetic reconstructions are not sufficient to assess the relative importance of strategies. The age of a particular divergence of two lineages does not necessarily correlate with the relative importance of any differences in their strategies. Likewise, the number of times a particular set of traits has arisen or the number of species that hold it is not sufficient for ranking different strategies. Neither is an analysis of the modern ecology of species, such as species' performances in modern environments, sufficient to rank strategies. The importance of factors in the selection of plants might not scale with their importance weighted by land area. The relative importance of factors in any one habitat is influenced by past selection and cannot be used alone to rank strategies.

If a given strategy is to be elevated over another, one should be clear about the criteria used to rank the strategies. At this time, there is no recourse but to arbitrarily elevate some factors over others, and therefore to elevate some strategies, too. In later chapters the strategies for success in environments with low availability of nutrients, light, water, and CO_2 are examined, as well as strategies for success in disturbed environments with high availability of nutrients, light, and water.

CHAPTER 2

The History of Plant Strategies

THIS CHAPTER reviews the origins of modern concepts of plant strategy as a prelude to laying the foundation for a new synthesis of resource strategies in the next chapter. The three ecologists who have contributed the most to modern plant strategy theory are Philip Grime, Terry Chapin, and David Tilman. For the purposes of understanding extant theories, it would be better to review their work after a formal analysis of terms, yet the upcoming synthesis of plant strategies rests firmly on the foundations laid by previous ecologists. The theories of Grime, Chapin, and Tilman are not critiqued in this chapter; only their research is reviewed up to the near present so that readers not familiar with the general arguments can begin to understand the tenor of the debates.

NUTRIENTS AND THE HISTORY OF PLANT STRATEGIES

A large component of the modern foundation of plant strategies is constituted by theories about the role of nutrients in plant growth and the performance and evolutionary consequences of a nutrient supply that falls below the demand of plants. Although nutrients are of central importance to modern plant strategy theory, they have not always been an integral part of the theories. Before we review the modern foundation, it is important to understand when nutrients were first recognized as a significant component of plant strategies and the subsequent development of theories about the roles of nutrients in plant strategies over the past 30 years.

Terry Chapin's "The Mineral Nutrition of Wild Plants," published in 1980, was a landmark paper. For many ecologists, it defined a major pattern in plant evolution and shaped thinking on the function of ecosystems. The paper differentiated the traits of crop plants and weedy plants (ruderals) from wild plants—those plants that have not been domesticated and are not adapted to a high-nutrient regime and high-disturbance environments. Unlike crops and weedy plants, wild plants were defined by Chapin as adapted to grow in soils with low nutrient availability. In contrast to fertile agricultural fields, rich in nutrients, the soils in which wild plants grow are infertile and poor in nutrients. Crop plants and ruderals have been selected to grow when nutrients are abundant. Wild plants have been selected to succeed when nutrients are scarce. Although in this book, all plants that have not undergone artificial selection are considered wild, Chapin was conjuring up just a small subset of wild plants when he analyzed the strategies of plants from low-nutrient habitats.

It is telling that arguably the most important paper published on plant strategies in 1980 focused on nutrients. Few articles in ecology have been cited more than this one, and in the more than 25 years since its publication, nutrients have played a central role in explanations of the strategies of plants. In contrast to the recent focus on nutrients, plant ecologists initially considered nutrients to be a minor component in explaining the traits of plants or their distribution and abundance. Sometime before 1980, a major shift occurred in the thinking of ecologists.

Early Plant Strategies

Ecologists in need of a historical perspective on evolutionary or ecological issues generally turn to Darwin. But Darwin is not the best person to consult to understand plant adaptations. Little is said about plants in the *Origin of Species*. It is true that after completing the *Origin of Species*, Darwin went on to write three books about plants, but they were primarily concerned with movement, sex, and carnivory. For Darwin, plants were not that different from sessile animals, much like the barnacles he studied for many years.

Instead of London and Darwin, a reader interested in tracing modern plant ecology in North America to its beginnings would start in Chicago with Henry Cowles (pronounced "coals"). Cowles would later join the faculty of the University of Chicago and become a pivotal figure in North American ecology as a teacher and adviser, and through his service to the ecological community. For example, Cowles helped create the Ecological Society of America in 1915 and served as its president a few years later. When Cowles started his doctoral studies in 1895, his adviser introduced him to the ideas of Eugenius Warming. Warming, a professor in Copenhagen, had published a book titled *Plantesamfund*, which had not been translated into English when Cowles's adviser referred to it. Cowles was so excited about Warming's ideas that he learned Danish to read the book. Cowles would later apply Warming's ideas to interpreting succession at a site on the dune shores of Lake Michigan, a short train ride east of Chicago. The paper that resulted from his dissertation, "The Ecological Relations of the Vegetation on the Sand Dunes of Lake Michigan" (Cowles 1898), is considered a classic in plant community ecology for its characterization of succession and its use of chronosequences.

Reading the 1909 English edition of Warming's book, *Oecology of Plants*, it is not hard to imagine what it must have been like for an impressionable student at the dawn of a new science to slowly decipher an attempt to describe the vegetation of the world. Warming lays the groundwork for the modern state factor approach to ecology, describing the ecological factors that affect plants, such as light, heat, water, and temperature. He discusses interactions among organisms, such as competition and symbioses. Another section covers the adaptations of plants, while others describe the vegetation communities of the world. Descriptions follow of a global survey of vegetation types of the world, from the Brazilian *Caa-tinga* to the Hungarian *pusztas*. For a modern plant ecologist, this is the equivalent of reading Darwin's *Origin of Species*. For all intents and purposes, this is where the modern quest to understand the forces that shape the world's vegetation began.

In describing the vegetation of the world, Warming reviewed attempts to classify plants according to their functional traits. These categorizations represent the first attempts to rank the factors involved in natural selection. Warming wrote, "Just as species are the units in systematic botany, so are growth-forms the units in oecological botany. It is therefore of some practical importance to test the possibility of founding and naming a limited number of growth-forms upon true oecological principles" (Warming 1909, p. 5).

Since the time of Alexander von Humboldt in the early 1800s, plant geographers have attempted to classify plants based on the traits that relate to their performance in a given environment, as opposed to their reproductive traits. European botanists would get on a ship and sail for some faraway land, collecting plants at lands they touched on. Parts of plants from forests, grasslands, and deserts, islands and continents, mountains and valleys would make their way to the botanist's press. Warming observed that when the travelers returned home, they would sort the species into functional categories differently, and it was quite a struggle to have piles with more than one species.

According to Warming, Humboldt piled his plants primarily into 19 categories that included palms, bananas, grasses, and ferns, which, as Warming correctly noted, mixed systematics and function. Later reshufflings of specimens attempted to group them by function. Griselbach established 60 functional piles for the world's plants, but admitted that more were likely. For northern Europe alone, Warming had 15 piles, with lots of subordinant piles. Roscoe Pound and Frederic Clements, Christen Raunkiær, and E.H.L. Krause all reshuffled the piles at different times, focusing on some different aspect they felt was most important for determining the functional groups. At the time Warming wrote his *Oecology of Plants*, there was little coherence to the sorting strategies of different phytogeographers.

Yet when botanists of today are pressed to rank environmental conditions in their importance for community assembly, it is clear from reading Warming and other geographers of the time such as Andreas Schimper that even a hundred years ago, the paramount environmental factor controlling plant distribution and plant form was considered to be water. Concerning the importance of water, Warming wrote:

> [N]o other influence impresses its mark to such a degree upon the internal and external structures of the plant as does the amount of water present in the air and soil (or medium), and that no other influence calls forth such great and striking differences in the vegetation as do differences in the supply of water.

If the world were binary, Warming's words would imply that plants were built to succeed either in the wet or in the dry. Plant assemblages were primarily distinguished based on water. There were deserts and there were rain forests. "The oecological importance of water to the plant is fundamental, and almost surpasses that of light or heat," Warming wrote (1909, p. 28).

In addition to water, Warming covered the influence of other environmental factors that affect plants. Of these, nutrients are discussed, but by no means does one get the impression that the relative availability of different nutrients was a central factor in categorizing the flora of the world. Warming mentions the differences between "rich" and "poor" soils and understood that nutrients could be limiting to growth. Yet, when Warming discusses nutrients, one does not get the impression that he felt that the low availability of nutrients was a major structuring factor for vegetation. From his descriptions, it seems he felt the soil's physical properties, such as particle size (e.g., how sandy the soils were), were the most important aspect of the soils, largely since particle size was associated with water availability. If nutrients were important, it was only when they were in excess. Soils might have too much zinc (calamine soils), magnesium (serpentine soils), calcium (soils dominated by calcicolous or dolomite plants), "salt" (halophilous plants), or silica (silicicolous), selecting for the rare plant that could tolerate the excess nutrients. Nitrogen is discussed, too, but in a similar manner to the other elements that might occasionally be in excess. Excessive nitrogen was considered poisonous, and "nitrophilous" plants were the ones that could tolerate high nitrate availability.

It is simplistic to state that there are just different approaches to ecology and that Warming focused on water while Terry Chapin, some 70 years later, focused on nutrients. Chapin is the academic great-great-great-grandson of Cowles. Warming's approach has been passed down from one academic generation to the next. Cowles's more noted student was

William Cooper, who studied plant communities from Isle Royale in Lake Superior to Glacier Bay, Alaska, which Chapin would in turn study many years later. Like Cowles, Cooper published little, and it is difficult to surmise his thoughts on what structured plant communities directly. Yet Cooper had many students who were influential in North American plant ecology, and none of the students proposed nutrients as a central structuring factor. For three generations after Cooper, there is little mention of nutrients. Cooper's students included Henry Oosting, who investigated succession in the southeastern United States. One of Oosting's students, Dwight Billings, served as adviser to Hal Mooney, who was Chapin's adviser. Oosting in *The Study of Plant Communities*, Billings in *Man and the Ecosystem*, and Chapin (with Mooney) in *Principles of Terrestrial Ecosystem Ecology* are essentially just updating Warming's *Oecology of Plants*, almost down to the chapter titles. In this lineage of thought, until Chapin, there is little indication of an approach in which the scarcity of nutrients was proposed as a major selective agent on plants.

Sometime between Warming and Chapin, something happened to elevate the importance of low nutrient availability for plant strategies. Between 1909 and 1980 a paradigm shift occurred, a new way to look at the world. A new idea was injected into the fundamental understanding of plants that was not present in the works of Chapin's adviser or anyone in his academic lineage. The research that first injected nutrients into plant strategies was pivotal to creating the modern foundations of the science. Although ideological events are difficult to pinpoint, it is fair to say that it was Philip Grime who first added low availability of nutrients to the recipe for natural selection.

GRIME

In 1979, Grime published his book, *Plant Strategies and Vegetation*. Like Warming's book, Grime's is a bold attempt to characterize the major plant strategies of the world. The most influential part of this book is a triangle in which Grime places the plant species and habitats surrounding Sheffield, England (figure 2.1). No other idea has had more of an effect on ecologists' thinking about classifying the growth of plants than this triangle. The three assumptions that underlie the triangle can be summarized as follows:

1. Plants are adapted to either a high resource supply or a low resource supply.
2. Plants that are adapted to a high resource supply can be adapted to either frequent or infrequent disturbance.

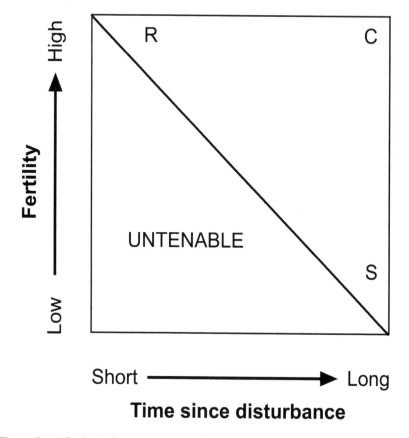

Figure 2.1. The basis for Grime's triangle of plant functional types: competitors (C), stress tolerators (S), and ruderals (R). In a factorial of environments that vary in time since disturbance and fertility, species cannot grow in low-fertility sites with high disturbance. Species Grime called "stress-tolerators" dominated low-fertility sites that had not been disturbed for a long time. High-fertility sites were dominated by ruderals if the sites had been recently disturbed, and by "competitors" if they had not been disturbed for a long time. Adapted from Grime 2001.

3. Plants that are adapted to a low resource supply cannot be adapted to frequent disturbance.

Grime proposed there were basic similarities in plant adaptations to all stressful environments. Not only were plants that dominated cold environments similar to those that thrived in environments of low resource availability, but strategies were similar regardless of whether water, nutrients, or light was the limiting factor. By 2001 Grime had suggested that not only are there general strategies for success when different resources are limiting, but also that plants that dominate in environments that are ultimately limited by different resources are all proximally limited by the same resource: nutrients. The similarities in traits among plants that are adapted to limitations in different resources were a consequence of water and light limitation generating nutrient limitation. Grime placed low nutrient availability at the core of his thinking on plant adaptations to survival in stressful environments.

Strategy for Survival in Stressful Habitats

In describing the dynamics of the vegetation around Sheffield, England, and erecting this triangle of nutrient supply and disturbance, Grime's emphasis on the general low availability of nutrients was nothing less than revolutionary. As mentioned earlier, prior to Grime, nutrients were of conceptual interest primarily from the standpoint of toxic levels in the soil. Although it had long been known that the growth of plants could be limited by individual nutrients, low nutrient availability was not considered a key aspect of habitats that shaped their evolution. Grime termed plants that inhabited sites with a low frequency of disturbance and low nutrient availability "stress tolerators." In Grime's descriptions, low-nutrient habitats and the species that inhabited them are characterized as follows:

1. Stress tolerator species have low maximum growth rates. These species grow slowly even when water, nutrients, and light are plentiful. In addition to growing slowly, stress tolerator species have leaves with low nutrient concentrations, and they allocate a lot of resource to defenses such as tannins.
2. In low-fertility habitats, nutrients are supplied in occasional pulses. The heterogeneous nature of nutrient supplies is embedded in most of Grime's more controlled experiments (Grime and Curtis 1976) and is a consistent general assumption of his regarding low-fertility habitats.
3. To succeed in these habitats, plants must be able to maintain biomass, if not growth, during times of low nutrient availability while waiting for pulses. Grime states that "the capacity of slow-growing plant species [i.e., stress tolerators] to dominate vegetation on infertile soils is related more to the ability to protect nutrient capital than to capture nutrients at low external concentrations" (Grime 2001, p. 45). Acquiring resources between pulses is less important than the ability to endure the low availability and the agents that cause disturbance in the environment until the next pulse arrives.
4. For the purposes of community assembly, competition is relatively unimportant at low nutrient supply. In low-nutrient-supply soils,

fast-growing species might dominate immediately after a disturbance, but differential susceptibility to stress agents or being eaten
preferentially eliminates fast-growing species in favor of the tough,
well-defended, slow-growing species that better conserve resources
in the face of these agents.

Two Strategies for Survival in Fertile Habitats

In contrast to the plants of low-fertility habitats, plants that inhabit high-
fertility, low-disturbance sites Grime called "competitors." In many respects, these habitats and the species that dominate them are the mirror
image of low-fertility sites.

1. High-fertility plants have high maximum relative growth rates
   (RGR_{max}). When given plentiful resources, their relative increase in
   biomass per unit time is greater than that of low-fertility plants. In
   addition to growing fast, high-fertility species have higher nutrient
   concentrations, a smaller fraction of their biomass is in cell walls,
   and they are less well defended chemically.
2. Although nutrient availability is high, plants that dominate high-
   fertility environments are more demanding of nutrients. Therefore,
   plants compete for nutrients. With higher growth rates and greater
   production, plants are also competing for light. Competition for
   nutrients and light is strongest in these environments.
3. To compete successfully in high-fertility habitats, plants must be
   able to project leaves and roots rapidly into unoccupied space to
   acquire light and nutrients. Fast-growing species are better able to
   project their roots into unoccupied soil and their leaves into unlit
   portions of the canopy than stress tolerators.
4. For the purposes of assembling plant communities, competition is
   more important than herbivory or stress. Competition for nutrients
   is a race to produce roots in areas of high nutrient availability but
   low root occupancy. Plants winning the competition preempt the
   supply of nutrients, acquiring nutrients before slower growing
   plants can produce roots in the soil. At the beginning of a growing
   season, plants race to acquire a general pulse of nutrients throughout the soil volume. After this nutrient pulse is acquired, plants continue to race to place roots into short-duration patches of nutrient
   availability or they race to respond quickly to a large pulse. Once
   widespread availability declines, competition is minimal, beginning
   again only when a new pulse initiates a new race.

The species that inhabit high-fertility, high-disturbance sites Grime
called "ruderals." These species are largely the same as competitors ex-

cept that their life cycle is completed in one year. Instead of starting from perennating organs, ruderals start from seed, but they also have high growth rates with high-activity roots and leaves. These plants also experience high initial light and nutrient availability, and then race to keep their leaves above other plants and to project their roots into unoccupied patches or respond to pulses.

Grime further elaborated on the contrasts among the low- and high-fertility species:

> [A] crucial genetic difference between competitive, stress-tolerant and ruderal plants concerns the form and extent of phenotypic response to stress. . . . [S]uch differences constitute one of the more fundamental criteria whereby the three strategies may be distinguished. . . . [T]he stress-response of the ruderal ensures the production of seeds, those of the competitor maximise the capture of resources, whilst those of the stress-tolerator allow the conservation of captured resources. (Grime 1979, p. 46)

Again, this focus on the general low availability of nutrients and how it shaped a broad set of species to conserve nutrients represented a marked departure from earlier descriptions of plant strategies. Warming, for example, described the adaptations of plants of xeric habitats to conserve water. Before Grime, low nutrient availability had not been considered to be central to the ecology and evolution of plants.

Foundations of the Triangle

Although building on earlier theories, Grime's own experiments and gradient analyses, the results of which were published from 1963 to 1968, formed the foundation of his later theories on the relationship between plant traits and the environment. Grime's early work (Grime 1963) centered on an observation whose pattern was noted by Warming. Some species, referred to as calcicole species, were more abundant on shallow calcareous soils, while other species (calcifuge species) were more abundant on deeper, more acidic, productive soils. Grime began to look at the mechanisms of these patterns and found that in the absence of competition, both types of species grew better in the more productive soils (Grime 1963). Contemporaneous work showed that plants that grow in areas of low nutrient availability have roots with low maximum specific rates of nutrient acquisition (Clarkson 1965). Grime interpreted this observation to mean that it was not a greater ability of the low-fertility species to acquire resources that led to their dominance. Grime also tested whether fast-growing species were eliminated because they were worse competitors for nutrients. Grime observed that instead, extreme water stress on the shallow calcareous soils (Grime 1963) caused fast-growing seedlings to die, and the fast-growing species were also more likely to be eaten than slow-growing species (Grime, MacPherson-Stewart, and Dearman 1968).

In 1973, Grime assembled these findings into a predictive framework. Grassland species from around Sheffield were each assigned a score reflecting variables such as RGR and maximum plant height. Sites from six different habitat types were characterized by the average score of the species within the assemblage. High-fertility sites were dominated by fast-growing species, leading Grime to suggest that the low incidence of fast-growing plants in some sites might be due to environmental stress, just as he found for calcifuge species on calcareous soils. Alternatively, disturbances, such as grazing or mowing, might prevent some fast-growing species from dominating, leading to a distinction between plants of fertile, disturbed areas and those of fertile, undisturbed areas (Grime 1977).

This approach to habitats and the relative roles of nutrients and disturbance are generally consistent throughout Grime's career. Almost 25 years after assembling his first triangle, in 1997 Grime and others synthesized more than two decades' measurements of traits on a diverse subset of the flora of Sheffield and were able to support his competitor-stress tolerator-ruderal (CSR) triangle (see figure 2.1). When the patterns of traits were analyzed, it became clear that one axis separated out Grime's stress tolerators, which had low leaf nutrient concentrations and low RGR, among other traits. Plants with high leaf nutrient concentrations and high RGR were differentiated along another axis that was characterized by differences in life history traits. The fast-growing annuals were Grime's ruderals and the fast-growing perennials were his competitors.

In 2001, Grime acknowledged that different resources are found in low availability in different environments. In some environments, nutrients are at conspicuously low availability, in others it is light that is deficient, while in yet others it is water. In attempting to explain the similarities in plant traits that are found among plants that dominate different environments, he proposed two alternative hypotheses. The first hypothesis held that similarities in traits across environments could be explained largely by convergence associated with selection driven by limitation of different resources: "The set of traits associated with stress-tolerance and conferring fitness at low productivity are selected regardless of the environmental factors constraining production" (Grime 2001, p. 65). The second hypothesis proposed commonality due to similar underlying conditions across environments: "The set of traits associated with stress-tolerance and conferring fitness at low productivity are selected only in circumstances where productivity is constrained by the same underlying limiting factor" (Grime 2001, p. 66).

The convergence and commonality hypotheses, as these are known, ask powerful, basic questions about the nature of plant strategies. In 2001, Grime stated that the reason why there are similarities in traits among plants that dominate habitats with low availability of different resources can be explained by the commonality hypothesis. Nutrients are a common limiting resource in many stressful environments.

Although Grime's favoring of nutrient stress and the commonality hypothesis is clear in 2001, it is interesting that one aspect of Grime's characterization of plants that changed over time was the nature of the stress of shade. The mechanism by which Grime proposed plants compete for light is the production of leaves above competitors' leaves. With a unidirectional light source, preempting the supply becomes a race to the top. Plants that find themselves below the canopy of others have to endure the stress of shade while waiting for resource availability to increase. Initially, Grime characterized this stress as one of low carbon availability. As early as 1965, he determined that shade-adapted tree species in North America have leaves with lower specific rates of respiration. They also have lower RGRs in full sun than non-shade-adapted species. Having a low RGR, Grime said, shade-tolerant plants must be better at tolerating stresses. Grime proposed that shade-adapted plants do not acquire light better when light levels are low but conserve their energy better:

> [P]hysiological studies suggest that natural selection in deeply-shaded habitats has been associated with the evolution of mechanisms of conserving energy rather than with those which increase the quantity of energy captured. In particular, it seems likely that low respiratory rates may be important in maintaining the carbon balance of plants exposed simultaneously to low light intensity and high temperature. (Grime 1979, p. 27)

By 2001, however, Grime was no longer giving primacy to the idea that the suite of traits associated with shade tolerance had been selected for their role in carbon dynamics. Instead, he hypothesized that the slow growth and associated traits of shade-tolerant plants resulted from intense competition for nutrients, which would result in low nutrient availability for understory plants (Grime 2001, p. 34). Commonality replaced convergence. Grime reasoned that mature canopy plants require a high quantity of nutrients to sustain their high productivity, which would leave little for understory plants. Also, as plants are shaded, they experience low carbon availability, which limits their potential for root growth, leaving plants starved for nutrients. As a result, understory plants are adapted not to conserve energy but to conserve nutrients.

Grime proposed a broad framework for understanding the diversity of plants, along with three general strategies for vegetative growth across environments. The second major figure in plant strategies, Terry Chapin, initially worked within Grime's nutrient framework. By the end of his active research career on plant strategies, however, he had compiled some of the evidence critical to a revision of the basic assumptions of Grime's theories and that would factor prominently in a new synthesis.

Summary of Grime's Research

Grime set out to characterize the major plant strategies of the world. Whereas previous phytogeographers had divided the flora of the world into a multitude of categories—the piles of the seagoing geographer-collectors—Grime proposed three major categories: plants of stressful habitats, plants of fertile, undisturbed habitats, and plants of fertile, disturbed habitats. The central role he proposed for nutrients in these strategies would turn out to be revolutionary. Other key aspects of his approach included explicit incorporation of stresses, in addition to general and selective disturbances.

In Grime's triangle of habitats and strategies, stressful habitats were characterized as having pulses of nutrients and plants were selected to endure the periods between the pulses of nutrient availability by conserving their resources in the face of herbivory. In contrast, fast-growing species in stressful environments would poorly acquire nutrient pulses, since their root systems have to regrow each time and they are more likely to be eaten by generalist herbivores. In high-nutrient-supply environments where there is little disturbance, fast-growing plants would be better able to compete for both light and nutrients, which are still supplied in pulses and patches. Slow-growing, low-nutrient plants are excluded from these environments by nature of their inferior competitive ability. Finally, high disturbance rates are associated with high resource availability and select for plants that can complete their life cycle in a short period of time, which requires them to grow fast.

In explaining similarities in traits among plants adapted to different environments, Grime had originally suggested that the similarities represented a convergence, but he later favored a common limiting resource among nutrient-poor, dry, and understory environments: nutrients.

CHAPIN

Terry Chapin published his landmark paper, "The Mineral Nutrition of Wild Plants," the year after *Plant Strategies and Vegetation* appeared. In his paper, Chapin first characterized the traits of crop plants such as barley, which he likened to Grime's ruderals. These plants had high inherent growth rates and high potential nutrient uptake rates. In contrast to the ruderal and crop species, Chapin did not characterize high fertility perennials or shade-tolerant plants but instead focused on the traits of plants that are most common in low-fertility ecosystems.

The Low-Nutrient Strategy

In describing low-nutrient species, Chapin built on the traits Grime had noted. The roots of low-fertility species have low nutrient uptake rates and low nutrient concentrations, and are thought to have high longevity. Leaves have low photosynthetic rates and low nutrient concentrations but differ in their resorption rates. At the whole-plant scale, these plants have high root:shoot ratios, which Chapin suggested might be due in part to higher root longevity or higher allocation belowground (figure 2.2).

Like Grime, Chapin characterized the nutrient supplies of low-nutrient habitats as being dominated by pulses of availability, with nutrient uptake concentrated during these times of high availability. For example, the nutrient pulse that occurs after the spring thaw dominates the nutrient supply of cold ecosystems. During these pulses, the low-fertility species have greater luxury consumption of nutrients. In between the pulses, plants must endure low nutrient availability and use the nutrients that were consumed during times of high availability to maintain growth. Like Grime, Chapin noted that the low-fertility species were also less susceptible to other stresses.

Chapin (1980, p. 253) summarized the low fertility strategy as follows:

> [I]nfertile soils are most successfully exploited by stress-tolerant species whose inherently low growth rates can be adequately maintained by their low capacities for photosynthesis and nutrient absorption. . . . A higher absorption capacity would provide little advantage in infertile soils, where diffusion of nutrients from bulk soil to the root surface is the step that most strongly limits absorption. These species maximize nutrient acquisition primarily by maintaining a large root biomass, and associated mycorrhizae, achieved in large part through slow root turnover. The long-lived nature of roots may in turn be partially responsible for their low root absorption capacity. The inherently low growth rates and the relatively small growth response to flushes of higher nutrient availability enable the plant to acquire and maintain nutrient reserves and in this way survive periods of exceptionally low availability in soil. The annual nutrient requirements of these species are low because of (a) slow rates of tissue production and (b) low nutrient loss rates through both senescence and leaching. This in large part explains the success of slowly growing stress-tolerant species on infertile

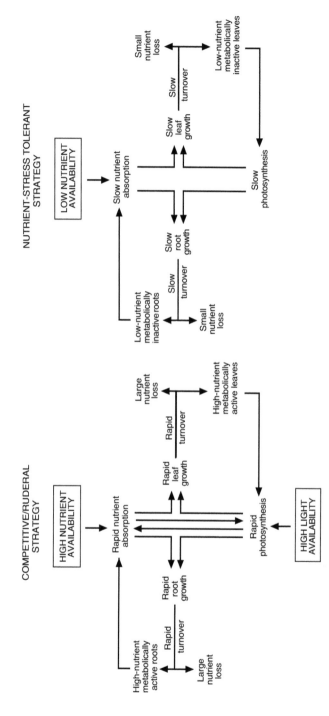

Figure 2.2. The series of physiological feedbacks that drove differences between the strategies of high-fertility species (competitive–ruderal strategy) and species of low-nutrient environments (nutrient–stress tolerant strategy). Adapted from Chapin 1980.

soils. In response to declining nutrient availability, tissue reserves and growth rate decline slightly, but the normal metabolic effectiveness is maintained. Because of higher survivorship and the longer time that growth can be maintained on limited plant nutrient reserves, stress-tolerant species outproduce competitive species on infertile soils over the annual cycle.

As with Grime's work, it is instructive to analyze the path that led to Chapin's seminal review. Before he wrote the review, most of Chapin's early work had centered on root nutrient uptake kinetics, which are a characterization of the rate of nutrient uptake at different solution nutrient concentrations. For example, for his dissertation he examined the nutrient uptake kinetics of plants taken from "stable" and "fluctuating" environments (Chapin 1974). Plants from stable environments, such as the Alaskan tundra, had low rates of nutrient uptake. Plants from fluctuating environments, such as a Southern California desert oasis, had higher rates of nutrient uptake and would increase their potential uptake rates more in response to increases in nutrient availability. These patterns foreshadowed his 1980 review, which held that plants from lower-fertility sites had lower specific nutrient uptake rates and were less responsive to increases in availability. Although much of his later work focused on nitrogen, the early research centered on the acquisition of phosphorus, both for uptake kinetics and for ecosystem cycling.

Chapin told me once that when he began to review the literature on the physiological traits of non-crop plants, the patterns that Grime described most closely matched his findings. Around 1980, the differences between Chapin and Grime were minimal. Chapin used many of Grime's assumptions and approaches. The focus on nutrient pulses in low-fertility ecosystems was similar to Grime's assumptions, although Chapin's focus on luxury consumption was a novel mechanistic development of persistence in between pulses. Chapin's focus on the mechanisms by which nutrients move in soil solution was also a novel addition and helped explain the lack of utility of high uptake rates at low nutrient supply. Plants that had high uptake rates under high nutrient availability regimes would not have higher uptake rates at low nutrient supply owing to inevitable declines in nutrient concentrations at the root surface.

Chapin continued to elaborate and change the low-nutrient strategy after publication of "The Mineral Nutrition of Wild Plants." For example, he found little difference in the efficiency of nutrient resorption among high- and low-fertility species. He made the first comprehensive measurements of the energetic costs of the tissues of different species, finding that high- and low-fertility species had similar energy contents (Chapin 1989). He was the first to show that some plants could directly take up organic nitrogen (Chapin, Moilanen, and Kielland 1993). He also helped develop a theory on nutrient limitation and co-limitation (Bloom, Chapin, and Mooney 1985; Chapin, Vitousek, and Van Cleve 1986) (see chapter 4). Although this was all important research, it did not have much immediate impact on the basic understanding of strategies for growing in low-fertility ecosystems. The framework remained the same, even though the research findings began pointing toward the eventual need for a fundamental revision of the theory of plant strategies in response to low resource availability.

Relative Growth Rates

Although the framework appeared to have been set irrevocably in 1980, for nearly 15 years after his review of plant strategies appeared, Chapin seems to have struggled to understand one of the central questions of plant strategies: why do some plants grow slowly? Chapin's attempts to explain the central trait to both his and Grime's theories introduced a notable wrinkle into the otherwise smooth fabric of understanding of plant strategies.

Because understanding the importance of RGR_{max} and its relationship to performance is a central component of plant strategies, the changes in Chapin's hypotheses regarding RGR_{max} over time are worth attention. In "The Mineral Nutrition of Wild Plants," Chapin provided three hypotheses as to why plants from low-fertility ecosystems had lower inherent growth rates. The first hypothesis was that slow-growing plants were less likely to exhaust nutrients in the soil. This hypothesis was quickly rejected in his review, as it conveyed group selection. Leaving nutrients in the soil would benefit only those plants that grow faster, which is not an evolutionarily stable strategy. The second hypothesis was that having a low RGR_{max} allows plants to function closer to their optimum. Chapin admitted that this hypothesis was vague, as there was no direct advantage to growing closer to an optimal rate, but he felt there was support for selection on RGR_{max}, and for low RGR_{max} as being advantageous in and of itself. The third hypothesis was that a slow growth rate would prevent plants from exhausting internal nutrient reserves. With a pulse of nutrients, plants acquire more nutrients than are needed to satisfy immediate requirements. This luxury consumption fuels their growth until the next pulse, whereas a faster growing plant would have used the nutrients or accumulated less reserves, causing some unspecified negative consequences before the next pulse.

In 1991, Chapin revisited the topic of the low RGR of some plants in an article titled "Integrated Responses of Plants to Stress," in which he introduced three new hypotheses. First, low growth rates could arise as a consequence of a low maximum specific rate of nutrient uptake. Although this might be true, Chapin makes no statement as to why having a low nutrient uptake rate would be advantageous. In his 1980 review, he had suggested that low uptake rates might be a consequence of having roots that lived a long time. Second, low RGR_{max} might be a consequence of a high allocation rate of resources to structures or activities not directly associated with growth, such as chemical defense or storage. This hypothesis was a new one for Chapin, echoing assumptions that Tilman had made (see below), and was supported by a study of the intraspecific relationship between leaf production rates and defensive allocation (Coley 1986) (figure 2.3).

Third, Chapin proposed that low RGR_{max} is a consequence of internally imposed constraints on growth rates. Again, there is no statement as to the direct advantage of slow growth rates, but this hypothesis represented an attempt to rectify past results. In 1980, Chapin had stated that wild plants had low nutrient concentrations. Yet in controlled experiments (Chapin, Follett, and O'Connor 1982), slower growing, low-fertility plants often had higher nutrient concentrations. As with the second and third hypotheses in the 1980 paper, low nutrient concentrations didn't cause a low RGR_{max}, but instead a low RGR_{max} allowed plants to store nutrients to continue growing through periods when nutrient availability was low. From this, Chapin noted there was a centralized stress response syndrome in plants that was hormonally activated. Across a broad suite of stresses, the same abscisic acid (ABA) trigger was pulled, slowing growth down. Chapin hypothesized that the slow growth of plants might be a consequence of high constitutive levels of ABA, as if the stress switch was always on.

The last formal attempt Chapin made to understand the low RGR_{max} of plants appeared in a paper published in *American Naturalist* in 1993, "Evolution of Suites of Traits in Response to Environmental Stress" (Chapin, Autumn, and Pugnaire 1993). The paper provides different hypotheses for the low RGR_{max} of plants. Slow growth in plants could be associated with (1) a slow turnover of tissues, (2) minimizing growth respiration, which is the respiration associated with producing new tissues, as opposed to maintaining them, and (3) the opportunity to use resources not allocated to growth for other purposes, which allows plants to resist stresses. Of the latter, the authors wrote, "slow growth indirectly confers stress resistance by reducing carbon demands for growth which thereby allows greater allocation to other processes that directly contribute to stress resistance." The causality in this last hypothesis is that low RGR values determine secondary allocation, not that secondary allocation slows growth rate.

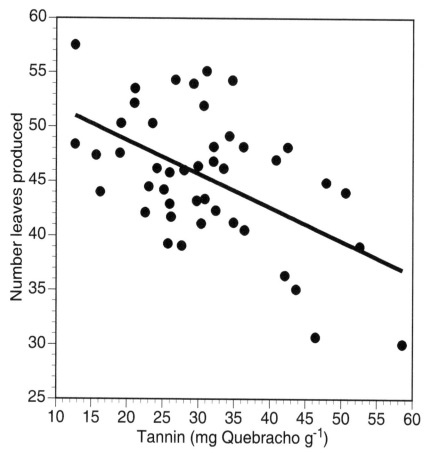

Figure 2.3. Relationship between foliar tannin concentrations and the number of leaves that an individual plant produced after 18 months for seedlings of *Cecropia peltata* grown under common conditions. Adapted from Coley 1986.

Summary of Chapin's Research

Chapin's research built on Grime's framework and first summarized in 1980 the broad suite of plant traits associated with low-nutrient-supply habitats. Chapin continued to develop the correlation of traits associated with low nutrient supplies and the functioning of habitats with low nutrient supplies. He contributed research on nutrient resorption from leaves, organic nitrogen uptake, and the carbon costs of structures of different plants. Through the mid-1990s his research continued to seek the proximal and distal reasons for low inherent growth rates of low-fertility plants. Over time, a range of hypotheses at different mechanistic distances from RGR_{max} was provided. Chapin appeared to struggle with the causality of the relationship between secondary allocation and slow growth, and with whether slow growth in and of itself confers advantage. He also noted that under common conditions, slow-growing plants do not always have lower nutrient concentrations than fast-growing plants, an observation he was never able to reconcile with the general patterns of tissue nutrient concentrations across environments.

Tilman

David Tilman's goals were as expansive as Grime's and Chapin's, if not larger, for he attempted to characterize the processes that structure assemblages along nutrient supply and disturbance gradients, as well as the traits of plants along the gradient. In contrast to Grime and Chapin, however, Tilman formulated his core ideas in aquatic, not terrestrial, ecosystems. Although he conducted experiments in terrestrial ecosystems, just as the other two did, he relied much more on mathematical models to structure his hypotheses and interpretation of results. It would be an oversimplification to appropriate the differences in the theories of Tilman and of Grime and Chapin to explain aquatic-terrestrial divides or empirical versus theoretical approaches. It would also be injurious to the concept of the scientific process to attribute any lack of rectification of their different ideas to the inferiority of one approach versus another or to an inability of researchers with fundamentally different approaches to synthesize a unified theory. That said, the hypotheses and conclusions that Tilman developed at different points during the period of 1980–95 stand in stark contrast to those of Grime and Chapin, and they have proved to be important building blocks for a more synthetic theory of plant strategies.

1. Differing from Grime, Tilman stated that competition was an important regulator of relative abundance of species in habitats with low nutrient supply.
2. From low nutrient supply to high nutrient supply, the importance of competition for light and the importance of competition for nutrients were not positively related but inversely. Whereas competition for nutrients was important at low nutrient supply, competition for nutrients was unimportant at high nutrient supply. Instead, it was mostly competition for light that regulated the relative abundance of species in the high-nutrient habitats.
3. If competition for nutrients was not important in a low-nutrient environment, that was because of disturbance and differences in colonization ability, not the stress of low nutrient supplies. Some plants might be better at dispersing into recently disturbed habitats, where competition for resources is poorly developed.

4. Slow-growing plants have a low RGR_{max} not because of how they build their leaves or roots but because they allocate resources away from light acquisition. In low-nutrient-supply habitats, the dominant plants grow slowly because of their greater allocation of resources to roots to compete better for nutrients. In high-nutrient-supply habitats, the dominant plants grow slowly because of their high allocation of resources to stems, which allow them to compete better for light.

5. Differing with the characterization of nutrients being supplied in pulses, Tilman assumed that most nutrients are supplied evenly over time. Although he discussed the consequences of pulses and patches of nutrient availability, the basic patterning of species could be explained with a uniform nutrient supply.

6. Whereas Grime and Chapin were ambiguous about the mechanism of competition (at least in comparison to Tilman), Tilman hypothesized that one species displaced another when nutrients were limiting by lowering the concentrations of nutrients in soil solution to levels lower than required for the growth of the competing species.

To understand how Tilman arrived at a point so fundamentally different from the hypotheses of Grime and Chapin, it is instructive to examine his early research, for many of his ideas were formulated early in his career. Some potentially key ideas of Tilman's can then be highlighted, such as the importance of competition in different habitats, the relationship between plant traits and strategies, and the mechanisms of competition.

Early Limnological Research

Tilman began his career by asking what controlled the relative abundance of two species of diatoms along a gradient in Lake Michigan (Titman 1976; Tilman 1977). At one end of the gradient, nearshore environments were dominated by one species of diatom and open-lake environments were dominated by another. Tilman also observed that the two parts of the lake had different ratios of two nutrients (silica and phosphorus) in water. Nearshore environments had higher relative concentrations of phosphorus and waters far from the shore had higher relative concentrations of silica. Tilman hypothesized that it was differences in the ability to compete for the two nutrients that led to differences in dominance of the two diatoms.

In the laboratory, Tilman was able to test the relative competitive abilities of the two diatoms. Tilman grew monocultures and mixtures of the two diatoms in chemostats, where he could manipulate the supplies of silica and phosphorus. Tilman found that the species with the higher RGR at a given ratio of silica and phosphorus supplies were able to reduce the concentrations of the limiting nutrient to a level below that required for sustained growth of the other species. Owing to its ability to lower the concentration of the limiting nutrient, it became the better competitor for the limiting nutrient (Titman 1976; Tilman 1977).

From his work with diatoms, Tilman offered the general hypothesis that the key to competition for a given nutrient in aquatic environments was reducing its concentration in solution. If one species could lower the concentration below the concentration required for a population of a competing species to maintain itself, it would become dominant. Tilman formulated this hypothesis using Jacques Monod's model of growth as a framework (Monod 1950), in which the concentration of nutrients in solution was denoted as R and the minimum concentration at which a population could maintain itself was called R^*.

Tilman (1990, p. 123) described R^*, and his theory of competition for nutrients, in the following way:

> R^* is the level to which the concentration of the available form of the limiting resource is reduced by a monoculture of a species once that monoculture has reached equilibrium i.e., once it has attained its carrying capacity. . . . Thus, R^* is the concentration of available resource that a species requires to survive in a habitat. . . . If all species are limited by the same nutrient, the species with the lowest R^* is predicted, at equilibrium, to displace all competitors.

Applying the Theory to Terrestrial Systems

After he began working at the Cedar Creek Natural History Area in Minnesota, Tilman identified a gradient that was analogous to his Lake Michigan gradient. Upland habitats at Cedar Creek were a mixture of native oak savanna and closed canopy forests, along with low-productivity grasslands that had been abandoned after being under agriculture at different times in the past. Productivity in the grasslands was primarily limited by the supply of nitrogen, which had been reduced by past agriculture (Tilman 1982) and was slowly increasing with successional age. The grasslands and native savannas formed a successional and nutrient supply sequence, from young fields with low soil nitrogen supply, to older fields with higher soil nitrogen supply, to native savannas with the highest soil nitrogen supply.

Like the Lake Michigan gradient, this successional sequence had different dominant species at the ends of the gradients. Tilman hypothesized that the gradient of species was driven by the changes in ratios of resource supplies. His initial hypotheses about the successional sequences were derived from his theories regarding the underlying abiotic factors that drove the differences in the relative abundance of species, with competition for resources driving the changes in the relative abundance of species. Instead of variation in the ratio of silica and phosphorus, Tilman hypothesized that the successional sequence was driven by changes in soil nutrients that caused variation in the ratio of nutrient and light supplies (Tilman 1982, 1985). Similar to the differences in the diatoms along the gradient, plants that occupied environments with relatively low nitrogen availability were postulated to be better competitors for nitrogen (figure 2.4). Those plants that occupied environments with relatively high nitrogen availability were hypothesized to be better competitors for light.

Applying the theory he had developed with diatoms, Tilman (1985, p. 846) proposed that differences in "the requirements of the species for limiting resources and the availabilities of the resource" drove competitive outcomes. Early-successional, low-nitrogen-availability fields were assumed to be dominated by species that required less nitrogen per unit of light. As such, those species would be expected to have higher growth rates at low nitrogen supply and would be able to extract more nitrogen from the low-nitrogen soils. These traits would lead to competitive superiority when nitrogen availability was relatively low. Species that dominated the later-successional grasslands with high soil nitrogen availability were assumed to be better competitors for light, and as such were hypothesized to require more nitrogen per unit of light, to have higher growth rates at high nitrogen than the "early"-successional species, and to reduce light levels more.

The research that followed these initial hypotheses was a complicated set of shifting ideas as Tilman struggled to reconcile empirical results with his theories of succession, competition, and plant strategies. This led to a chain of hypotheses and theories over time. Disentangling the changes in the theories of succession, competition, and plant resource strategies as empirical results were collected and compared with results predicted from theoretical work is not straightforward. A constructive solution is to describe the different theories that Tilman articulated over time rather than attempting to characterize what Tilman himself thought was true at any one time. The flow of Tilman's theories can be difficult to follow over time as different ideas were revised, and by the end of his active research into plant strategies, around 1995, it is difficult to know what body of theory remained from his earlier ideas (Craine 2005). Some of the different and potentially important ideas that Tilman contributed on the topics of succession, competition, and plant strategies are highlighted in the next section.

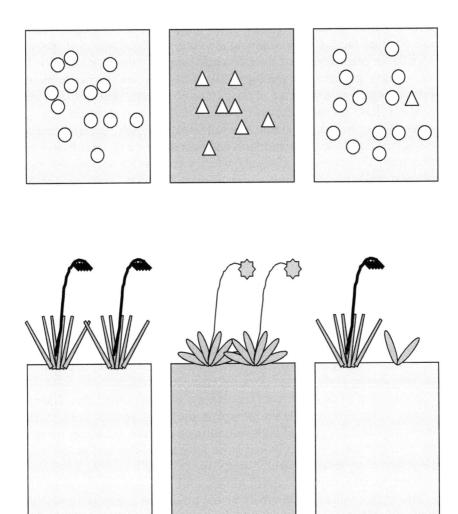

Figure 2.4. Cartoon showing the concentration reduction hypothesis (R^*) as applied to algae in water (upper panel) and plants in soil (lower panel). In its simplest form, for a constant rate of supply of a nutrient that is limiting to growth for two species, the hypothesis predicts that the organism that can reduce the concentration of the limiting nutrient in solution (shown with shading) to the lowest level at equilibrium will competitively exclude the other species when grown together, all other things being equal.

Succession

Tilman's initial misunderstanding of the importance of competition relative to other factors in determining the successional gradient of species abundance caused some of the mismatch between theory and results. If successional gradients are representative of the different types of habitats different species encountered in the past or encounter currently, then the gradients have the potential to elucidate different plant strategies.

Along the successional gradient of soil nitrogen supply, Tilman hypothesized that competition for nutrients and light drove the changes in species over time. Yet his empirical results, which were at odds with his theories of plant growth, competition, or succession, suggested that the lack of species that dominated old grasslands in early-successional grasslands was not due to competition. For example, Tilman grew individual plants of different species for 12 weeks across a soil nitrogen gradient (Tilman 1986). Early-successional species acquired more nitrogen than late-successional species, consistent with the idea that the early-successional species were better competitors for nitrogen. Just as with diatoms, better competitors for nutrients grow faster at a given resource supply. Yet late-successional species *were not growing faster* at high soil nitrogen content than early-successional species. With this departure from expectations, some part of his theory had to be revised. The link between growth rates and competitive ability might have been wrong, or the relative importance of competition along the successional sequence could have been misunderstood. With this departure from theory, it is interesting that Tilman offered alternative hypotheses to explain the lower growth rates of the late-successional species at high soil nitrogen content, including the hypothesis that the late-successional grass *Schizachyrium* was less susceptible to herbivory than early-successional species in soils with high nitrogen content, an idea very reminiscent of Grime's.

Tilman had initially discounted the importance of dispersal into early-successional habitats, and as a result had overemphasized the importance of competition for early-successional fields. Ken Thompson (1987), in a critique of Tilman's theories, suggested that "early colonists of most secondary successions owe their success firstly to good dispersal or a long-lived seed bank and secondly to rapid growth and reproduction under conditions of plentiful resources and low competition." A few years later, Tilman presented differences in colonization ability from the outset (Tilman and Cowan 1989). Early-successional species were considered to be better at dispersing, the species that dominated the late-successional grasslands were considered better competitors for nitrogen, and the species that dominated the forests and savannas were considered better competitors for light.

In the end, Tilman provided a set of ideas regarding the potential strategies of plants. First, plants might have evolved to disperse into habitats where competition from other species for light or nutrients might be relatively unimportant. This does not mean that competition is unimportant in these habitats, only that the absence of some species cannot be explained by competition. Second, after colonization by other species has occurred in soils with low nutrient availability, the relative abundance of species is determined by competition for nutrients. Third, given enough time for colonization in habitats with a high soil nitrogen supply, competition for light determines the relative abundance of species.

Differences among Plants in Traits

Initially, Tilman had offered little description of the differences among plants in the traits that led them to be better competitors for nutrients or light, beyond vague statements of differences in "resource requirements." With the ALLOCATE model (Tilman 1988), Tilman suggested that the differences in competitive ability were driven by differences in the allocation of resources among rather than within organs. Tilman had observed that plants that dominated the grasslands where competition for nutrients was supposed to be important had a high fraction of biomass in roots. Trees have a large fraction of their biomass in stems and leaves and, as a result, dominate relatively undisturbed environments with a high nitrogen supply.

Tilman proposed that differences in the relative allocation of resources among organs were also associated with differences in RGR_{max}:

> [I]t is necessary to assume that species-to-species differences in morphology are much greater than species-to-species differences in nutrient- and light-saturated rates of photosynthesis per unit biomass or respiration rates per unit biomass. This assumption is probably a valid first approximation. Terrestrial plants range from soil algae that are functionally almost 100% "leaf" to canopy trees that are less than 1% leaf. Within a given geographic region, the maximal specific rates of photosynthesis under field conditions typically vary by less than tenfold (see papers in Chabot and Mooney 1985). However, after morphology, the next major determinant of maximal growth rates is likely to be maximal rates of photosynthesis. (Tilman 1988, p. 60)

Tilman's evidence for the importance of allocation over physiology and morphology of organs was that "thousands of years of selection for highly productive cultivars of various crop plants have had little effect on physiology but a major effect on allocation patterns and morphology (Fitter 1986). Gifford and Jenkins (1981) found that allocation to leaf was a stronger determinant of growth rates of crop plants than maximal photosynthetic rates." This is the sum of the evidence that he initially provides for the lack of importance of organ-level construction.

Although the importance of allocation among organs and the linkages with RGR_{max} were a potentially unique contribution to the understanding of plant strategies, Tilman quickly began to modify his ideas about the causes of differences in RGR_{max} and the centrality of differences in the allocation rate of resources among organs. Shipley and Peters (1990) questioned the necessary link between allocation and RGR_{max}, to which Tilman responded that there might be no need for allocation rates and RGR_{max} to be associated. Tilman stated that "leaf area ratio may thus be a better measure of allocation to photosynthesis than percentage leaf mass" and that there are "equally interesting and important trade-offs that plants face in allocating protein (i.e. nitrogen) to alternative physiological functions" (Tilman 1991, pp. 1270, 1271).

After attempting to match RGR_{max} and relative allocation rates one more time (Gleeson and Tilman 1994), Tilman apparently rejected the central importance of allocation among organs in plant strategies. Field studies had shown that slow-growing plants had a high fraction of biomass in roots, which was interpreted as representing high allocation to roots. Yet in seedlings grown in nutrient-rich conditions in a greenhouse over a two-month period, there was no relationship between relative allocation to root, leaf, and stem and RGR_{max}. If anything, late-successional plants allocated less to roots, not more. The stark contrast led Gleeson and Tilman to conclude that "seedlings may have markedly different allocation than adults." The authors still asserted that allocation was important, but they also suggested that resource use efficiencies might be the key to understanding "growth rate, optimal allocation, and potentially competition and succession" (Gleeson and Tilman 1994, p. 543) (figure 2.5).

The Mechanism of Competition

Throughout his career, Tilman offered little on the mechanism of competition for light besides general statements about the ability to reduce the "availability" of light (but see Dybzinski and Tilman 2007). The one factor that was constant in Tilman's theories was that competitive displacement of one species by another when nutrients were limiting was due to differences in the abilities of the species to lower the concentrations of nutrients in soil solution. Tilman never repudiated the fundamental assumptions of the models that he derived for diatoms. The relative importance of competition along the Cedar Creek successional gradient changed over time as he incorporated Thompson's observation of the superior colonization ability of some species.

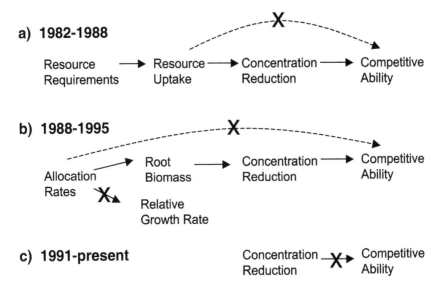

Figure 2.5. The progression of David Tilman's theories regarding the relationships among plant traits, resource availability, and competitive ability. An X indicates that the pathway had been largely falsified and would reject the causal set of mechanisms. From Craine 2005.

Tilman also revised his ideas about trait differences among species leading to differences in their ability to reduce resource levels. Initially the mechanism was differences in demand and the ability to grow at different resource ratios. Later it was allocation among organs that led to the differential ability to reduce the concentration of nutrients in soil solution and the availability of light at different heights. For a time, plants that allocated a large fraction of their biomass to roots were best able to reduce concentrations of nutrients in soil solution and therefore were competitively superior for nutrients (Gleeson and Tilman 1990, p. 1144). By 1994, Tilman had all but rejected the centrality of organ-level allocation in determining the ability to reduce soil solution nutrient concentrations. Yet he never rejected the metric of R^*, even if it was based on models that should have been rejected or revised based on empirical results.

LAYING THE FOUNDATION OF PLANT STRATEGIES

Others have contributed to our understanding of the growth of plants under different nutrient availability regimes. Peter Vitousek's research on ecosystem development showed the importance of differentiating low nitrogen availability and low phosphorus availability, as well as patterns of nutrient use efficiency (Vitousek 2004). Rien Aerts and Frank Berendse contributed knowledge on the potential components of nutrient use efficiency and the mechanisms by which plants could attain a high-nutrient-use efficiency (Berendse, Elberse, and Geerts 1992; Aerts 1995). Hans Lambers and his colleagues emphasized partitioning growth around leaf morphology and provided many species comparisons that quantified differences in resource use, such as respiration rates (Lambers and Poorter 1992). Peter Grubb put forth a set of theories regarding plant strategies based primarily on plasticity of traits rather than on mean differences (Grubb 1994, 1998).

There are differences among the theories of Grime, Chapin, and Tilman, but their contributions should not be scored or scanted. Competing hypotheses are important to scientific progress; a plausible but ultimately incorrect hypothesis is just as important as one that ends up being accepted. More important—and for this the greatest debt exists—the work reviewed here produced the components of a robust foundation by establishing what plant strategies must include. These can be enumerated as follows:

1. The first set of stresses that must be acknowledged as shaping plant strategies are those of low resource availability. In low-nutrient ecosystems, plants are likely to be stressed for nutrients. The nature of the stress, whether due to acquisition by neighboring plants or inherent to the environment, should be explicit. In other systems, some plants can be energy stressed owing to the shading of taller plants. Other stresses that should be accounted for include environmental extremes, such as high or low temperatures, and soil moisture. Although environmental stresses of this sort might be independent of nutrient or light stress, it is important to know whether species have differential susceptibility to these environmental stresses and whether they are more susceptible to other stresses or disturbances when a given resource has low availability.

2. Disturbances are a major factor that reduces the reproduction of plants, if not outright kills individuals. Plant strategies must acknowledge the probabilities of disturbance agents in different environments. Grime acknowledged selective herbivory as a factor that preferentially removed certain species from low-fertility habitats and nonselective disturbances as favoring ruderals. Both general and selective disturbances should be considered when delineating strategies.

3. The mechanisms by which nutrients are supplied to plants must be explicitly incorporated into a strategy for acquiring them. For example, Chapin's explanation for low-fertility species with low specific

nutrient uptake rates relied on the low diffusion rates of nutrients. As plant strategies are identified and developed, it is crucial to identify the degree to which nutrients are supplied to plants in pulses, come from patches, or are delivered uniformly in space and time in different habitats.

4. Not all traits are of equal weight in a given plant strategy. The role of RGR_{max} appears to be central to plant strategies. For example, it is important to understand why plants that dominate habitats with low nutrient supply have low RGR_{max}. The correlations of traits that make up a given strategy should also include resource activity levels—photosynthesis, nutrient uptake, respiration—as well as secondary allocation such as chemical defenses.

5. The theories developed by Grime and Tilman appear to differ in the relative importance each assigned to competition for resources in low- and high-fertility environments. As both acknowledge, competition for light and nutrients is an important component of resource acquisition and therefore reproduction, which would have been part of the natural selection of plants. It is important to be specific about the mechanisms of competition for light and nutrients and to characterize the absolute and relative importance of each, as it likely reflects the relative contribution to the overall selection of plants in different environments.

6. As strategies relate to the performance of plants in different environments, they should have predictive capacity regarding plant performance. Both Grime and Tilman sought to test the predictive capacity of strategies in experiments and natural gradients, and this approach is an important confirmation of the importance of a strategy.

7. It is important to identify the traits that plants of different environments have in common, and then to understand the reasons why these similarities exist. There are likely multiple levels of causation for the similarities that should be acknowledged and tested. First, traits are interconnected, and the presence of some traits likely has consequences for the presence of others. Second, the proximal limiting resources, stress agents, or disturbance agents among environments should also be investigated. For example, Grime suggested that the traits of species in different environments can be similar as a result of convergence or as a result of common proximal limiting resources.

Over the next four chapters, the basic principles of the functioning of assemblages and ecosystems are laid out to set the stage for understanding the strategies plants use to be successful in different environments. Although it may seem that many basic topics have been considered long enough by ecologists to be fully worked out by now, some fundamental questions about plant performance in different environments still remain. The nature of stress and disturbance and how plants respond to them are discussed in chapter 3. Chapter 4 updates the basic concept and application of resource limitation. For example, nutrient cycling has become much better understood over the past two decades, with little concomitant change in theories of nutrient limitation. Chapter 5 addresses competition for resources, formalizing new theories on how plants compete for nutrients and revising concepts of light competition. Finally, at the heart of plant strategies is understanding which factors have been important in the natural selection that formed the strategies, as well as which factors are important currently. Chapter 6 considers how importance is assessed over ecological and evolutionary time scales and the importance of different factors at low and high nutrient supply.

CHAPTER 3

Stress and Disturbance

ALL OTHER THINGS being equal, an individual plant should reproduce as much as possible. There is no advantage for a plant to hold back on reproduction over its life span, as its genes would diminish in frequency in a given population in which other plants were reproducing more. As a result of differences in the ability to acquire and maintain resources in a given environment, some plants produce fewer offspring than others and the frequency of its genes in the population decreases, while other, more successful plants produce more offspring and their genes increase in frequency.

The important first principle of natural selection is that agents of natural selection cause some plants to reproduce less than others, leading to a decrease in their abundance. Agents can reduce reproduction by reducing the viability of propagules, for example when seeds are attacked by pathogens. Yet most of the reduction in potential reproduction for a given plant occurs as a result of agents affecting the ability of plants to acquire resources, maintain them, and allocate them for future resource acquisition. A plant that has its net resource gain reduced has fewer resources to allocate to reproduction at a later time.

Two main sets of factors reduce growth and hence have been the main agents of natural selection, stress and disturbance. In this chapter, definitions of each are developed, and the major causes of plant stress and disturbance are discussed. The traits that allow plants to resist being stressed or disturbed by different agents are then covered, followed by the traits that allow plants to respond better after being stressed or disturbed. Much of the following treatment of stress and disturbance is relatively general; their effects and how plants respond to them are topics developed further in subsequent chapters. The one exception is herbivory, which is discussed in this chapter in some detail. The nature of herbivory is complicated, as are the evolutionary responses of plants to herbivory.

DEFINING STRESS AND DISTURBANCE

Two general categories of factors restrict net resource acquisition. Although it might make sense to categorize these factors as those that restrict the uptake of resources and those that increase their loss, that is not the traditional classification for natural selection.

Defining Stress

The first set of factors that reduce plant growth are called stresses. Grime has a simple definition of a stress: "the external constraints which limit the rate of dry matter production of all or part of the vegetation" (Grime 2001, p. 48). Stresses by definition reduce the growth of plants but do not immediately kill plant biomass. Generally, the rate of resource acquisition or biomass production is used as a proxy for reproduction. Plants that acquire a lot of resources or accumulate biomass at a relatively high rate are more likely to reproduce the most.

Reductions in growth result from either reductions in the acquisition of resources relative to a maximum potential uptake or increases in the loss of a resource (not resulting from biomass destruction). The *supply* of a resource is not equivalent to the *availability* of the resource to plants. The supply of a resource is *the rate at which a given resource becomes available*, scaled to a relevant abiotic unit, such as volume of soil or ground area. Nutrient supplies are generally scaled per unit of ground area. As an example, $10 \text{ g N m}^{-2} \text{ y}^{-1}$ would be a possible rate of supply of nitrogen. Often it is relevant to scale nutrients to a volume of soil, such as when comparing plants that differ in the volume of soil they explore. As such, supplies can often be calculated per unit of ground area to a certain depth, such as $10 \text{ g N m}^{-2} \text{ y}^{-1}$ for the soil between 0 and 20 cm depth, or stated per unit of soil volume, such as $50 \text{ μg N cm}^{-3} \text{ y}^{-1}$. Light is often best assessed per unit of ground area.

Supplies of resources might be influenced by plants but are expressed independent of plant traits or the assemblage that an individual is growing in. Availability, on the other hand, is *the supply of a resource that is experienced by an individual*. Nutrient availability is hard to quantify, but qualitatively it is clear that factors exist that cause the supply of nutrients to a plant to be lower than the supply of nutrients in the soil volume that a plant is exploring. For example, the presence of competitors does not lower supplies but does reduce the availability of nutrients to a plant. Similarly, taller plants reduce the availability of light to lower plants. The instantaneous concentrations of nutrients in soil are often used as an index of availability, but concentrations are only a proxy for availability.

Stress is often induced by low availability of a resource. For example, when nutrients enter soil solution at a lower rate than a plant can acquire them and use them for productive purposes, the plant is under stress. The plant's acquisition of nutrients can be reduced by a low resource supply rate, and the decreased acquisition causes a lower rate of growth than if the supply rate were higher. Alternatively, availability can be reduced by factors such as competition that reduce the supplies to an individual rather than the overall supplies. As another example, a decrease in soil moisture that causes plants to close their stomata and reduce the rate of photosynthesis can be a stress, provided the growth rates of the plant are reduced as a consequence of the low soil moisture. Stress can also be caused by factors that reduce the supply of resources to leaves instead of roots. Cloudy skies that cause a reduction in energy gain can cause stress in plants.

Myriad stresses can increase the rate of loss of a resource. Acidity in rainwater can cause leaves to lose nutrients at a faster rate than with neutral rainwater and would be considered a stress if the loss of nutrients reduced growth rates. High temperatures can be a stress by causing plants to increase their respiration rates and suffer net losses of carbon, or by increasing transpiration rates and reducing the water potential of leaves. High ultraviolet radiation can denature proteins, causing chemical energy to be lost, which slows growth as the plants allocate resources to repair the damage caused by ultraviolet radiation.

Stress can also occur as a result of excessive acquisition of a resource. Resources present in excess can interfere with metabolic processes and require the reallocation of other resources from primary growth to repair and coping strategies. For example, plants grown in soils high in available heavy metals may expend extra energy to exclude the metals from their roots (Marschner 1986). Although outside the purview of a book on the resource strategies of plants, other agents increase vegetative growth rates but are a stress with regard to reproduction, since resources are allocated away from reproduction to vegetative growth.

Not all plants are equally stressed by a given factor, which is why it is better to refer to a factor as an agent of stress rather than a stress (or stressor) per se. For example, drying soils can reduce the photosynthesis of a drought-sensitive plant but have little effect on a plant that is able to acquire water just as well at lower soil water potentials as at higher ones. For one plant the low soil water is a stress, for the other it is not a stress. Factors such as lower soil moisture, low nutrient supplies, or high temperatures are agents that can cause stress. Whether they are realized as a stress depends on a plant's traits and its current condition.

Defining Disturbance

Like stresses, disturbances also reduce the reproduction of plants, but they do so by removing or killing biomass. Again, Grime's definition of disturbance is useful here: "the mechanisms which limit the plant biomass by causing its partial or total destruction" (Grime 2001, p. 80). The removal of a leaf by an herbivore is a disturbance. High winds that knock over a tree are a disturbance. Disturbances directly cause a reduction in a plant's RGR by increasing the loss of biomass, but they also affect future growth rates by reducing the ability to acquire new resources. Disturbances generally increase the loss of multiple resources, but they also indirectly decrease the acquisition of new ones.

Like stresses, some disturbances can reduce growth more than would be expected based on the amount of biomass lost. Some biomass has a greater role in future growth than other biomass. For example, the loss of a leaf a week before it would have senesced has less of an effect than the loss of an equal biomass of active meristems. And just as with stresses, not all plants suffer equal losses of biomass when exposed to the same agent of disturbance. Some of the variation that determines whether a given factor becomes a disturbance is associated with the plant's traits. For example, high-velocity winds are likely to be less damaging to a tree with a strong trunk than one with a weak trunk. Similarly, the local environment of a tree contributes to determining its likelihood of being disturbed. A tree that emerges above a forest canopy is more likely to be damaged by high-velocity winds than one that resides below the forest canopy.

There can be a fine line between calling something that increases resource loss a stress or a disturbance. If an agent kills cells or any larger aggregation of cells, it would be considered a disturbance. If an agent removes resources but doesn't kill cells, it would be considered a stress. As an example, a sucking insect that feeds on phloem would be an agent of stress to the plant, while a chewing insect that crushes or eats cells would be an agent of disturbance.

Defining stresses and disturbances as factors that reduce reproduction or more proximally growth but differentiating them by whether they kill biomass or just reduce the net acquisition of resources leads to a situation in which a given agent can be either an agent of stress or an agent of disturbance. Low soil moisture that reduces the growth of a plant is solely a stress until biomass begins to die, then it also become a disturbance. If a given agent is simultaneously reducing the net acquisition of a resource and also killing biomass, then it would be both stressing and disturbing the plant. The agent could be considered to cause both a stress and a disturbance, although the relative importance of a net reduction in resource acquisition and biomass loss could be ranked to allow one to think of the agent categorically. How the magnitude of negative effects should be compared is addressed in chapter 6.

Major Causes of Stress and Disturbance

Plant stress is created by agents that cause reductions in the acquisition of resources or increases in the loss of resources. Disturbances cause the death of biomass from the cellular level on up. Because stresses and disturbances are the primary agents of natural selection, understanding the causes of stress and disturbance is an important component of understanding both plant strategies and the dynamics of ecosystems. This section reviews the major agents of stress, focusing first on agents that restrict the acquisition of resources and then on those that increase the loss of resources. Thereafter the major agents of disturbance are reviewed. By definition, all increase the death of biomass.

Agents of Stress

Reductions in the acquisition of resources can result from decreases in supplies of resources to the plant. For example, if nutrients or light are supplied at a relatively low rate, the internal availability of resources can decline, slowing growth. The causes of an inadequate supply of nutrients or light and how they have created pressure for the selection of particular plant traits are complex topics and are discussed separately in the next two chapters.

Other agents cause stress by decreasing the ability of plants to acquire resources at a given supply rate. For example, low soil temperatures can slow the uptake of nutrients by plants by decreasing the metabolic activity of roots and consequently the rate at which roots can actively take up nutrients (Chapin 1979). Low temperatures can also cause embolisms in a plant's xylem, limiting transpiration rates (Pearce 2001), while high temperatures can denature the proteins required for photosynthesis.

In contrast to decreasing the acquisition of a resource, some agents stress plants by increasing the loss of a resource. Abiotic agents that cause stress include high temperatures, which can increase the rate of respiration of plants, and excess ion availability in the soil, which causes plants to expend more energy to exclude the excess ions.

Biotic stressors include insects, parasitic plants, and pathogens. Each stresses plants by tapping into resource supplies, which decreases resource availability to other plant parts. Sucking insects such as aphids can tap into the resources that are carried in the phloem or xylem and divert the resources from their intended destination. Parasitic plants form direct connections into a plant's xylem or phloem and, like insects, redirect resources to themselves. Pathogens, which can be fungal, bacterial, or viral in origin, redirect resources away from vegetative growth to their own growth. Although the disease is often initially contained entirely within the plant, usurpation of plant resources by the diseases still increases loss rates.

Agents of Disturbance

Any agent that stresses a plant can cause the death of biomass, if the stress becomes severe enough. A mild drought that decreases water availability, if prolonged or of increasing severity, can cause plant biomass to die.

Sucking insects can remove enough resources to starve biomass downstream, rather than just slow the growth rate.

Some disturbances concentrate biomass removal aboveground, others belowground, and yet others kill biomass both above- and belowground, if sometimes not the entire plant. The selectivity of the disturbances also varies, in part with the traits of the plants. Some disturbances can be relatively indiscriminate, regardless of the traits of the plants present. These are referred to as *general* disturbances. Other agents target individual species out of a diverse assemblage. These disturbances are referred to as *selective* disturbances.

The ways in which abiotic disturbances remove plant biomass are generally not complex. High winds can blow trees over and snap limbs. Fires directly remove biomass via combustion or denaturing and can kill meristematic tissues, limiting future growth or girdling trees. Freezing soils and drying soils can cause soil movement, which can sever roots. In contrast, pathogens and herbivores cause disturbance (and stress) in a myriad of ways. What is understood about herbivory is described in the next section.

How Herbivory Works

Biotic disturbances are the most complex set of disturbances that exist. There are many ways in which herbivores can damage tissues. This section does not provide a comprehensive treatment of herbivory but instead lays out ways in which plants are eaten, focusing on the feeding strategies, physiologies, and resource requirements of herbivores. These concepts are paired later in this chapter with the evolution of plant responses to the presence of herbivores. The eventual goal is to understand how pressure from herbivores varies across environments, and subsequently how defenses against herbivores contribute to strategies for success in different environments.

There are three major categories of herbivores: insects, mammals, and birds. They differ mainly in their mouthparts, which determine how biomass is removed from a plant; their digestive system, which determines how food is processed; and their general physiological requirements, which determine the resource requirements of the herbivores.

Why Animals Eat Plants

Herbivores eat plants to acquire the two resources that most limit their growth: energy and protein. There are other nutrients that plants provide herbivores, but these can also be acquired from other sources, such as mineral licks, and are less frequently limiting to the growth of herbivores.

There is no doubt, for example, that sodium is an important element for herbivores, since it is the only element essential to animals that is not essential to plants. By and large, however, energy and protein are the most important constituents of plants for herbivores. There is no other manner for herbivores to acquire them except to eat plants, and the spatial and temporal availability of energy and protein in plants is a major determinant of the relative abundance of different species of herbivores and their performance in different environments.

Any given part of a plant can be roughly divided into the materials contained in its cell walls and the contents of the plant cells (Van Soest 1982). Herbivores can acquire energy from both the contents of cells and the cell walls. Energy in the cell contents is generally more labile than that in the cell wall, but cell walls generally make up a higher fraction of plant biomass. Although cell contents can be digested easily by herbivores, because of the recalcitrance of the compounds in the cell wall, herbivores need to culture microbes in their guts to acquire energy from cell walls. Some cell wall fractions are recalcitrant enough that their energy is essentially unavailable to any herbivore. Protein is almost exclusively contained in the cell contents.

The quality of the plant biomass for herbivores depends in part on the traits of the herbivore but is generally determined by (1) the amount of labile carbon in the cell, (2) the amount of protein in the cell, and (3) the amount of secondary chemicals that affect digestion or physiology. An optimal diet for a given herbivore has a good balance of protein to available energy. Deviations from optimality are dependent on the digestive system of the herbivore and can happen for many reasons. For example, for some herbivores, plant biomass can have too little available protein as a result of having too low a ratio of cell contents to cell wall; for example, senesced leaves have little cell content left. In general, when food has too little available energy, herbivores respond by altering the rate at which material passes though its digestive system. Some animals end up eating more biomass, some eat less. In general, when plant biomass has too little available protein, either from having too low a fraction of cell contents or through the action of secondary compounds that restrict protein availability (see below), some herbivores can alter the rate of passage of material through their gut or supply nitrogen to microbes by recycling urea to the gut, while some herbivores that rely on microbial communities in their gut for digestion are obligated to break down muscle to maintain microbial communities.

The patterns of responses to herbivores to variation in food quality are somewhat complex for generalizing statements across all herbivores and are more easily understood when analyzed by herbivore class. Secondary compounds also vary in their effects on herbivores.

Insects

Insects are the herbivores with the most diverse set of mouthparts. Some insects are able to tap into vessels with piercing mouthparts, while others consume plants by biting off and chewing small pieces of biomass. Some insects can masticate entire sections of leaves or roots, while others concentrate on the consumption of individual tissues within an organ. For example, miners concentrate on consuming the tissues between the upper and lower epidermis of leaves, while bark beetles concentrate on the cambium of trees. Other insects consume the entire cross section of biomass but are restricted in where they attack plants, for example, concentrating on the biomass between the hard veins in a leaf.

After ingesting the plant biomass, insects digest only the contents of the cells. Cell walls that are ingested pass through the insect gut undigested. When insects are forced to rely on plant biomass that has too little protein or too little available energy for optimal growth, they can often increase their intake rate in order to compensate for the low quality. For grasshoppers, the uptake of protein is limited by absorption capacity in the gut. When fed a diet that is balanced in carbohydrates and protein, grasshoppers retain food in the gut longer than when the stoichiometry of carbohydrate and protein is suboptimal (Raubenheimer and Simpson 2004). Poor diets pass through the digestive system quicker. The excess carbohydrate in the diet is still absorbed into the bloodstream of the grasshopper and metabolized (i.e., burned off) through a currently unknown pathway. When the stoichiometry of the plant biomass that insects feed on becomes highly skewed, other factors besides retention time become bottlenecks. For example, over longer time scales, grasshoppers can increase the capacity of their digestive system (Yang and Joern 1994). One key for insect nutrition is that when the quality of the diet declines, insects cannot completely compensate by increasing passage rates; insects grow more slowly, and the time between instars increases. Empirically, it appears that when the protein concentrations of a grasshopper's diet approaches 6% protein, approximately 1% nitrogen, molting stops, and most individuals die before reaching the next instar (Raubenheimer and Simpson 2004; S. J. Simpson, personal communication; see also Joern and Behmer 1997; Clissold, Sanson, and Read 2006).

Termites are the one exception to the rule of minimum nitrogen requirements among insects. Termites have a specialized gut that harbors a microbial flora that can fix atmospheric nitrogen (Brune and Friedrich 2000). Although they prefer to eat biomass with higher nitrogen concentrations, termites can subsist on nitrogen-free substrates. Largely restricted to ecosystems where temperatures do not get below freezing, they can be large consumers of low-protein vegetation such as wood and senesced leaves. The ability to produce protein on a low-protein diet has ramifications for herbivory in some low-nutrient habitats and for how plants defend themselves.

Mammals

Mammals differ from insects in the way they obtain vegetation, in their digestive systems, and in their much greater size. After the sheer height of the animals, which enables them to access more biomass, the removal of biomass by mammals is determined largely by their lips, tongue, and teeth. Some mammals pull off biomass by grasping it first with their lips. Others, such as giraffes, sometimes wrap their tongues around a branch and strip it. Most mammals pull or shear biomass with their teeth. In almost all acquisition strategies, biomass is chewed in the mouth as the first part in the digestion process.

Mammals have three major types of digestive systems. For mammals, the simplest digestive system is analogous to that of insects. Like insects, species such as panda bears and most primates largely digest cell contents. Other herbivorous mammals have adaptations that allow them to culture microbes (Van Soest 1982). The microbes digest cell walls under anaerobic conditions, and then the energetic by-products of anaerobic fermentation or the microbes are digested. Foregut fermenters, such as cows and kangaroos, culture microbes before the plant material reaches the stomach. Microbial acids generated under anaerobic conditions are used as an energy source by the mammals, and the microbes themselves are digested for protein. Hindgut fermenters, such as horses, elephants, and lagomorphs, foster microbial fermentation in the colon. Again, anaerobically produced acids are absorbed by the mammal and used as an energy source. For hindgut fermenters, there is no chance to digest microbes and acquire microbial protein in the colon. When protein deficient, animals such as rodents, lagomorphs, and even horses may practice caecotrophy and reingest feces to digest the microbial protein that had developed during digestion (White 1993).

Although hindgut fermentation is less efficient in some ways than foregut fermentation, fermentation in the colon allows animals to selectively pass coarse, low-protein material such as plant stems. Foregut fermenters such as cows have a sievelike structure (omasum) before the true stomach that requires them to attempt to digest coarse, low-quality material to a small particle size, which is a slow process that reduces the rate of digestion.

When the availability of plant biomass is sufficient, there are few situations in which the availability of energy is limiting for fermenting mammals. Instead, fermenting mammals are generally faced with a lack of protein. When hindgut fermenters are faced with insufficient protein concentrations, the animals can speed up the rate of passage of plant material through their digestive system, compensating for the low quality with greater quantity and allowing microbial populations to be maintained to provide energy for the animals. As with insects, passage time can only be increased to a certain point, and hindgut fermenters can ultimately be limited by protein concentrations. For foregut fermenters, passage time cannot be increased to compensate for low protein concentrations. Because of the omasum, all particles in the fermentation chambers must be digested until a small size is reached that can pass through the omasum to the stomach. In the face of low protein concentrations, to maintain microbial activity, digestion, and energy production, foregut fermenters break down muscle and supply some of it to microbes.

The minimum nitrogen concentrations required to maintain condition for foregut fermenters is approximately 10 mg N g^{-1} biomass (1% nitrogen by mass). When feeding on biomass that has nitrogen concentrations below this threshold, foregut fermenters lose muscle. Even higher threshold concentrations exist if foregut fermenters are to meet the demands of reproduction. The threshold protein concentration for growth can be lower for hindgut fermenters. Yet the lower nitrogen concentrations must be caused by the inclusion of coarse material that dilutes the overall nitrogen concentration but can be passed through the gut without being digested. Digestible material still must have about 10 mg N g^{-1} for microbial populations to grow and provide energy to the animals. For example, horses can gain weight eating grass that is 5 mg N g^{-1}, but only if the leaves have a nitrogen concentration greater than 10 mg N g^{-1} and more than half the biomass is stem, with relatively little to no protein.

Beyond the different digestive systems affecting mammalian herbivory, there are variations in the energy and nitrogen concentration requirements of mammals with different body mass that result from differences in metabolic rates and gut capacity (Demment and Van Soest 1985). Smaller animals require a higher quality diet than larger animals, but these differences are secondary to the basic patterns of herbivory associated with differences in digestive systems.

Birds

Although birds are not thought to be as important herbivores as insects and mammals, they can consume large amounts of vegetation. For example, geese can consume a large fraction of aboveground production in arctic marshes (Cargill and Jefferies 1984). Before human settlement, New Zealand did not have herbivorous mammals, and herbivory was dominated by a range of birds, from shrub-eating moas to grass-eating takahe. Instead of the soft mouthparts of mammals, birds have a hard beak. However, they do not have the hinged jaw that allows shearing, requiring biomass to be plucked off plants. The simple digestive system of birds allows them to digest only cell contents. Only the hoatzin (*Opisthocomus hoazin*), a South American folivorous bird, is known to encourage microbial fermentation in its gut (Dominguezbello et al. 1993), but others are suspected to do so (Pacheco et al. 2004). As such, in general, birds have high energy and protein requirements, and they select for plant biomass that has a high ratio of cell contents to cell wall.

Growth in the Face of Stress and Disturbance

Minimizing the effects of agents that cause stress or disturbance follows three well-known evolutionary approaches: resistance, response, and avoidance (Macgillivray et al. 1995). Resisting agents of stress or disturbance requires allocating resources away from structures that directly increase resource acquisition to structures that reduce the ability of stress agents to reduce growth or the ability of agents of disturbance to remove biomass. In the absence of a specific agent, plants that do not allocate resources to these structures grow faster than ones that do. The specific structures associated with low availability of resources are covered in subsequent chapters, while defenses against herbivory are discussed later in this chapter. In general, to resist agents of stress and disturbance, plants have been selected to allocate resources to compounds with no primary benefit (secondary compounds), as well as to defensive mechanisms such as thicker cell walls, greater wax production on leaf surfaces, and greater production of bark on trees.

Not all compounds and structures that do not have a primary function would have been selected for as a way to resist stress and disturbance agents. If agents of stress or disturbance are not (or cannot be) resisted, some plants gain an advantage through being able to respond better after the stress or disturbance has passed (see below).

Finally, when agents of stress or disturbance are somewhat predictable and limited in temporal scope, plants can avoid them entirely by reducing growth or susceptibility in advance of the onset of these agents' actions. For example, in temperate regions, the cold temperatures of winter are predictable, and plants can recover nutrients in leaves before freezing temperatures arrive.

Structural Defenses against Herbivory

Any factor that leads to a decrease in herbivory can be thought of as a defense. Defenses against herbivory by definition reduce the rate of resource or biomass removal by herbivores and can be identified by determining whether their presence benefits plants in the presence of herbivores.

Although there are multiple possible hierarchies for classifying plant defenses, the biggest categorical difference is that between structural and chemical defenses (figure 3.1). The most obvious structural defenses are of the thorn class and include thorns, spines, and prickles. Although the three types differ in the tissues from which they originate—thorns are modified stems, spines originate in stipules, and prickles originate in epidermis—from a resource perspective, all three are primarily composed of wood and require little nitrogen to produce. Thorns are produced on stems, branches, and even underground on tubers, where they protect against fossorial mammals. Here, all of these structures are collectively referred to as thorns.

Thorns do not absolutely eliminate herbivory, but they do reduce the feeding rate of mammals (Wilson and Kerley 2003). For example, straight spines force mammals to select leaves carefully. Hooked thorns point toward the base of the stem and prevent herbivores such as giraffes from curling their tongue around a stem and stripping the leaves off by pulling. By slowing down the rate of biomass acquisition by mammalian herbivores, the structural defenses can reduce the rate of herbivory by a single herbivore and encourage herbivores to select other plants. In addition to reducing leaf browsing, thorns have the potentially more important purpose of protecting meristems. Without thorns, herbivores could consume entire shoots, removing not only leaf and stem biomass but also meristems, thus reducing the potential for future growth.

Thorns slow the feeding rate of mammals on leaves but are less effective at protecting leaves against the hard beaks of bird. Browsing birds such as rheas, emus, ostriches, and the extinct moas and elephant birds feed in a uniquely different manner from mammals. Birds have a hard beak but lack a hinged jaw, and so cannot shear stems (Bond, Lee, and Craine 2004). Birds can only pluck at plants, grabbing shoots and pulling back. In places where browsing birds have had a significant selective pressure on plants, plants have developed a unique structural defense called the wire plant defense (Bond, Lee, and Craine 2004). This involves (1) narrow, strong stems that do not snap when pulled, (2) a concertina-like structure to stems, which elongate when pulled, thus reducing the force that a bird can apply to the stem, and (3) a cagelike three-dimensional structure that prevents wholesale swallowing of biomass by birds, which

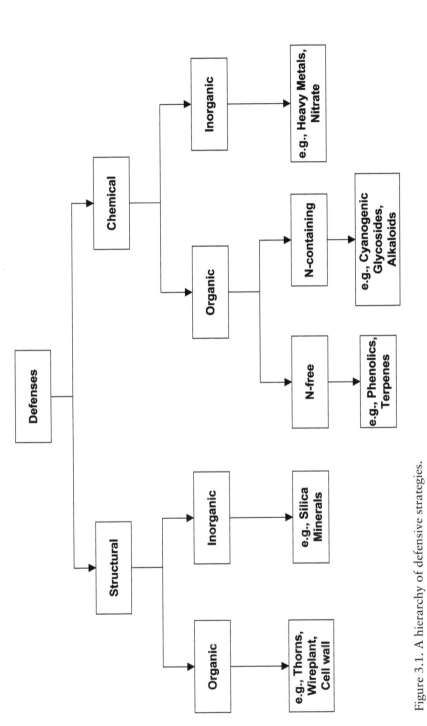

Figure 3.1. A hierarchy of defensive strategies.

are poor at manipulating the biomass. Latex, which reduces the ability of herbivores to chew, is probably best considered a structural defense, although it can carry other compounds that serve as chemical defenses (Zalucki, Brower, and Alonso 2001).

Last among the organic structures that provide defense against herbivores are cell walls themselves (Lucas et al. 2000; Sanson 2006). There is considerable interspecies variation in cell size and the thickness of cell walls, and in the compounds embedded in cell walls. Although hard, tough cell walls provide resistance to other stresses, their presence increases the force required to shear or crush tissues, essentially making it harder to chew. More cell wall material also decreases the quality of the tissue for herbivores, diluting cell contents and lowering protein concentrations (Van Soest 1982). If cells are hard to crush, cell contents are protected from absorption. For example, grasshoppers have difficulty absorbing the contents of cells associated with the sclerotic bundle sheaths of C_4 grasses (Barbehenn and Bernays 1992).

Cell walls can be stiffened not just with organic structures but also with inorganic crystalline structures. The most widespread crystalline structure with defensive properties is silica (McNaughton et al. 1985; Lucas et al. 2000). In addition to providing cell rigidity, which increases the force needed to shear or crush cells, silica wears down herbivores' teeth and abrades soft tissues (Sanson 2006). In some cases, high silica concentrations can cause urolithiasis in mammals, in which condition silica builds up in the urethra and reduces or blocks urination, although in modern times this is a rare event (Parker 1957). Other inorganic structures, such as those derived from oxalic acids or minerals (McManus, Robinson, and Grout 1977), can serve similar purposes.

Chemical Defenses against Herbivory

Plants protect themselves not only structurally but also chemically. Chemical defenses are generally stored within specialized cells, within vacuoles of cells, or within specialized ducts. Chemical defenses can be inorganic or organic. Most inorganic compounds that have defensive purposes are structural in effect. Yet many species can accumulate heavy metals to levels that are toxic to herbivores (but see Noret et al. 2007), while others can accumulate NO_3^- in vacuoles that binds to hemoglobin in mammals but has little effect in insects.

Organic defensive compounds make up the most diverse set of defenses. Organic defensive compounds can be strictly composed of carbon, hydrogen, and oxygen, or they may also contain nitrogen. Non-nitrogen-containing compounds generally are quantitative in nature, being required in large amounts (relative to those defenses considered qualitative).

They generally act by reducing the availability of energy or protein to herbivores on ingestion, while others have diuretic properties (Dearing, Foley, and McLean 2005).

The most common classes of organic, nitrogen-free quantitative chemical defenses are the phenolics. Phenolics are often stored in specialized individual cells or in ducts, and act to reduce the digestibility of food. Polyphenolics such as tannins are stored within specialized cells and bind with protein under neutral to acid pH, reducing protein availability to herbivores (Hagerman et al. 1992; Reed 1995). It has long been known that there are many other nitrogen-free chemical defenses against herbivory (Levin 1976; Bennett and Wallsgrove 1994). Among the other compounds, furanocoumarins are prevalent in plants such as those of the Apiaceae family. In the presence of ultraviolet radiation, furanocoumarins bind to DNA (Berenbaum, Nitao, and Zangerl 1991). Other nitrogen-free chemical defenses include terpenes, coumarins, and cardiac glycosides, all of which have unique effects on herbivores.

Nitrogen-containing chemicals are generally qualitative and affect the nervous system or cellular respiration. Cyanogenic glycosides in the presence of the right enzymes and oxygen release cyanide. Present in more than 2,000 species, including *Prunus*, cyanide effectively short-circuits the electron transport chain and stops cellular respiration (Bennett and Wallsgrove 1994). Glucosinolates are present in many families of plants (mainly of the order Capparales) but are especially abundant in members of the Brassicaceae family (Bennett and Wallsgrove 1994). Glucosinolates are evolutionarily related to cyanogenic glycosides but have a central carbon atom bonded to both nitrogen and sulfur (Halkier and Gershenzon 2006). On tissue damage, glucosinolates are enzymatically hydrolyzed to other compounds that have a host of chemical properties, including reacting with proteins and causing goiter in mammals. Alkaloids are the other major class of nitrogen-containing defensive chemicals. More than 10,000 forms of alkaloids have been identified that again have a large range of effects, such as impairing liver function (Bennett and Wallsgrove 1994). Nonprotein amino acids substitute for amino acids in proteins and cause the proteins to become malformed.

Another feature differentiating defenses is that some defenses are inducible, such that plants can be triggered to increase the production of the defenses, while others are constitutive and not subject to stimulation. Jeffrey Harborne stated that one of the most important advances of the past 25 years in understanding plant-animal interactions is that some plants respond to damage by increasing the production of defenses (Harborne 2001). Although the frequency of having inducible defenses has not been estimated, they are not omnipresent. Some inducible defenses have a direct negative effect against herbivores, while others indirectly reduce feeding by attracting parasitoids or predators of the herbivores without having any primary effect on the herbivore. The timing of induction is variable, but gene regulation can be induced within minutes of attack, while it might take days for the induced defense to be expressed (Kessler and Baldwin 2002).

Circumventing Defenses

For every defense against herbivores, there seems to be a strategy herbivores can use to circumvent the defense. Structural defenses can be circumvented, as it is almost a given that structural defenses do not offer total protection to plant biomass. Prickles can stop slugs from crawling up stems but have little effect in protecting leaves. Thorns have little impact on insects, and nimble-mouthed large mammals or hard-beaked birds can eat around them. High tissue density has little effect on strong-jawed mammals, while in mammals with high-crowned teeth, there are few short- to medium-term effects of silica grinding (Lucas et al. 2000; Sanson 2006).

Protein-tannin complexes disassociate at high pH, and the midgut pH of many insects, such as gypsy moth larvae and *Alsophila* and *Anisota* caterpillars (White 1993), can be above 10. Mammals can produce low-molecular-weight proteins in their saliva to sacrificially bind with the tannins (Robbins et al. 1991). The secretory canals that carry latex or resin, which also can contain terpenes or alkaloids, can be severed at the base of a leaf, reducing the leaf's defenses (Robbins et al. 1991). Phloem feeders can avoid the canals entirely (Becerra et al. 2001). Some insects, colloquially known as leaf rollers, spin webs to wrap themselves in a leaf. Rolling the leaf around them shades them from ultraviolet light, and the furanocoumarins are never activated (Berenbaum 2001).

Not only can nitrogen-based defenses be circumvented, they can also be used to advantage by some herbivores. Monarch butterfly caterpillars can sequester the alkaloids of plants such as milkweed, using them ultimately as a defense against predators. Some species, such as humans and butterflies, can metabolize cyanogenic compounds, while others sequester cyanogens for defense (Gleadow and Woodrow 2002). Sucking insects do not initiate cyanide production as they do not disrupt the cells, and the cyanogens and glucosidase never come into contact. Nonprotein amino acids can be metabolized by some beetles. For example, *Dioclea* species, which are in the Fabaceae family, produce arginine analogs, but these can be metabolized by bruchid beetles (Rosenthal 1977). Heavy metals or tannins in leaf tissue have no effect on phloem feeders.

It has been argued that the net effect of any given defense is not to reduce the herbivory rate, just the number of herbivores that feed on the species. As such, plants generally have multiple defenses. For example, *Acacia* trees have both spines and tannins in their leaves (Brooks and Owen-Smith 1994). Once a given defense or set of defenses is circumvented, defenses then serve the primary purpose of reducing the feeding rate. Thorns slow down mammal feeding, while chemical defenses such as nicotine slow the growth of specialist herbivores, which invest resources in detoxification (Cresswell, Merritt, and Martin 1992). The benefit of any given defense or set of defenses is therefore not to halt all herbivory but instead to slow herbivory to the point where new growth can exceed herbivory. It is also possible that if plants can slow herbivore feeding rates, the herbivores may become more vulnerable to predators, indirectly limiting herbivory rates (Coley and Barone 1996). In fact, plants have other approaches to increasing the likelihood that predators find herbivores. Some plants release volatile organic molecules upon damage by herbivores that predators cue in on (Baldwin 2001).

Responding after Stress and Disturbance

Some stresses or disturbances are unavoidable, and there is little a plant can do to limit the severity of the effects. In such cases, it is more beneficial to store resources to regrow after the stress or disturbance has passed than to try to limit the effects of the agent (Chapin, Schulze, and Mooney 1990; Iwasa and Kubo 1997). Storage has been distinguished from accumulation (Millard 1988). The accumulation of resources occurs when resources are supplied in excess of the plant's immediate ability to use them and comes at little immediate cost to growth. In contrast, storage competes with immediate growth and comes at the cost of slowing growth. Separating accumulation and storage is not trivial, especially when they are assessed in the field.

Storage occurs on multiple scales, from daily, associated with diurnal variability in light availability, to interannually, to cope with rare events. Although the details of storage are largely outside the purview of this book, storage allows plants to use the resources supplied during large pulses and thereby gain competitive advantage where competitive interactions are asymmetric. To respond to disturbances and stresses, plants store carbohydrates as well as nutrients (Nordin and Nasholm 1997; Bausenwein et al. 2001). The optimal storage size increases with the age and longevity of the plant and varies with the frequency of disturbance or stress.

Responding to disturbance or stress with increased growth rates also often requires the presence of dormant meristems that can be turned on after the stress or disturbance has passed. For example, many plants have "bud banks" that can respond to the greater availability of resources following disturbances or can utilize stored resources when appropriate (Vesk and Westoby 2004).

THE LINKS TO RESOURCE AVAILABILITY

The particular approaches to resisting and responding to stress and disturbances can be matched with the general strategies associated with differences in resource availability. For example, there are clear patterns linking the environments that favor species that use nitrogen-based chemical defenses with other traits those species hold. These relationships between environment and traits are determined in part by differences in resource stress among environments. As such, the subject of the next chapter is low resource availability as a stress, and resource limitation. The chapter covers how nutrients are supplied to plants and what factors limit the supplies of nutrients. Stress caused by the acquisition of resources by other organisms (competition) is considered in chapter 5.

SUMMARY

Stresses and disturbances reduce the growth of plants and consequently their ability to reproduce. Stresses reduce the rate of net resource acquisition either by reducing the rate of resource acquisition or by increasing the rate of resource loss. Disturbances cause the loss of biomass, which is arbitrarily defined to occur at the cellular level in order to constitute a disturbance. Whether a particular agent or condition causes stress or disturbance cannot always be clearly distinguished. Severe stress can become a disturbance if biomass begins to die, and the same agent can cause stress and disturbance. Because of the differential susceptibility of species to agents of stress and disturbance, stresses and disturbances may be either selective or general, if all species are more or less equally affected.

Resisting stresses and disturbances or responding to them once they have passed requires that resources be allocated to processes that do not lead directly to more resource acquisition. Resisting stresses and disturbances can require (1) the synthesis of compounds that reside in the cytoplasm, (2) modification of the cell wall, or (3) the production of new tissues altogether. In other cases, physiological processes are reduced ahead of time or biomass is prematurely senesced to reduce losses of resources. Preparedness to respond in the aftermath of stresses or disturbances generally entails producing stores that can be remobilized for later growth.

Because herbivores can evolve in response to evolution in plants, herbivory is the most varied of disturbances, yet the basic themes are the same. Defense requires allocating resources away from growth or sacrificing biomass prematurely. The most basic sorting of defenses is into chemical or structural types. Chemical defenses can be inorganic, such as heavy metals, organic but not containing nitrogen, such as polyphenolics, or organic and containing nitrogen, such as alkaloids. Inorganic and nitrogen-free organic chemicals generally must be produced in large amounts to be effective, while organic, nitrogen-containing defenses are more qualitative and are effective in lower concentrations. Some defenses can be induced, others are constitutive.

In the end, no one defense is adequate to deter all herbivores over the long term. Thorns are of little deterrence to insects, tannins can be disassociated from protein in the high-pH gut of gypsy moths, and many insects can metabolize or sequester nitrogen-containing chemicals. Most plants have multiple defenses. In the end, the minimal purpose of defenses is to slow herbivory sufficiently that plants can experience positive growth, rather than eliminate herbivory altogether.

CHAPTER 4

Resource Limitation

WHEN THE SUPPLY of a resource to a plant is less than is required for growth, stress develops, and plant growth becomes limited by the low availability of that resource. Any essential resource can be limiting to growth, and there is no necessary limit to the number of resources that can limit growth at a given time. Similarly, different plants growing in the same habitat can be limited by different resources for a number of reasons, including differences in demand ratios or in the amounts of essential resources required for growth. An important part of plant strategies has to do with differences in resource demands among species. Natural selection has often worked to alter not only demands but also how plants acquire resources when the resources are limiting.

Stress and limitation are intertwined for resources such as light and nutrients. The nature of resource stress is tightly linked to theories of resource limitation. Many of the current theories on stress and limitation derive from a time when scientific understanding of how resources become available to plants and how plants use resources to grow was underdeveloped. Therefore, a quick review of the history of the development of nutrient cycles is warranted before introducing recent advances. Key questions that relate to plant strategies include how nutrients become available to plants, as well as the spatial and temporal heterogeneity of resource availability. For both light and nutrients, the plant strategies that arise if limiting resources are supplied at a low, uniform rate are qualitatively different from those associated with resource supplies that are temporally heterogeneous.

The other key advance in understanding limitation is the concept of co-limitation of growth by multiple resources. Co-limitation is much more common than would be predicted from the most widely accepted basic principles of limitation (Elser et al. 2007) and likely has played a large role in shaping plant strategies in different environments. The original theories of resource limitation, which have been little developed since they were first formulated 150 years ago, are inadequate to explain why co-limitation occurs as often as it does, which resources are most likely to be co-limiting in a given environment, and the ecological and evolutionary impact of co-limitation. In many cases, natural selection is driven by co-limitation of resources rather than by single-resource limitation, and that has affected everything from the patterns of plant defenses to allocation strategies among species and environments.

THE CONCEPT OF SINGLE-RESOURCE LIMITATION

When a resource is supplied to a plant at a rate that is less than the plant's demand for the resource, the plant is said to be under resource stress. When a plant is under resource stress, alleviating that stress should increase growth. If so, the growth of the plant is considered to be *limited* by the supply of that resource. The idea that a single resource could limit growth dates back to the time before ecology was a recognized discipline. The concept of limitation was developed to understand the mineral nutrition of crop plants at a time when the understanding of both resource supplies and plant growth was quite rudimentary.

The Law of the Minimum

The concept of limitation is derived from agricultural research in the first half of the nineteenth century. In 1837, the chemist Justus von Liebig was asked by the British Association for the Advancement of Science to comment on the application of chemical principles to agriculture. In the resulting 1843 work, titled *Chemistry and Its Application to Agriculture and Physiology*, Liebig began to lay out the principles of limitation and articulate the theory of plant stress. In 1862 he formulated what would become known as the law of the minimum. This law, which was restricted in its application to just nutrients, has three essential parts.

First, *growth is limited by the resource that is supplied at the lowest rate relative to the demands of the plant*. Liebig stated, "By the deficiency or absence of *one* necessary constituent, all the others being present, the soil is rendered barren for all those crops to the life of which *that one* constituent is indispensable" (Liebig 1855, p. 24).

The general concept embodied in the first part of Liebig's law of the minimum seems straightforward: where there isn't enough of a given nutrient, growth is restricted. If there isn't any of the resource, there is no growth. Yet what constitutes a deficiency is unclear. The effect is clear: demand needs to exceed availability. But what conditions lead to a deficiency? Liebig assumed that nutrients were needed in a fixed ratio for a given species, but he knew little about the processes by which nutrients are made available to plants.

Second, *growth is proportional to the rate of supply of the most limiting resource*. This second statement addresses the consequences of the presence of limitation as well as relieving limitation. An increase in the supply of the limiting resource should be matched by an increase in growth. Having growth be proportional to the rate of supply implies that the resource in question is the only resource that is limiting, in which case a 50% increase in supply, for example, should theoretically be matched by a 50% increase in production.

Third, *growth cannot be increased by increasing the supply of a nonlimiting nutrient*. This last part is somewhat axiomatic, but is important in that it functionally separates limiting and nonlimiting nutrients.

In stating the law of the minimum, Liebig echoed what another agricultural chemist, Carl Sprengel, had stated in 1828: "when a plant needs 12 substances to develop, it will not grow if any one of these is not available in a sufficiently large amount as required by the nature of the plant" (cited in van der Ploeg, Bohm, and Kirkham 1999). Sprengel's work was an important source of understanding for Liebig, and Sprengel has recently come to be considered the co-originator of the law of the minimum with Liebig. Although Sprengel had first stated that plant growth is limited by the nutrient in shortest supply, Liebig offered a clearer set of rules for resource limitation, and his formulation is used here.

Co-limitation versus Serial Limitation

Liebig had little to say specifically about co-limitation of resources, but his concept of co-limitation is clear from the metaphor of limitation as a barrel with uneven staves from which water is flowing (figure 4.1). Liebig himself did not use this analogy, as it was not until 1906 that German advertisements for inorganic fertilizers depicted limitation with uneven staves in a barrel (Holloway and Paris 2002). In the staves-on-a-barrel metaphor, the height of the staves represents the supply of a given nutrient relative to the demand of the plant. When a given nutrient is supplied at a high ratio relative to the demand of the plant, its stave is tall. Short staves represent nutrients that are supplied in a low ratio relative to the demand of a plant. The shortest stave represents the most limiting nutrient and determines the level of the water, analogous to the productivity of the vegetation.

According to Liebig's law of the minimum, when the supply of the limiting nutrient is increased, productivity increases until another nutrient becomes limiting, after which adding more of the originally limiting nutrient does not increase productivity. Now, only addition of the secondarily limiting nutrient leads to increases in productivity. In this case, the two

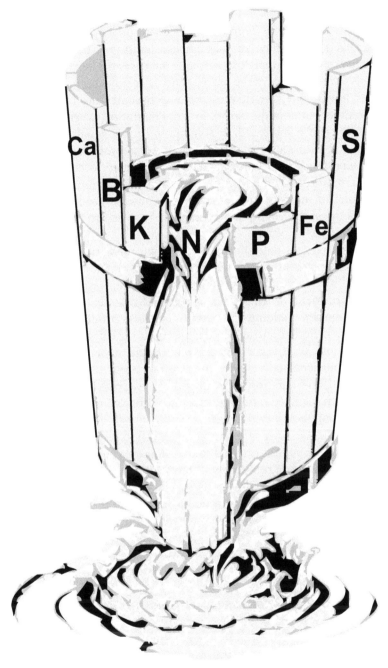

Figure 4.1. Liebig's law of the minimum, shown as a bucket analogy. The height of an individual stave of the bucket represents the supply of the individual nutrient relative to the demand of the plant. Plant productivity is equivalent to the level of the water in the bucket, which is determined by the height of the shortest stave.

nutrients are *serially limiting*: one nutrient limits growth until its supply exceeds demand, then another nutrient limits growth (figure 4.2).

Increasing the supply of a resource increases the height of the stave and leads to more water in the barrel. Once that stave becomes taller than the next lowest one, the new lowest one becomes the factor limiting the amount of water in the barrel. In serial limitation, when the supply of the first nutrient is increased, at some point it just equals demand, because demand is also constrained by the supply of another nutrient. At this point the supplies of the two nutrients are considered to be co-limiting. With co-limitation as formulated in Liebig's law of the minimum, an increase in either of the two nutrients does not increase production. Both staves are of the same height, and both must be raised to increase the level of the water in the barrel.

This model of limitation generates two predictions regarding the responses of vegetation to nutrient addition. First, if production is co-limited by two nutrients, production should not respond to the addition of two nutrients when each is applied individually. With Liebig's law of the minimum, if adding one nutrient increases production, then the addition of a different nutrient in the absence of the first should not increase production. Yet if vegetation responds frequently enough to the addition of two nutrients individually, then the law needs to be revised.

Second, co-limitation of production by two nutrients should be rare. If a species has a fixed ratio of demand for different nutrients, then the odds that the supplies of two nutrients exactly match demand are exceedingly low. As a result, only rarely should vegetation respond to the addition of two nutrients but not respond to the addition of one. Although this is not the best place for a full review of fertilization experiments, in some cases the patterns of observed responses to fertilization fit the law of the minimum paradigm: vegetation responds initially to the addition of only one nutrient. Yet increases in productivity with the individual addition of two or more nutrients are frequently seen, and co-limitation occurs much more often than one would predict from first principles.

HISTORY OF THE NITROGEN CYCLE CONCEPT

Nitrogen and phosphorus are the two nutrients most likely to be limiting to the production of terrestrial vegetation. Research on both dates back to the early to mid-1800s, when researchers such as Sprengel and Liebig investigated the role of the two nutrients as fertilizers for agricultural crops. The adumbration of the nitrogen cycle from the time Liebig first formulated the law of the minimum through approximately 1900 marks the beginning of the era of the classical nitrogen cycle. The neoclassical

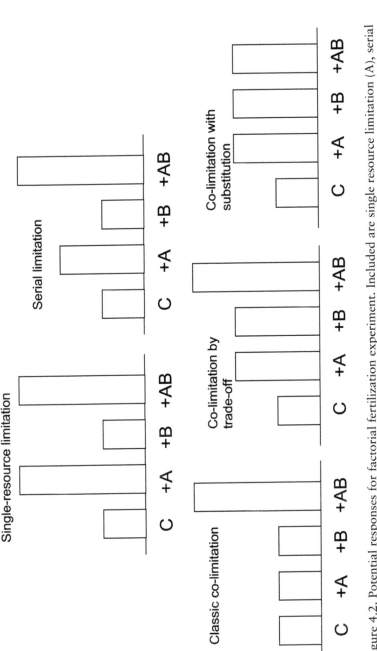

Figure 4.2. Potential responses for factorial fertilization experiment. Included are single resource limitation (A), serial limitation (B), classic co-limitation (C), and co-limitation by trade-off (D). Co-limitation for substitutable resources or co-limitation by trade-off, in which responses to the resources together become limited by another resource, can produce similar, less than additive responses (E). What is called serial limitation (first A, then B) is best considered a mixture of single resource limitation and classic co-limitation (first A, then A and B).

nitrogen cycle dates roughly from 1980. The lessons of the neoclassical nitrogen cycle are still being elaborated, but it is clear that concepts such as limitation and plant strategies must be revised in its ascendancy.

The Nitrogen Cycle to 1900

Before Liebig's treatise, it was generally accepted that nitrogen was provided to plants in organic form. At the time, it was well-known that the addition of manure, in which nitrogen is present in an organic form, could increase the productivity of fields. One of Liebig's contributions to ecology was to promote the idea that the humus theory of nutrient supply had been disproved. Sprengel had conducted experiments showing that plants could grow solely on inorganic nutrients, including nitrogen (van der Ploeg, Bohm, and Kirkham 1999). Sprengel's work is considered the foundation of the modern understanding of the mineral nutrition of plants, and rejection of the belief that nitrogen had to be supplied organically was an important first step toward a full understanding of the nitrogen cycle.

In disproving that nutrients had to be provided to plants in organic form, Liebig began to tease out the rudiments of what would become the modern nitrogen cycle. Liebig characterized the nitrogen cycle as organic nitrogen being mineralized to ammonium, which in some environments was transformed (nitrified) to nitrate. When Liebig formulated the law of the minimum, he thought the primary source of nitrogen to plants was ammonia from the atmosphere. In his 1843 treatise, he knew that plants could grow in charcoal supplied only with rainwater and that ammonium was present in rainwater. Knowing that atmospheric N_2 was relatively unreactive, he proposed that the major source of nitrogen to plants was NH_3 in precipitation. As organic matter decayed, NH_3 was released to the atmosphere, to return later in precipitation. Liebig knew that in some systems nitrate was more common, but he felt that the primary source was NH_3.

There were a few loose ends regarding the nitrogen cycle that Liebig had difficulty tying together. First, what was the ultimate source of nitrogen if it didn't come from atmospheric N_2 via the action of plants? Liebig had suggested volcanoes as the ultimate source of nitrogen but left this point largely unconsidered. Second, and more contentious, what was the role of legumes in fallow systems? It was well-known that leaving fields fallow for a period would increase productivity the following year, especially if legumes were present in the fallow fields. Liebig proposed that legumes had different stoichiometric requirements for nutrients that allowed other nutrients limiting to crop plants to accumulate in the soil. As an alternative, he proposed that some plants exude poisons into the soils.

Keeping a field fallow allows detoxification, and legumes are particularly good at detoxifying the soils.

With Liebig's hypotheses regarding limitation, nitrogen cycling, and fallow fields, intense debates arose between Liebig and two men from Rothamsted, John Lawes and Joseph Gilbert that foreshadowed the modern recognition of deficiencies in Liebig's concept of limitation. Lawes and Gilbert acknowledged that rotation of crops with legumes increased nitrogen in plant biomass, yet they found that plots fertilized with inorganic nitrogen also maintained yield. This called into question whether legumes had different requirements for nutrients that allowed nutrients to accumulate or whether legumes could somehow increase nitrogen supplies. As a note, Liebig responded that the mere fact that fertilization with nitrogen could maintain productivity for a few years did not refute the law of the minimum or his concept of nutrient supplies. This caused Lawes and Gilbert to maintain their fertilization plots in what would become the longest running fertilization experiment, still ongoing today, more than 150 years later.

The debate over the role of legumes and the nitrogen cycle would span nearly five decades of research and bring to light a major hole in nitrogen cycling as it was conceptualized. In 1838, France's Jean Baptiste Boussingault had carried out experiments in which different species were grown in bell jars supplied with nitrogen-free water. The results of the experiment suggested that clover and peas, but not wheat and oats, could extract nitrogen from the air (McCosh 1975). Although this result suggested that legumes could somehow fix atmospheric N_2, these findings were forcefully debated. Georges Ville through the early 1850s provided evidence that nonleguminous plants could also fix atmospheric nitrogen. Later it would be concluded that Ville's experiments suffered from contamination, providing additional nitrogen for nonleguminous plants. No definitive experiment emerged from Boussingault's laboratory to support his earlier findings, as when the experiment was repeated, the legumes were unable to fix atmospheric N_2.

With conflicting results at hand, Lawes and Gilbert took up the question. They surmised that if rotating crops with clover increased crop uptake of nitrogen the following year and if crop yield could be sustained with inorganic nitrogen additions, then legumes must be able to access either a unique source of nitrogen from the soil or atmospheric nitrogen. They then tried to replicate Boussingault's experiments, using large jars that were supplied with air that was passed through sulfuric acid to remove any ammonia. Lawes and Gilbert found no evidence that legumes could increase nitrogen availability. On the whole, European scientists were flummoxed by the role of legumes for 50 years after Boussingault first grew clover in bell jars.

It is known today that legumes increase nitrogen availability through their symbiosis with bacteria. The experimental work of Boussingault and of Lawes and Gilbert failed because these researchers were too rigorous to allow contamination with rhizobial bacteria. Not until 1862 was it shown that any bacteria could fix nitrogen. In 1888, Hermann Hellriegel and Hermann Wilfarth conducted a set of experiments in which they varied not only the species, under controlled conditions, but also the presence of inoculum (Nutman 1987). Not until Martinus Beijerinck isolated nitrogen-fixing bacteria in 1893 was the source of nitrogen to ecosystems settled.

When Liebig worked out the law of the minimum, he had not known much about how nutrients were supplied, or even that atmospheric nitrogen could be fixed. That fact alone should have caused official revision of the concept of limitation. At the rise of the classical nitrogen cycle, the law of the minimum was already somewhat outdated, a situation that only progressed as more was learned about the nitrogen cycle.

The Classical Nitrogen Cycle

After the discovery of N_2 fixation by legume-rhizobia symbioses, the foundation for the classical nitrogen cycle was set. Under the classical nitrogen cycle, plants can acquire NH_4^+ or NO_3^- that is supplied in excess to microbial demands. Nitrogen does not accumulate indefinitely in the soil, as excess nitrogen can be lost as NH_3 and NO_3^- can be converted to gaseous forms ("denitrified," the process of which was discovered in 1885) or leached from the soil as NO_3^-. Some plants have access to atmospheric N_2 through their symbioses with bacteria in the soil.

From this point, most of the research from 1900 to 1980 sought to quantify the pools and fluxes of nitrogen in the environment as opposed to restructuring the basic nature of the nitrogen cycle. Conceptually, parts of the nitrogen cycle were refined. Beginning in the 1960s, soil scientists worked to build a model of the movement of nitrogen in soils (Tinker and Nye 2000). Originally, it was hypothesized nutrients might migrate to roots along the surfaces of clays. Later calculations showed that the nutrients diffused through soil solution and that diffusion was more important for delivering nutrients to roots than mass flow when nutrient availability was low. From these calculations, it was clear that if a plant was limited by nutrients, increasing transpiration rates would have little effect on nutrient supply to roots.

With the classical nitrogen cycle, the amount of nitrogen that is supplied to a plant could be considered a function of the volume of soil that a plant explores, the rate at which nitrogen is supplied in a given volume of soil, and the partitioning of supplied nitrogen among individuals, that is, competition for nitrogen among plants. For plants growing in the classical nitrogen cycle, nitrogen is made available in soil water as a result of microbial decomposition. That rate of decomposition per unit soil volume is determined by soil organic matter concentrations and the decomposition rates of a given unit of organic matter. There are still lots of unanswered questions about what determines soil organic matter content in soil, but for the classical nitrogen cycle, decomposition rates are largely determined by the C:N ratio of plant biomass and climate (Gholz et al. 2000). Unless the plants are associated with N_2-fixing bacteria, there is little plants can do to alter supplies. Inorganic nitrogen is then supplied to plants via diffusion, in the form of either nitrate or ammonium.

Of importance to understanding nutrient limitation in plants, and therefore a major factor in natural selection, is the process by which nitrogen is transformed to an inorganic state: decomposition. Most nitrogen is supplied to plants as a result of the decomposition of plant biomass by microbial communities. As microbes work to decompose plant biomass, the higher the ratio of decomposable carbon to labile nitrogen that is in litter, the more likely microbes are to acquire nutrients from the soil solution and the less likely they are to release nitrogen acquired from the litter. The inflection point of litter C:N at which microbes release nitrogen versus immobilizing nitrogen is determined by the metabolic requirements of microbes to build and maintain their biomass and is generally considered from empirical data to be about 20:1 (Chapin, Matson, and Mooney 2002). Assuming a typical carbon concentration of plant biomass of 450 mg C g^{-1}, a C:N ratio of 20:1 is about the same as 22 mg N g^{-1} by mass.

The Neoclassical Nitrogen Cycle

Beginning around 1980, the foundations for the neoclassical nitrogen cycle began to become set. Research on these topics is ongoing, but as more is learned about the nitrogen cycle, it is becoming clear that these findings are changing concepts about limitation as well as natural selection. Over the past 30 years, there has been little advance in understanding the differences among plants in the volume of soil they explore. Revisions regarding competition for nitrogen are covered in the next chapter. The major changes in the scientific understanding of nitrogen cycling have to do with the rate at which nitrogen is supplied in a given volume of soil, namely, the ability of plants to acquire organic nitrogen and the ability of plants to affect the supplies of nitrogen.

Whereas in the classical nitrogen cycle, plants were thought to acquire only inorganic nitrogen, early studies showed that ectomycorrhizal fungi not only increase solubilization of organic nitrogen but also acquire amino acids (Read 1991). With this finding, some plants were indirectly able to increase nitrogen supplies by transferring carbon to ectomycorrhizal fungi (and later ericoid mycorrhizal fungi). Further research has indicated that plants have even greater ability to influence the decomposition of organic matter through their release of labile carbon. When nitrogen availability is low, labile carbon in the soil is used by free-living microbes such as white rot fungi to produce enzymes that decompose recalcitrant carbon (Sinsabaugh and Moorhead 1994; Waldrop, Zak, and Sinsabaugh 2004; Sinsabaugh et al. 2005; Craine, Morrow, and Fierer 2007). Recalcitrant carbon is often complexed with nitrogen. Decomposition of the recalcitrant carbon is energetically neutral at best, but provides a supply of scarce nitrogen. This mining of recalcitrant carbon is apparently greatest when nitrogen availability is low and labile carbon availability is high. As such, when plants are limited by nitrogen, if they can release labile carbon into the soil environment, it is likely to increase the supply of organic nitrogen.

With plants able to increase nitrogen supplies, plants that associate with mycorrhizal fungi could reap differentially by acquiring organic nitrogen before other microbes mineralize the nitrogen. Chapin and colleagues in 1993 showed that the ability to acquire organic nitrogen was not restricted to mycorrhizal fungi (Chapin, Moilanen, and Kielland 1993). Nonmycorrhizal sedges common to arctic tundra acquired more than half of their nitrogen from amino acids. To date, organic nitrogen uptake appears to be more common in cold, wet ecosystems where mineralization is restricted, with little current evidence that organic nitrogen uptake by plants is prevalent in warmer, drier ecosystems.

The ability of plants to increase nitrogen supplies raises questions about what limits plants in their ability to increase nitrogen supplies. In addressing questions of co-limitation, it is important to ask whether nitrogen-limited plants that can increase nitrogen supplies should be considered co-limited by the resource that limits their ability to increase nitrogen supplies. The understanding that plants can increase organic nitrogen supplies as well as directly or indirectly acquire organic nitrogen calls into question whether nitrogen is supplied largely in occasional or periodic pulses or is better characterized as a slow, uniform bleed.

In addition to plants being able to increase nitrogen supplies, as more was understood about decomposition, it was clear that plants could also decrease nitrogen supplies. The main mechanism by which plants decrease nitrogen supplies is by producing biomass with high C:N ratios (Aerts and Chapin 2000). As discussed for the classical nitrogen cycle, it became clear as the neoclassical nitrogen cycle was being revised that plants differ in the quality of the litter that they produce. As such, plants that produce litter with a high C:N induce microbial immobilization of nitrogen, decreasing the rate at which inorganic nitrogen is released. In addition, plants that produce some secondary compounds also reduce nitrogen mineralization. For example, plants that have high tannin concentrations in their leaves return tannin to the soil, where the tannins bind with proteins, just as they do in herbivore digestive systems. In sum, many questions remain about the proximal mechanisms by which species produce litter of varying quality, whether plants actually experience reduced nitrogen supplies at different time scales, and whether there would be any selective advantage for an individual to reduce nitrogen supplies.

Beyond these two main points, the neoclassical nitrogen cycle is still being revised with additional factors whose consequences are less certain for the performance of plants in ecosystems with low nitrogen availability. For example, the soil contains many organisms that graze the bacteria and fungi that are the primary drivers of decomposition (Clarholm 1981). How soil food web dynamics affect nitrogen cycling in different ecosystems and whether such dynamics have affected natural selection for plants growing in low-nitrogen environments are unclear. Also, plants not only compete against other plants for nitrogen, they likely compete against microbes. As such, in some ecosystems plant nitrogen supplies might match up better with gross mineralization rates (the rate at which nitrogen cycles among microbes) as opposed to just net mineralization rates (the rate at which excess nitrogen accumulates in the absence of plant uptake).

Pulses or Slow Bleeds?

How nitrogen is supplied to plants is a place to start in understanding the strategies of plants when nutrients are in short supply. A related question that guides the interpretation of plant strategies for low-nutrient ecosystems has to do with the temporal pattern of nutrient supplies (figure 4.3). Are limiting nutrients typically supplied infrequently in pulses, with intervening periods of low supply? Or are nutrients supplied at a low rate that is relatively uniform over time? If nutrients are largely supplied in rare pulses, then Grime's model of stress tolerators dominating low-nutrient ecosystems as a consequence of their ability to persist during periods of low nutrient availability between pulses might be a good model. With infrequent pulses, a stress tolerator is best suited to persist between pulses and to have roots present when the next pulse occurs. In contrast, if nutrients are supplied at a low but constant rate, plants never experience high nutrient availability, making chronic competition for nutrients among plants more likely, or at least changing the concept of tolerance of low nutrient supplies.

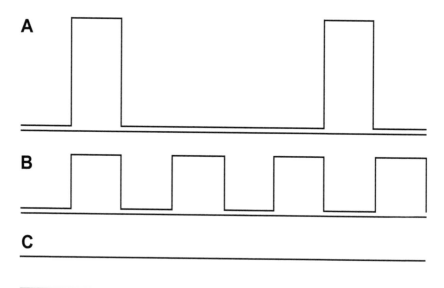

Figure 4.3. Comparison of different resource supply regimes in which the total supply is constant. Resources can be supplied in infrequent, large pulses (A), in more frequent, smaller pulses (B), or evenly over time (C).

From the many published studies of nutrient cycling in different ecosystems, it is clear that nutrients can be supplied in pulses at times. In ecosystems with soil freezing, a pulse of availability follows soil thawing as microbes are damaged and the nutrients once contained in them enter solution (Deluca, Keeney, and McCarty 1992; Smith, Munson, and Coyea 1998; Schimel and Bennett 2004). Severe drying of soils leads to analogous pulses of nutrient availability on rewetting (Reynolds et al. 1999). Herbivores can return localized pulses of nutrients to the soil in their urine and feces. Fire causes a widespread pulse return of the nutrients that remain behind in ash while also removing litter that can cool soils and restrict mineralization of soil organic matter (Hobbs et al. 1991; Cook 1994).

Although pulses of availability occur at some magnitude in all ecosystems, in most low-nutrient ecosystems natural selection has selected for plants that are best able to acquire nutrients supplied more or less uniformly in space and time, for three reasons. First, many factors that produce nutrient pulses are not important in low-nutrient ecosystems. For example, herbivores can return nutrients in pulses, but in low-nutrient ecosystems only a small fraction of the nutrient supply to plants passes through herbivores. Tissue quality in low-nutrient ecosystems is generally too low to support high densities of herbivores. In some low-nutrient ecosystems, termites consume large amounts of biomass, but nutrients are generally concentrated in termite mounds and represent moderate-sized patches of high nutrient availability in a matrix of low nutrient availability. Although plant biomass in low-nutrient ecosystems is more likely to burn than to be eaten, and fires do return pulses of nutrients, ecosystems that burn often are more likely to be limited by nitrogen than by phosphorus or other nutrients that are returned in the pulses of ash. With fire volatilizing most of the nitrogen in biomass that burns, the nutrients made available in pulses after fire often are not the nutrients that are most generally limiting.

Reinforcing the concept of the lack of pulse generation in low-nutrient ecosystems, there is little empirical evidence for autogenic pulses of nutrients in the absence of fire, herbivory, and freezing soils in low-nutrient ecosystems. For example, Wedin and Tilman (1996) determined the concentrations of inorganic nitrogen in soil solution in unfertilized Cedar Creek grasslands and found little evidence of temporal or spatial heterogeneity in available inorganic nitrogen concentrations.

There is a second reason for the lack of importance of pulses of nutrient availability in low-nutrient ecosystems. In ecosystems where pulses of nutrients consistently occur, the pulses often are produced at times when plant physiological activity is low. As such, the pulses of supply do not constitute a large fraction of the annual nutrient uptake of plants. For example, when soils thaw in the spring in temperate ecosystems, many roots have been killed by the same freezing that killed microbes. In roots that were not killed, physiological activity is low as a consequence of the low soil temperatures. By the time soil temperatures are warm enough that root physiological activity is significant, nutrient availability has likely declined as a consequence of microbial uptake or loss from the soil.

Many published studies on ecosystems with freezing soils have mischaracterized the relative contribution of pulses to supplies to plants out of ignorance of the organic nitrogen cycle. The lack of early-season pulses of uptake and the likely importance of slow bleeds of organic nitrogen are evident from examining the patterns of nutrient contents in plants over the course of the growing season. For example, Chapin and colleagues in work published in 1978 had characterized nutrient cycling in the tundra as a system dominated by an annual spring pulse followed by intervening times of low nutrient availability, with nutrient uptake concentrated in the spring. Likewise, Chapin's (1980) characterization of plants growing in low-nutrient ecosystems as being highly dependent on pulsed nutrient supplies was derived from a time when inorganic nitrogen was considered to be the only source of nitrogen to plants. The only time that inorganic nutrients were found in any significant concentration in soil solution and mineralization was measured was after the thaw. Hence, it seemed logical to characterize plant uptake as dominated by pulses also.

Contrary to the initial characterization of pulsed resource supplies, amino acids should be made available throughout the growing season because of their consistently rapid turnover, and likely they are made more available when soil temperatures are highest in the summer. Chapin actually measured the plant nutrient content of *Eriophorum vaginatum*, the dominant sedge in Alaskan tundra, over the course of the growing season. Had spring pulses been the predominant source of nitrogen that plants acquired, with excess nitrogen accumulating in plant tissues, plant nitrogen content should have been highest during the spring, with little increase, if not declines, during the summer. Yet Chapin showed that contents increased during the summer (Chapin, Shaver, and Kedrowski 1986). Our understanding of nitrogen uptake in the tundra is still developing (Schimel and Bennett 2004), but it appears that nitrogen is acquired throughout the growing season (J. Schimel, personal communication), especially as organic nitrogen (Weintraub and Schimel 2005), and is also acquired in the fall, under the snowpack (Andresen and Michelsen 2005). *Eriophorum vaginatum* roots are produced throughout the growing season and into the fall, suggesting that uptake, though not constant over time, occurs throughout the year. Although it was the ecosystem on which Chapin had based much of his theoretical work, the tundra did not appear to fit the pulse and tolerate model.

A third reason for natural selection in low-nutrient ecosystems favoring plants able to acquire nutrients uniformly in space and time depends on empirical evidence of competitive ability for pulses. When pulses of nutrients are experimentally manufactured in low-nutrient ecosystems, the dominant plants in the assemblage do a relatively poor job of acquiring the pulsed nutrients. Nutrient pulses are often disproportionately acquired by less abundant plants. For example, at Cedar Creek, ^{15}N-labeled inorganic nitrogen was applied to soils of mixed native grassland vegetation at three different times in the growing season (McKane, Grigal, and Russelle 1990). Aboveground biomass was harvested approximately 50 days after the pulse of nitrogen was added. Consistently, disproportionately more nitrogen was acquired by the less abundant species than by the dominant species. The dominant species of low-nutrient ecosystems do not have root systems optimized for infrequent pulses of nutrients.

Although pulses of nutrients certainly occur, the empirical patterns of nutrient supplies in low-nutrient ecosystems reveal that the dominant pattern in low-nutrient ecosystems is a slow bleed of nutrients. As such, the strategy for plants in low-nutrient ecosystems cannot be merely to tolerate low nutrient availability while waiting for a pulse. Instead, they must be able to actively grow well at low nutrient supplies. In chapter 7, the traits of plants are reviewed to show that natural selection pressure on plants growing in low-nutrient ecosystems has predominantly reflected an evolutionary history in low-nutrient ecosystems for these slow bleeds of nutrients. In the next section the similarities and differences between the nitrogen and phosphorus cycles are addressed, then the discussion turns to co-limitation in a post-Liebigian world.

PRIMER ON THE PHOSPHORUS CYCLE

Understanding of the phosphorus cycle has developed less dynamically than that of the nitrogen cycle. The differences in plant strategies for success when phosphorus rather than nitrogen is limiting can be understood by investigating a few main differences in the phosphorus and nitrogen cycles. First, in contrast to the nitrogen in soil, the ultimate source of phosphorus for plants is rocks, not the atmosphere. Second, unlike nitrogen, phosphorus in soils can also become unavailable to plants by becoming incorporated into minerals. Also, phosphorus does not become bound to recalcitrant organic matter as nitrogen does; organic bonds with phosphorus are relatively weak. Fourth, phosphorus also behaves differently in solution from nitrogen. The diffusion rates of phosphorus in soils are much lower than the diffusion rates of organic or inorganic nitrogen, lowering the volume of soil from which a single root or hyphal strand acquires phosphorus. Phosphorus diffuses much shorter distances in soil than nitrogen, causing a given root to be able to acquire phosphorus from a much smaller soil volume than nitrogen.

Also in contrast to nitrogen, pulses of phosphorus can be important for the phosphorus budget of some plants, although not in the manner that was generally characterized by Grime or Chapin. Many species of plants that inhabit low-phosphorus environments generate localized pulses of high phosphorus availability by releasing organic acids into the soil (Shane and Lambers 2005). For example, species that produce dauciform roots, which are dense aggregations of fine roots, create transient patches of high phosphorus availability by releasing acids into the soil. The patches and the roots that produce them are short-lived. As such, although at the whole-plant scale phosphorus supplies are more than likely relatively even, at the local scale they can be short-lived. This becomes important when the root traits of the plants that dominate low-phosphorus environments are examined.

Although there are many differences between the nitrogen and phosphorus cycles, there are also many similarities, which become important for generalizing the concepts of limitation beyond nitrogen. For example, the proximal source of much of the phosphorus supplied to plants is organic matter. Plants can also increase the solubilization of phosphorus, although through means such as lowering soil pH or releasing phosphatases. Additionally, there are trade-offs in allocation in acquiring both nutrients. In both cases carbon can be released into the environment to increase the availability of the nutrient.

CO-LIMITATION IN A POST-LIEBIGIAN WORLD

Co-limitation among Nutrients

In a Liebigian world, co-limitation between nutrients such as nitrogen and phosphorus should occur rarely. For Liebig, nutrients were supplied independent of plant activity, and more likely than not one nutrient would be supplied at a low rate relative to the rate of supply of other nutrients and the demands of plants. This one nutrient supplied at a relatively low rate would become the limiting nutrient. On rare occasions, two limiting nutrients could be supplied in exactly the same ratio as demanded by vegetation, leading to co-limitation.

Since Liebig's time, understanding of the nature of the interaction between nutrient supplies and plant demand has developed to the point where co-limitation might be expected to be less the exception than the rule (e.g., Sinclair and Park 1993; Elser et al. 2007). One reason why nutrients are more likely to be co-limiting to vegetation than expected in a Liebigian world is that limiting nutrients are often retained more strongly in the ecosystem than nonlimiting nutrients. Nitrogen is a good example here. When nitrogen is supplied in excess of plant demand, volatilization of ammonium, microbial denitrification, and NO_3^- leaching into groundwater all serve to remove excess nitrogen from the soil, making nitrogen more likely to be a limiting nutrient. For nutrients that are limiting, plants conserve the nutrients and reduce their availability in the soil, which in turn tends to reduce the probability that they are lost via leaching.

Another reason why vegetation is likely to be co-limited by nutrients is that species differ in their stoichiometric demands for nutrients. Plants whose stoichiometric demands most closely match the supply ratios should be favored, as they can use a greater fraction of the joint resource supplies for productive purposes. There are important questions regarding the degree plants differ in their stoichiometric demands for primary growth, some of which are addressed in chapter 7. It is clear, however, that plants differ in their use of nutrients for secondary purposes, such as defense. For example, when nitrogen is in excess, species that use nitrogen for secondary purposes are likely to be favored over plants that use more limiting resources for the same purposes. Although the allocation of excess nutrients to secondary purposes might not increase primary productivity, it likely decreases susceptibility to agents of stress and disturbance.

If the ratio of supplies of different nutrients is variable over time, plants can store resources to ensure that over long time scales resources are more likely to be co-limiting (Chapin, Schulze, and Mooney 1990). Economic theory suggests that natural selection would favor plants that accumulate or store resources that are currently abundant but are expected to be more limiting in the future. In doing so, although a plant might be limited by only a single resource at a given time, over long time scales it is likely to be co-limited. For example, early in a growing season, nitrogen availability might exceed current demand, while phosphorus is limiting to growth. Later in the growing season phosphorus might be more available and nitrogen less available. Plants that stored nitrogen early in the season would be less limited by nitrogen later in the season and more likely to be co-limited by nitrogen and phosphorus.

Although differential loss of nutrients from ecosystems, differences among species in stoichiometric demands, and the ability to store resources are likely to contribute to the prevalence of nutrient co-limitation, the major reason why plants are likely to be co-limited is that nutrients are not supplied independent of demands. Individual plants adjust their allocation patterns to increase the availability, if not supply, of limiting nutrients, while the relative abundance of species in an assemblage can shift among species to favor species that increase the supply of the more limiting nutrient. For example, when nitrogen is limiting, plants might allocate more carbon to ectomycorrhizal or ericoid fungi, which mine nitrogen from soil organic matter. Other plants might release more labile carbon into the soil to promote nitrogen mining by free-living microbes. When phosphorus is limiting, plants can allocate more carbon to mycorrhizal fungi, lower soil pH, or release more phosphatases into the soil to increase phosphorus availability. Where the ability of a given species to increase limiting nutrient supplies is limited, species replacement often occurs, favoring plants that can increase the limiting nutrient. In low-nitrogen environments, N_2-fixing plants would be favored, while in low-phosphorus environments, plants that can increase phosphorus availability would be favored.

The Economic Basis for Co-limitation

Some of the rationale for the prevalence of co-limitation was laid out by Bloom, Chapin, and Mooney (BCM) in 1985 (Bloom, Chapin, and Mooney 1985). BCM applied economic principles to ecology and assumed that just as in economics, decisions or alternative approaches can be analyzed by quantifying the costs and benefits of different options. In drawing on economic analogies, BCM come to the conclusion that natural selection should produce plants that allocate resources so that *many* resources are co-limiting to growth. Like a business, a plant must acquire resources and turn them into a product (biomass). There are costs to acquiring different resources, and different options in how those resources are spent realize different rates of return. Just as businesses work to maximize profits, plants should be selected to maximize biomass or reproduction.

BCM present four economic theorems based on the assumption that plants allocate resources in order to maximize biomass, which they consider a strong correlate of reproductive ability. For example, BCM's first theorem was that

> a profit-maximizing firm buys resources at the lowest price and uses them when they are most valuable. . . . Plants can maximize their primary productivity (profits) by "buying" low and by making timely "reinvestment," i.e. by acquiring a resource when it is abundant, storing it, and utilizing it when it provides maximum enhancement of productivity. (Bloom, Chapin, and Mooney 1985, p. 366)

In short, when resources are supplied heterogeneously over time, plants that can selectively store resources are more likely to be co-limited by multiple resources than are plants that cannot store resources.

In addition to an economic basis for storing resources for later use, BCM provide a conceptual basis for plants to adjust their allocation patterns so that multiple resources are co-limiting at any one point in time. BCM state that "A profit-maximizing firm tends to equalize the ratio of marginal product over cost for all resources. . . . In biological terms, the marginal product of a resource is simply the response of primary productivity to a change in the availability of carbon, nutrients, or water. . . . By this theorem, a plant should adjust allocation so that, for a given expenditure in acquiring each resource, it achieves the same growth response: Growth is equally limited by all resources."

Here, costs are defined as resource spent to acquire new resources. Immediate costs can be assessed as resources are allocated from stores to biomass. As some of these resources can be remobilized, over long time scales, costs are determined to be the amount of resources lost from the plants to acquire new resources. Marginal product is the ratio of biomass production to the amount of internal resource spent to acquire the external resource. Restating the theorem in terms of plant resources, plants that maximize biomass production allocate internal resources so that biomass production is increased the same regardless of which external resource that internal resource is allocated to acquire.

One particularly important criterion for co-limitation is that for two resources to co-limit growth, they must have separate costs (Gleeson and Tilman 1992). For two resources to have separate costs, there must be trade-offs in allocation whereby allocation of resources to one function results in acquisition of one resource but not another. If a resource allocated to a particular function returns two resources, they do not have separate costs. Trade-offs in allocation and separate costs are generated when different resources are acquired by shallow and deep roots or by mycorrhizal fungi and roots, or when resources are allocated to increase nitrogen supplies versus phosphorus supplies.

Whereas Liebig's assumptions would predict that co-limitation among resources should be rare, economic analogies predict that co-limitation should be common. In addition, where there are trade-offs in allocation generating co-limitation, production should increase with the addition of either co-limiting nutrient, and not just from the addition of both. When the availability of one nutrient increases, allocation should shift toward acquisition of the other co-limiting nutrient (and vice versa). As such, productivity would increase in response to increases in availability of either nutrient.

Co-limitation of Light and Belowground Resources

If more than one nutrient can limit plant biomass at any one time, can light and nutrients co-limit production? Although some studies decrease the light supply to vegetation, there has been only one reported study that increased light supply to an ecosystem (Johnston et al. 1969). That paucity of empirical data aside, there is good indirect evidence that light should at least be limiting to production in many ecosystems.

In general, the supply of solar energy is a major axis describing variation in global net primary productivity (NPP) and the distribution of vegetation (Whittaker 1975, Stephenson 1990). At the stand level, for stands with leaf area index (LAI) greater than 1, as the intensity of light supply increases, light acquisition also commonly increases. Although leaves high in the canopy may be light-saturated, leaves lower in the canopy continue to increase their photosynthetic rate (Johnston et al. 1969; Pearcy 1990; Chazdon and Pearcy 1991). This leads to a nonsaturating increase in stand-level carbon uptake with increases in light supply of up to 2,000 μmol m^{-2} s^{-1} for some vegetation types (Ruimy 1997). Thus, although certain parts of the canopy may be light-saturated, the entire canopy is not light-saturated.

If vegetation can be limited by light, then can ecosystems be co-limited by light and nutrients? The uncertainty regarding the nature of light limitation of NPP in nitrogen-limited ecosystems reflects both the lack of direct experimental tests of light limitation and the lack of conceptual frameworks for testing and evaluating light limitation. Without storage of light in the environment, whether light is likely to co-limit production with nutrients cannot necessarily be evaluated in the same manner as co-limitation among nutrients. Whereas nitrogen that is not immediately acquired by plants can still remain in soil solution to be acquired later, light instantaneously is absorbed or reflected away. As such, the case that promotes co-limitation where unacquired light is more likely to be lost when nonlimiting does not hold.

Still, light is likely to be co-limiting with nutrients. Although plants cannot increase light supplies, they can often increase the light they acquire by increasing allocation of resources to leaves. In addition, there are clear trade-offs in acquisition of light versus nutrients. For example, energy and nitrogen are required for both light and nitrogen acquisition. Biomass can be allocated to leaves or roots, but not both simultaneously. As long as there is a marginal benefit of allocating additional resources to both roots and leaves (i.e., more nutrient or light is acquired), then light is likely to be co-limiting with nutrients.

Proving that vegetation is co-limited by light and nutrients requires specific experiments that increase both resources in factorial. In lieu of that, much circumstantial evidence and theory suggest that plants should be co-limited by light and nutrients. As discussed in the next section, moving from an assumption of limitation to an assumption of co-limitation changes how costs are evaluated in cost-benefit analyses of different allocation strategies and determines the types of defenses that are used in different environments. In addition to structuring predictions of responses of vegetation to changes in resource availability, it raises new hypotheses for the efficiency by which plants in different environments use resources. The assumption of co-limitation and the assumption that natural selection favors plants that are co-limited by light and nutrients change expectations about the patterns of competition across nutrient supply gradients.

EVALUATING COSTS IN A CO-LIMITED WORLD

The prevalence of co-limitation changes the way that costs in cost-benefit analyses of alternative allocation strategies are evaluated (Craine, Bond, et al. 2003). For example, in assessing the strategies of plants in low-nutrient ecosystems, there are questions about the relative costs and benefits of different types of defenses. How are the relative resource costs of producing a given mass of tannin versus an equal mass of an alkaloid that contains nitrogen evaluated? If nitrogen was not limiting and carbon was limiting as a consequence of light limitation, the costs of the defenses might only be their energetic costs—the amount of energy required during photosynthesis to reduce the CO_2 to the carbohydrates that are the building blocks of the defenses. If carbon was not limiting and only nitrogen was limiting, tannins might have little cost, and the cost of the alkaloid might be assessed by its nitrogen content. Conversely, if both carbon and nitrogen are limiting, how should the costs be assessed when both carbon and nitrogen have costs?

Attempts to calculate the resource costs and benefits of structures such as these different defenses have generally not included the relative value of limiting resources (Bloom, Chapin, and Mooney 1985; Bazzaz et al. 1987). Generally, defense costs have been calculated based solely on the energy cost of the synthesis and maintenance of the defense. Most of the cost of nitrogen, such as the amount of carbon that is spent to acquire the nitrogen, is ignored. Yet more than half of a nitrogen-limited plant's carbon budget can be allocated belowground, much of which can be thought of as a cost of acquiring nitrogen. Determining the costs and benefits of biomass and allocation of resources has been limited by the inability to calculate the cost of multiple resources in a common currency. Without being able to express the value of carbon and nitrogen in a common currency, there is no way to know if a unit of biomass that uses 45 mg of carbon and 2 mg of nitrogen is more expensive than one that contains 60 mg of carbon and 1 mg of nitrogen.

The relative value of carbon and nitrogen can be derived from the exchange rates of the two resources at the whole-plant or stand level (Bloom, Chapin, and Mooney 1985; Craine, Bond, et al. 2003). In human economies using barter to exchange goods and services, the relative value of a commodity is assessed on the empirical exchange rates determined between the parties to the transaction. For example, if on average three loaves of bread are exchanged for two pounds of butter, the relative value of one pound of butter is 1.5 loaves of bread. Analogously for plants, the relative value of two resources can be inferred from the exchange rates, that is, how much carbon is spent by a plant relative to how much nitrogen it acquires and vice versa.

Quantifying these exchange rates is best assessed at the whole-plant level, not at the level of individual roots or leaves (Poorter 1989). For example, the costs of roots acquiring nitrogen cannot be separated from the costs of leaves acquiring reduced carbon, which is then used to support the roots. If at the whole-plant or stand level, x g of carbon is acquired per y g of nitrogen lost, the relative value of nitrogen in terms of carbon is x/y. Using this exchange rate, the cost of nitrogen in leaves can be expressed in terms of carbon. Assuming approximate steady-state conditions, acquisition and loss should be nearly equivalent and can be substituted for one another. It is important to note that both resources need to

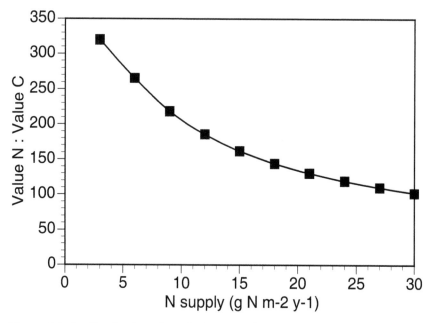

Figure 4.4. Decline in the value of nitrogen relative to carbon as the nitrogen supply increases. Data are derived from a stand-level model of photosynthesis and nitrogen uptake. Data from Craine et al. 2003.

be co-limiting to growth for their relative value to be calculated. If a resource is not limiting, then theoretically it has no value, since additional units of the resource that are acquired do not lead to the acquisition of more resources.

When assessed at the whole-plant level, the cost of nitrogen in terms of carbon can be high. Stand-level exchange rates between carbon and nitrogen can be as high as 300 g to 1 g (Craine, Bond, et al. 2003) (figure 4.4). Put another way, if carbon and nitrogen are co-limiting, then it costs 300 g of carbon to acquire 1 g of nitrogen. Referring back to the example of comparing biomass with different carbon and nitrogen contents, when the relative value of nitrogen in terms of carbon is 300, biomass that has 60 mg of carbon and 1 mg of nitrogen has the same total value of biomass as has 45 mg of carbon and 1.05 mg of nitrogen. Thus, 45 mg of carbon and 2 mg of nitrogen would be the equivalent of 360 mg of carbon and 1 mg of nitrogen.

Although the use of relative exchange rates potentially offers a wide range of insights, the technique has yet to be commonly used in cost-benefit analyses to determine the relative value of resources. The relative costs of carbon and nitrogen influence the types of defenses used in different environments. Beyond this, no other analyses of plant allocation strategies have been undertaken, and the application of this approach to evaluating costs and benefits is limited, though promising.

TRADE-OFFS IN USE EFFICIENCY IN A CO-LIMITED WORLD

Use efficiencies can be determined for any resource. For example, at the stand or plant level, light use efficiency (LUE) is the ratio of production to intercepted light, while nutrient use efficiency (NUE) is the ratio of production to nitrogen acquisition or loss rates. Whether a plant is limited by one or multiple resources, the efficiency with which a plant uses resources to produce biomass should be under strong natural selection pressure. All other things being equal, plants that use a given limiting resource inefficiently should be less favored than plants that use the resource efficiently.

Although the underpinnings of the theories are a bit too complex to develop here, the theoretical relationship between resource use efficiencies and resource supply rates can be generated from economic analogy. A plant that is limited by one resource should maximize the efficiency with which the limiting resource is used in biomass production in order to maximize productivity. For co-limiting resources, if a stand acquires all the limiting resources that are supplied to it and is near steady-state in terms of vegetation development (Rastetter and Shaver 1992), then the stand that maximized NPP would utilize the limiting resources in the same ratio as they are supplied (criteria no. 4 in Rastetter and Shaver 1992). As such, a plant that was co-limited by light and nitrogen where the ratio of light to nitrogen was relatively high would have a low LUE but a high NUE.

If one assumes that plants are co-limited by two resources, there are two main hypotheses that arise regarding the patterns of allocation and changes in use efficiency among plants in environments with different resource supply ratios. First, the ratio of light to nitrogen supplies is inversely related to the ratio of use efficiencies of light and nitrogen. Increasing the nitrogen supply should decrease NUE and increase LUE. With an increase in the nitrogen supply, the relative value of nitrogen would decline and the relative value of light would increase. If plants are acquiring nearly all the supplies of limiting resources, use efficiencies must change in this ratio as more nitrogen is acquired per unit of light, leading to less biomass being produced per unit of nitrogen relative the amount of biomass produced per unit of light. Second, if not all of the supplies are acquired, then increasing the supply of one resource should be associated with a shift in allocation to acquire the other resource. As the relative value of light increases with increasing nitrogen supply, plants should allocate more resources to acquiring the more limiting resource. Additional nitrogen that was acquired should be more likely to be allocated to light acquisition, such as the production of leaves, than to nitrogen acquisition, such as production of roots.

The best and most compact line of evidence for inverse relationships between LUE and NUE across a nutrient supply gradient comes from fertilization experiments in Hawaii (Harrington, Fownes, and Vitousek 2001). In the forests there, with fertilization, NUE declines as a consequence of increasing foliar nutrient concentrations. In contrast to the decline in NUE, LUE increases. As such, NUE increases while LUE decreases. In addition, regarding the second hypothesis about changes in allocation rate, Harrington et al. found a typical increase in LAI with nutrient fertilization, indicating a relative shift of resources from roots to leaves and from nutrient acquisition to light acquisition.

Other empirical evidence is scattered but appears consistent with these hypotheses. Under increased nitrogen supply, the total amount of light captured increases (Pastor 1984; Wilson and Tilman 1993; Belanger, Gastal, and Warembourg 1994; Runyon et al. 1994), associated with increases in LAI (Runyon et al. 1994; Ryan et al. 1996; Fahey, Battles, and Wilson 1998). The relative increase in energy acquisition is less than the relative increase in aboveground net primary production, leading to an increase in LUEacq. As a caveat, in these studies, only aboveground production is considered in calculation of LUEacq. If belowground production decreases with increasing nitrogen supply, the increases in aboveground net primary productivity (ANPP) could potentially be offset and lead to decreases in NPP and therefore decreases in LUE_{acq}. This scenario seems unlikely. For example, in one tundra ecosystem (Chapin et al. 1995), a complete cessation of belowground NPP (approximately 35% of NPP in the ecosystem of study) would be required to offset the approximately 40% increase in aboveground NPP associated with increased nitrogen supply. Studies that have measured LUE_{acq} directly under decreased light supply (Sameshima 1996; Cruz 1997) show that LUE_{acq} increases with declining light supply.

If it is assumed that the plants in a stand are allocating resources in order to optimize biomass production, the direction of natural selection in different environments is clear. Optimizing production involves optimizing the balance of resource use efficiencies between co-limiting resources. With co-limitation, plants aren't allocating to maximize acquisition of one resource. It is more likely that plants balance net acquisition of multiple resources. Plants that have been selected to perform well in low-nutrient ecosystems should use nutrients efficiently, but energy derived from light should be used inefficiently. Plants selected to perform well when nutrient supplies are high should use light efficiently, with less pressure to use nutrients efficiently. In a related manner, detailed in chapter 10, plants increase their water use efficiency by sacrificing NUE.

Although the direction of changes in resource use efficiencies with changes in nutrient supplies is congruent with these general predictions, these theories assume that plants have been selected to optimize biomass production. As discussed in the next chapter, plants have also been selected to compete well against other plants, which does not necessarily optimize biomass production. Competition does not necessarily select for plants that are more efficient with limiting resources as much as it selects for plants that are better competitors. The mechanisms by which plants compete for resources and its consequences for natural selection are the subject of the next chapter.

Summary

Resource stress and limitation are tightly coupled. The law of the minimum, which describes the basic ecological concept of limitation, was established at a time when little was known about nutrient cycling, and it was not initially applied to limitation by light. The three parts of Liebig's law of the minimum are as follows:

1. Growth is limited by the resource that is supplied at the lowest rate relative to the demands of the plant.
2. Growth is proportional to the rate of supply of the most limiting resource.
3. Growth cannot be increased by increasing the supply of a nonlimiting nutrient.

In the Liebigian world of limitation, generally only one nutrient could be limiting at a time. Plants were inflexible in their demands for nutrients and could do little to increase the supplies of any particularly limiting resource. As more was understood about how nutrients were supplied to plants and how plants used resources to grow, the approach to assessing plant strategies had to be adjusted.

1. To increase the supplies of strongly limiting resources, plants can use resources that normally would not be acquired, or would be allocated to produce biomass, or would accumulate in excess. Plants can also decrease the supplies of resources, although this is of uncertain adaptive value.
2. Although there are mechanisms by which nutrients are supplied in pulses, by and large, limiting nutrients in low-nutrient ecosystems are best characterized as being supplied at low, uniform rates.

3. It is likely that there is co-limitation to growth among different resources, not just serial limitation. Co-limitation is more likely to
occur than would be predicted from Liebig's law of the minimum
because (a) nutrients supplied in excess are more likely to be lost,
(b) species differ in the stoichiometry of demands for optimal
growth, (c) plants can store resources to balance temporally variable
rates of supply, and (d) plants can increase the availability of the
most limiting resource. Building on the latter point, if there are
trade-offs in acquisition between different allocation strategies,
whether for increasing supplies or for acquiring a greater fraction
of a given supply, co-limitation is likely to occur.

4. As a consequence of trade-offs in allocation, light and belowground
resources are the most likely co-limiting resources, but there can
also be co-limitation among different belowground resources, if not
nutrients.

5. Resource co-limitation in the post-Liebig world manifests not only
in productivity responses to the addition of two resources, with no
increases if only one resource is added. As a consequence of alloca-
tional trade-offs, plants can be co-limited by multiple resources and
can respond to individual resources independently.

6. When resources are co-limiting, costs for different allocation strategies or the production of different structures should be evaluated
with a dual-currency model. Evaluating costs with just one resource
ignores the often great cost of the second resource.

7. Natural selection favors plants that adjust their allocation strategies
such that multiple resources are co-limiting. As such, plants are also
selected to balance their resource use efficiencies to match resource
supply ratios. For example, plants that grow with high relative limitation of nitrogen should have higher NUE to LUE ratios than plants
that grow in environments with greater relative limitation by light.
Increasing nutrient availability should also result in a shift, either
physiologically or through changes in the relative abundance of species, to vegetation allocating relatively more resources to light than
to nutrient acquisition, lower NUE rates, and higher LUE rates.

CHAPTER 5

Competition for Nutrients and Light

IT HAS LONG BEEN CONSIDERED that competition among plants generates significant stress for plants, and consequently serves as an important component of assembly and natural selection. In observing the high diversity of plants that could be grown in botanical gardens where plants are grown isolated from competitors, Warming surmised that competition among plants must be important in determining their distribution. In the *Oecology of Plants* he wrote, "Plants are evidently in general, tolerably impartial as regards soil, if we except certain chemical and physical extremes. . ., so long as they have not competitors." Although Darwin did not devote much of the *Origin of Species* to plants, he felt that competition was universal and important for plants. As such, he wrote, "Not until we reach the extreme confines of life in the arctic regions, or on the borders of an utter desert, will competition cease" (Darwin 1859, p. 78).

Early ecologists were certain that competition was important in determining the relative abundance of plants, but it would be a relatively long time before ecologists began in earnest to quantify the relative importance of competition and how it had shaped the modern flora. In Warming's time there was little knowledge as to what resources plants were competing for and by what mechanisms some plants outcompeted others for resources.

Competition for resources has indeed shaped plants, but in ways not imagined by Darwin and Warming. Before the importance of competition for abundance and natural selection is discussed, concepts of competition must be reconsidered. It is important to revisit what has been learned about resource cycles to understand the mechanisms by which plants compete for resources. This chapter focuses on competition for nutrients and light, and how such competition can structure assemblages. Understanding the mechanisms that underlie competition for nutrients and light is a prerequisite for understanding how resource competition has shaped the evolution of plants and the role that competition plays in plant strategies.

In what follows, different types of competition are discussed first, and then a working definition for competition for resources is developed. The mechanisms that underlie competition for nutrients when nutrients are supplied uniformly in space and time are then covered. Obviously, no supply is perfectly uniform, but the ideal case is instructive. Even though it does not appear that nutrient supplies in low-nutrient environments are best characterized as dominated by pulses of availability, concepts of competition when nutrients are supplied heterogeneously in space and time—that is, in patches and pulses—are examined here. After nutrients, competition for light is reviewed, along with the philosophical questions that have arisen around light as a resource. The chapter concludes with the question of whether plants can compete simultaneously for light and nutrients, which follows directly from the discussion of the nature of co-limitation in the previous chapter.

DEFINITIONS AND TYPES OF COMPETITION

The basic definitions relevant to competition among plants for resources (also known as exploitative competition) seem to be fairly well agreed upon. The definitions of resource competition have been startlingly consistent for quite a long time. John Weaver and Frederic Clements (1938) defined competition as occurring "where two or more plants make demands for light, nutrients or water in excess of the supply." Grime defined resource competition as "the tendency of neighbouring plants to utilize the same quantum of light, ion of a mineral nutrient, molecule of water, or volume of space" (Grime 1973), and Tilman stated that his approach to competition is "essentially identical to that stated in Grime's definition" (Tilman 1987a, p. 307), although it is difficult to find a clear definition of resource competition from Tilman.

Recent adjustments to the definition of competition have not necessarily improved on the definitions of Weaver and Clements or Grime. Welden and Slauson (1986) reformulated Grime's definition to generalize the "resource items" for which organisms might be competing (as opposed to light, nutrients, and water), and explicitly included the need for the resource to be limiting. They also took issue with the word "tendency," since they felt it "betrayed the teleological nature of competition." The definition they ended up with was "competition is the induction of strain . . . in one organism as a direct result of the use of resource items by another organism." Although including the induction of strain, which indicated that the resource supplies must be limiting to plants, was a step forward, altering the definition of competition in this manner was a step backward for one important reason: the process of competition must have mutually negative consequences for the competing plants. As defined by Welden and Slauson, if one plant acquires resources that would otherwise be acquired by a second plant, but if acquisition by the second plant has no effect on acquisition by the first, then the two plants would still be considered to be competing. When Grime included the word "neighboring" in his definition he was invoking the idea that there is no hierarchy to the acquisition. A plant in a river upstream of another plant is not competing with a downstream plant for nutrients. When there is complete asymmetry to resource acquisition, the interaction ceases to be competitive in the short term, but there are important implications for lengthening the reference period beyond the immediate term.

The different definitions of competition that have been offered are consistent on one point: two plants are considered to be competing for a limiting resource when the resources acquired by one plant could have been acquired by the other, and vice versa. Since the resource is limiting, if one plant acquires some of the resource that the other plant could have acquired, the reduced acquisition by the second plant induces resource stress and slows growth. The working definition of competition is *the process by which two or more individuals differentially capture a potentially common, limiting resource supply.* It is important to note that the supply must be "potentially common," such that acquisition by either plant decreases acquisition by the other, and that the resource supply must be limiting to both plants.

Resource competition has been contrasted to interference competition (Case and Gilpin 1974), in which plants do not reduce the acquisition of nutrients by other plants by acquiring the resources but by indirectly decreasing the ability of other plants to acquire resources by altering the environment of the plant (Rebele 2000; Goldberg et al. 2001). For example, plants can interfere with the growth of other plants by lowering the supply of nutrients or decreasing the ability of the plants to take up nutrients, such as releasing into the environment allelochemicals that interfere with the plants' functioning.

Defining resource competition is relatively easy. For the past 70 years, there has been virtually no change in the definition. Yet confusion and debate over competition still reign, and not because of the core definition used but how that definition is applied. For example, what does it mean to have the potential to use the same resource supply? Over how long a time scale is the potential to use the same resource supply integrated? Do competing plants have to have the potential to use the same unit in the next day, year, or until it is no longer available? Does competition apply only to individuals, or can it extend to the next generation? How is competition detected? Besides the presence of competition between plants, is there any way to quantify the degree of competition and possibly compare it with other factors that might induce stress? These questions are central to understanding natural selection and the major plant strategies that have arisen.

This chapter focuses on resource competition. Interference competition and the importance of reducing nutrient supplies are discussed in chapter

7, although allelopathy is not addressed in this book. This is not because allelopathy is never important but because it does not appear to be consistently associated with one strategy more than another.

Nutrient stress is determined not only by the volume of soil that is explored by roots and the supply rate of nutrients per unit of soil volume but also how difficult it is to acquire the nutrients that are supplied in a given soil volume. With resource competition, the presence of neighboring plants induces nutrient stress in plants as neighbors acquire nutrients that could have been acquired by the target plant.

Although the history of research into competition is relatively long in ecology, analyses of the mechanisms of resource competition were largely phenomenological before Tilman's research on phytoplankton in Lake Michigan. Before Tilman's work, most research examined the growth of an organism or group of organisms in the presence of a potential competitor relative to growth in its absence. For nutrients and water more so than for light, there was little research into the specifics of competition and little evaluation of the proximal and distal mechanisms by which one plant was able to outcompete another for a limiting resource supply.

Concentration Reduction Theory of Competition

When Tilman transferred his theories of competition from aquatic to terrestrial ecosystems, he brought with him a clear approach and set of mechanisms that he theorized determined competitive outcomes. As discussed in chapter 2, Tilman theorized that competitive superiority resulted from the ability to reduce nutrient concentrations in solution. When Tilman applied this idea to terrestrial ecosystems, he used the amount of nitrogen in soil organic matter as a first approximation of available nitrogen (Tilman 1987b, 2006). Only later was soil solution inorganic nitrogen actually measured (Wedin and Tilman 1990). It should be noted that although the concentration reduction theory is based on *concentrations* of nutrients in soil solution, in practice, R^* at Cedar Creek has been reported as soil solution content, the mass of nutrient per unit mass dry soil, not soil solution concentrations (the mass of nutrient per unit of water in the soil) (e.g., Tilman and Wedin 1991). Soil solution nitrogen concentrations among soils were always standardized for differences in soil moisture. This approach could be explained by trying to account for the temporal variability of soil moisture due to precipitation events, but it is uncertain whether soil solution concentrations or contents would be better predictors of competitive outcomes if soil moisture varied among the monocultures that were used to predict competitive outcomes. That said, the key in focusing on soil solution nutrient concentrations (even standardized for differences in soil moisture) is that plants could now be compared in (1) their ability to lower the "availability" of nitrogen and (2) the traits that led to differences in their ability to reduce nitrogen availability.

Tilman had made specific assumptions to arrive at the conclusions that plants displace one another when competing by reducing the concentration of available nutrients in soil solution and that the competitively superior plant is the one that is able to reduce the concentration of nutrients to the lowest concentration. There are two assumptions that, if they held, would end the story here. First, Tilman assumed that soil solutions are well mixed, such that uptake is a function of average soil solution concentrations. The second assumption is that plant growth (or population growth) ceases at a minimum average soil solution concentration.

At the time that Tilman formulated his theories on concentration reduction, it was known that soil solutions were not well mixed and that concentration gradients surrounded roots. Criticisms of the theory often cited these facts as objections (Huston and Deangelis 1994), although the critics could not offer examples where this assumption had caused erroneous predictions. In defense of the concentration reduction theory, any theory is an abstraction of the real world and is judged by its utility relative to that of other theories in explaining the real world. Concentration reduction could have been considered just an abstraction, like every other theory. As such, it would have captured the essence of competitive interactions and would have been sufficiently well grounded in mechanism to be plausible and to have predictive utility. But averaging soil solution concentrations and minimum concentrations seemed to make some ecologists nervous.

As Tilman tested the concentration reduction theory of nutrient competition, the theories regarding partitioning of nutrient supplies and competition for nutrients that arose from soil science were qualitatively different from the concentration reduction theory, which originated in the study of aquatic ecosystems. To generalize, soil scientists did not characterize availability in terms of average soil solution concentrations but usually in terms of supplies from the soil to the root (Tinker and Nye 2000). For example, the definitions of nutrient supplies, availability, and stress offered in chapter 3 are most closely aligned with soil scientists' definitions of supplies. Soil solution concentrations are not uniform in a given soil volume but form gradients around roots. Soil scientists devote considerable effort to characterizing diffusion coefficients for different nutrients in different soils to understand the rate at which nutrients diffused through the soil to roots. Uptake of nutrients by roots is not a function

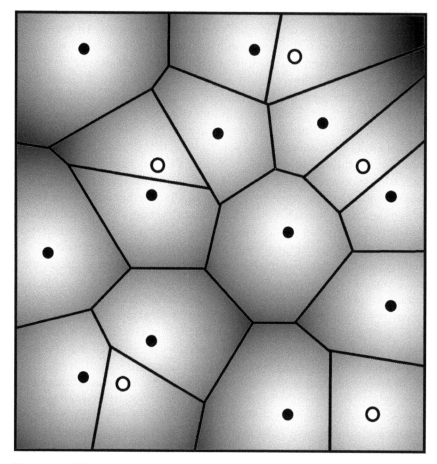

Figure 5.1. Hypothetical map of soil solution nutrient concentrations (gradient from high to low is from black to white) for two plants with roots in a soil volume (black circles and white circles). Lines show partitioning of supplies between roots.

of average soil solution concentrations but of nutrient concentrations at the root surface. Nutrient supplies are partitioned spatially among roots, as characterized by Voronoi diagrams or Thiessen maps (figure 5.1). These were perhaps unnecessary details for understanding the broad patterns of competition, but they led to different approaches that loom important in understanding competition.

Supply Preemption Theory of Competition

Independent of the theoretical framework utilized by Tilman, Phil Smethurst and Nick Comerford (1993), publishing in the *Soil Science Society of America Journal*, used a computer model to predict the uptake of nutrients in soils by the static root systems of two plants, with the goal of understanding partitioning of resources—that is, competition—between generic grasses and loblolly pine (*Pinus taeda*). The model was based on analytical equations that were solved to determine the concentration of nutrients at the root surface. With the equations, they were able to vary nutrient uptake kinetics (V_{max}, K_m, and C_{min}), root diameter, and root length density, as well as soil parameters such as soil moisture. Of all the parameters, partitioning of the nutrient supply between two plants was most sensitive to root length density. Increasing the root length density of one plant greatly increased the fraction of the nutrient supply that it acquired. Increasing nutrient uptake kinetics, making roots thicker in order to have more surface area did not. Root length density was never a parameter in the concentration reduction models, but it was held to be the key to understanding partitioning of nutrient supplies among plants.

It should be stated that Smethurst and Comerford did not perform a full sensitivity analysis as they analyzed the importance of different parameters for partitioning nutrient supplies between two plants. They only compared the response in uptake to a twofold increase in a given parameter, although, for example, plants might have the ability to increase uptake kinetics 10-fold. In their defense, the modeling exercise was mostly to test the ability of analytical solutions rather than numerical models to determine partitioning of nutrient supplies. The importance of root length density in competitive outcomes was written almost as an afterthought, and for more than ten years their results did not penetrate the ecology literature. Even then, it was uncertain whether the concentration reduction and supply preemption approaches were compatible.

The Smethurst and Comerford paper was a linchpin in the understanding of root systems. For example, in monocultures of grassland species at Cedar Creek, competitively inferior plants can reduce soil solution nitrogen concentrations to lower levels than competitively superior plants (Craine, Wedin, et al. 2003; Fargione and Tilman 2006) (figure 5.2). For example, *Solidago rigida* could reduce inorganic N concentrations well below those of competitively superior species, such as *Schizachyrium scoparium*. In some senses, the root systems of these two species are quite similar. For example, in both the root systems are dense and extend more than a meter in depth. *Schizachyrium scoparium*, however, has a higher density of roots per unit of soil volume. Competition seems to follow from root length density, not soil solution nutrient concentrations.

In another experiment, root length density was shown to predict the relative uptake of N from small patches of high availability in the soil. Hodge et al. (1999b) grew two grass species (*Lolium perenne* and *Poa pratensis*) alone and in mixtures. Plants were grown in thin (3-mm) micro-

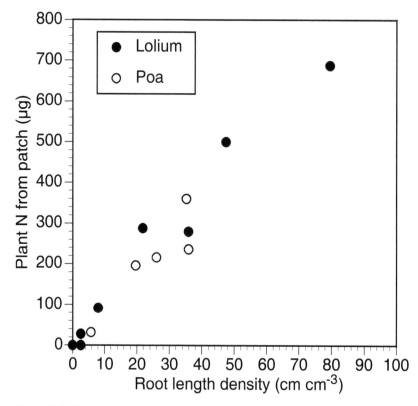

Figure 5.2. Relationship between root length density of a plant in a patch of high nitrogen availability and the amount of nitrogen acquired from the patch. Data from Hodge et al. 1999.

cosms. Patches of high nitrogen availability were created by adding ^{15}N-enriched grass leaves to the soil. The amount of nitrogen acquired by a plant was proportional to its relative root length density in the patch (figure 5.2). Just as with the Smethurst and Comerford approach, a higher relative amount of root length provided a higher fraction of the nutrient supply (Robinson et al. 1999).

Although it was not clear whether these observations were enough to refute the concentration reduction theory, root length density seemed to be key to understanding partitioning of nutrient supplies. Changing root uptake kinetics or root surface area does not increase uptake, since uptake is limited by the supply of nutrients to the root surface and there is little a plant can do to make nutrients flow to it faster. Even increasing transpiration rates apparently did little to pull nutrients to the root faster. Diffusion, even of nutrients with low diffusion rates in a given soil, is much faster than mass flow associated with transpiration.

In 2003, in a multi-author paper (Reich, Wright, et al. 2003, p. S155), I summarized my understanding at the time of competition for nutrients when nutrients are supplied uniformly in space and time:

> A root in soil that has low N supply generally can take up N faster than it is supplied, and plant roots cannot increase uptake by increasing specific rates of uptake or surface area (Leadley, Reynolds, and Chapin 1997; Robinson et al. 1999). As such, at low N supply the functional unit of uptake is root length. . . . [C]ompetition for nutrients is likely to involve supply preemption. . . . Preempting the supply from reaching roots of other plants means having more root length than competitors. . . . The higher the fraction of root length that an individual has, the higher fraction of the N supply that it preempts, and therefore the higher the fraction of the N supply that it acquires.

The concept of supply preemption was based on extrapolating the results of the analytical models of Smethurst and Comerford beyond their narrow goals and observations of the traits of plants when grown in monoculture. It incorporated the focus on supplies and flowed logically from the Thiessen maps of nutrient concentrations and uptake.

Testing Hypotheses with Models

The first numerical model of nutrient diffusion and uptake at a fine scale was published by Raynaud and Leadley in 2004. Echoing Smethurst and Comerford and the concept of supply preemption, they found that when the diffusion of nutrients was relatively slow, nutrient uptake was determined by the fraction of root length in the soil volume (see figure 5.2). The ability to preempt the supply from competing plants was due to what they called space occupation. The greater the soil volume from which a plant could preempt supplies, the better the plant was as a competitor. Echoing the Thiessen map approach, a plant preempts supplies by occupying space, much as animals occupy territories and collect the resources within their territory.

In their article, Raynaud and Leadley extended the soil science perspective and attempt to rectify their findings with Tilman's concentration reduction. They identified conditions where R^* might not predict competitive outcomes correctly, such as when there is heterogeneity in nutrient availability or slow diffusion of nutrients. Raynaud and Leadley were not the first to suggest that concentration reduction be dumped for mechanistic reasons. For example, Grime had stated that "the assumption of a uniform draw-down of nutrient levels is justified for phytoplankton populations in well-mixed solutions (Titman 1976) but does not capture the realities of localized resource depletion experienced by plants exploiting fertile soils" (Grime 2001, p. 35).

Raynaud and Leadley's statements are more cautioning than prescriptive in that they never showed concentration reduction to make incorrect predictions of competitive outcomes. In general, plants that are better able to preempt nutrient supplies reduce soil nutrient concentrations to a lower level when grown in monoculture. As root length density increases, the average distance from a given point in the soil to the surface of a root decreases. Since nutrient concentrations increase with distance from a given root, decreasing the average distance among roots decreases the average nutrient concentration in the soil solution. Thus, one would expect that in general, plants that were able to produce and maintain a higher root length density, and so better be able to preempt nutrient supplies, would also have lower soil solution nutrient concentrations.

If there were no differences in concentration reduction and supply preemption to predict competitive outcomes, any separation between the two as the mechanism would be semantic. What if the cautioning statements of Raynaud and Leadley were correct, and concentration reduction incorrectly predicted competitive outcomes? Empirical results are often used to falsify theories. Yet in the few cases where testing of the concentration reduction theory was attempted, concentration reduction predicted competitive outcomes each time (Wedin and Tilman 1993).

Recently, Fargione and Tilman (2006) examined the relative explanatory power of soil solution nutrient concentrations and root length density in predicting the relative abundance of plant species when grown in mixtures. The authors measured both soil solution inorganic nitrogen concentrations and the root length density of grassland plants grown in monoculture. These data were used to predict the relative yield of plants grown in mixture versus monoculture. For relative yield, the aboveground biomass of species in mixture was expressed as a ratio of the biomass of the species in monoculture and represented an index of competition. Species with low relative yield would have less biomass in mixture than monoculture, while species with high relative yields would be relatively unsuppressed by the presence of other species. In general, soil nitrate and root length density each explained similar amounts of variation in relative yield (figure 5.3). Yet in Fargione and Tilman's experiment, individual species were found to reduce soil solution concentrations to a low level in monoculture, but they seemed to be competitively displaced.

Identifying cases where concentration reduction did not predict competitive outcomes and supply preemption would not disprove that concentration reduction was the mechanism of competitive outcomes. For example, as mentioned earlier, at Cedar Creek, the C_3 tallgrass forb *Solidago rigida* consistently reduced soil solution N concentrations to lower

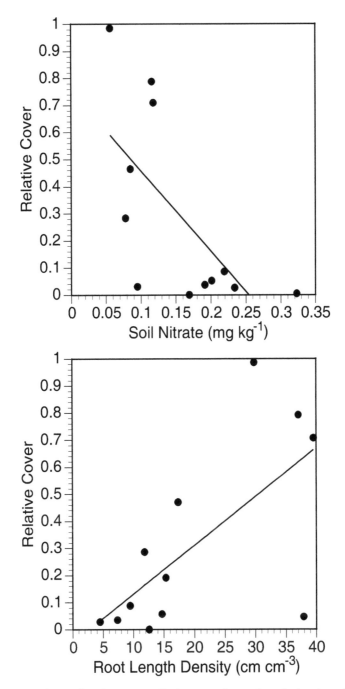

Figure 5.3. Relationship between soil nitrate and root length density of herbaceous species grown in monoculture and their relative cover in a diverse mixture. Data from Fargione et al. 2006.

levels than did the competitively superior C_4 grasses. More complex mechanisms could explain why *Solidago* had lower soil solution N concentrations without requiring the concentration reduction hypothesis be rejected. *Solidago* could dry out soils or release allelochemicals and reduce mineralization, but these mechanisms would not give it increased competitive ability.

After examining empirical patterns, the next step in comparing concentration reduction and supply preemption is to find theoretical examples where supply preemption explains competitive outcomes better than concentration reduction. Craine, Fargione, and Sugita (2005) published results obtained using a numerical model that allowed explicit comparisons of concentration reduction and supply preemption in predicting theoretical competitive outcomes. As in the Raynaud and Leadley model, a thin cross section of soil was divided into a grid and the soil was populated with roots of two species of plants. Nitrogen was mineralized into the soil solution, diffused along concentration gradients, and taken out of solution by roots. Root systems were not static, but instead roots were allowed to die and new roots were produced at a rate proportional to the rate of nutrient uptake.

With the model, the plant that was able to produce and maintain higher root length density was competitively superior. Yet these plants also had lower soil solution nutrient concentrations. We then asked what would happen if the species that had higher root length also lowered soil moisture to a lower level. Lowering soil moisture slows the diffusion of nutrients and leads to higher average soil solution nutrient concentrations for the high-root-length-density plant. Therefore, the concentration reduction theory would predict that the plant would be competitively inferior. When grown together, however, the high-root-length-density plant was competitively superior. One could argue that concentration reduction theory was never meant to explain differences in competitive outcomes when plants are allowed to grow at different soil moisture concentrations. On the other hand, a supply preemption approach could explain competitive outcomes when plants are grown at different as well as similar soil moistures.

Bayes, Popper, and the Mechanism of Competitive Exclusion

In the end, no combination of theoretical or empirical research is enough to disprove the concentration reduction hypothesis. In a Popperian sense, no single empirical study can refute the hypothesis. Concentration reduction was always to some degree an abstraction. For any empirical finding there are always more complicated mechanisms to explain why concentration reduction did not predict a particular set of competitive outcomes. For any theoretical finding there are always ways to restrict the scope of the original model so that the theoretical case does not apply. Allowing simultaneous changes in soil moisture with changes in soil nutrients extends the applicability of the original hypothesis beyond its original purpose.

Instead of a Popperian approach, a Bayesian or likelihood approach is the best way to approach these competing hypotheses for nutrient competition (Hilborn and Mangel 1997). In a Bayesian approach, the total explanatory power of each model or hypothesis is compared. This generally conjures up a meta-analysis of published data or large experiments, like that of Fargione and Tilman (2006), but when one is evaluating conceptual models, comparing explanatory power is not necessarily the best approach. Both supply preemption and concentration reduction have been shown to have similar explanatory power. In individual cases, results are predicted incorrectly by each model.

Supply preemption matches the behavior of models about the behavior of nutrients in soil much better than does concentration reduction. The assumptions that concentration reduction theories make might be considered simplifying, while others might state that they are incorrect. R^* does predict competitive outcomes. It is true that competitive outcomes rely on reducing the level or availability of nutrients in soil solution, as Tilman phrases occasionally. But it would be a poor characterization of nutrient supply and acquisition by co-occurring root systems to state that the average soil solution concentration determines competitive outcomes. Instead, the supply preemption approach used by Comerford, Smethurst, Hodge, Robinson, Raynaud, Leadley, and myself is a much better characterization of competition.

To put supply preemption on the same theoretical footing as concentration reduction, it is important to identify the analog of R^*. What metric allows a comparison of the competitive ability of two species, recognizing the importance of supply preemption for competition for nutrients? The focus on supplies and root length leads to the hypothesis that the plant that produces the greatest length of root (or equivalent in mycorrhizal hyphae) per unit supply is competitively superior. For a given nutrient supply, plants that can produce more root length per unit supply acquire a larger fraction of the nutrient supply. If one assumes that plants do not affect the nutrient supply, one should be able to examine the root length density of the plant in monoculture as an index of competitive superiority. If plants also affect nutrient supplies, then, for example, a species that reduced nutrient supplies might have lower root length in monoculture than a species that didn't, but might have greater ability to produce root length at the same nutrient supply and therefore preempt a shared nutrient supply. As such, both supplies and root length need to be measured in order to calculate the root length per unit supply. Future endeavors in this field should be exciting and promise to solidify an important aspect of ecological theory.

In summary, plants acquire nutrient supplies in proportion to their relative root length density in a given soil volume. Plants compete against one another by preempting the supply of nutrients in a given soil volume. Plants that can produce higher root length densities partition the larger fraction of a nutrient supply. The plant that has the lowest supply requirement per unit root length should be able to produce the highest root length densities and competitively displace other plants when nutrients are supplied uniformly in space and time. From these precepts, it is clear that producing more root length than a neighboring plant is the key to acquiring the bulk of the nutrient supply. The next section tackles the evolutionary consequences of competition manifesting itself through preemption and shows the profound implications of such competition for natural selection and for the shape of plants that must compete for nutrients.

How Much Root Length?

If high root length density is the key to competitive success, it is important to understand what regulates root length density and what the optimum root length density is for a plant in a competitive environment. For example, if just a few roots per plant were sufficient to acquire enough nutrients to maintain maximal growth rates in the absence of competition, what root length density would represent the most evolutionarily stable strategy when plants compete for nutrients?

It turns out that the optimal root length density when plants are competing for nutrients is much higher than when they are not. This high root length density of plants that comes as a result of competition can be better understood as an unregulated race to acquire nutrients, with little difference whether the competition is intra- or interspecific, or likely even against microbes. Using a fine-scale model of soil nutrient dynamics and plant growth, I used a cost-benefit approach to assess optimal allocation rates for plants that accounted for the relative value of both carbon and nitrogen (Craine 2006). The costs of roots were the amount of carbon and nitrogen invested in biomass and respiration rates, while the benefits equaled nitrogen uptake. Using a high relative value for nitrogen in terms of carbon, characteristic of low-nitrogen-supply ecosystems, the net benefits of different strategies could be assessed for a plant in the absence as well as in the presence of competing plants.

In the absence of interplant competition, resource benefits are maximized with very little root length, just a few percent of what is seen in

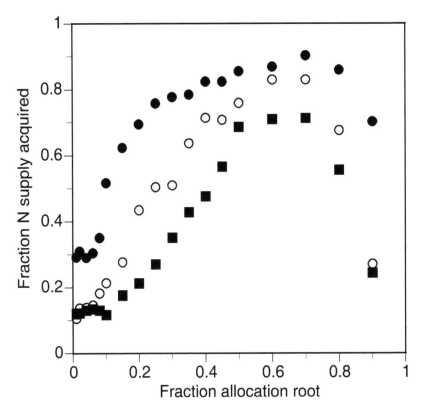

Figure 5.4. Relationship between the fraction of biomass that a plant allocates belowground and the fraction of the nitrogen supply that it acquires when competing against a plant that allocates 10%, 25%, and 40% of its biomass belowground (closed circle, open circle, and closed square, respectively). Data from Craine 2006.

low-nutrient species. In the presence of a competitor, the allocation rate of biomass to roots that maximizes net resource benefits is much greater (figure 5.4). This allocation also increases as the ability of competitors to produce root length increase. As one plant increases its root length production, the same amount of nutrients is acquired by plants in the soil, but a higher fraction is acquired by the plant with more roots. This differential kicks off an evolutionary race to produce as much root length as possible. Competition for inorganic nitrogen among plants generates a classic aspect of the tragedy of the commons, known as the "race for fish" in fisheries literature (Hilborn et al. 2003). Faced with a common nutrient supply, competition favors plants that produce more roots than is optimum in the absence of competition.

Although the model focused exclusively on relative allocation rates, similar considerations apply when evaluating other factors that affect root length. Plants that are competing for nutrients could also maximize root length density by producing thin roots that live a long time. There are multiple trade-offs associated with each factor, but it is likely that plant roots might be built thinner than would be optimum in the absence of competition, and plants might invest in roots so that they lived longer than would be optimum in the absence of competition.

INTERFERENCE COMPETITION

Besides preempting supplies from competitors, plants can reduce the availability of nutrients to neighbors by lowering nutrient supplies, which may affect the relative abundance of species (Suding et al. 2004). Plants primarily accomplish this by producing litter that induces feedbacks to nutrient availability. For example, if plants return litter to the soil that has a high C:N ratio, microbes mineralize nitrogen from the biomass at a slower rate and are more likely to immobilize ambient nitrogen. Hence, a high C:N biomass reduces the net mineralization of nitrogen and reduces the nutrient supply to all plants in the soil.

Although the ability of plants to lower nutrient supplies has been known for more than 20 years, there is a poor conceptual basis on which to judge why this would be advantageous to a given plant. For example, Blumenthal, Jordan, and Russelle (2003) mixed different amounts of a mixture of sucrose and sawdust into field plots and then seeded in equal amounts of native prairie species and plant species (mostly annual) considered noxious weeds. As more carbon was added, available NO_3^- declined and light penetration of the soil increased. Total weed biomass decreased from approximately 900 g m^{-2} to 500 g m^{-2} across the soil carbon gradient in the first year, while prairie species increased in biomass from close to 0 g m^{-2} to 20 g m^{-2} by the second year. The differences in absolute magnitude of the species are considerable, and many questions could be asked about the specifics of the results. Yet if plants could decrease soil nitrogen availability in a manner analogous to the carbon additions, might they acquire not only a relative advantage over other species but an absolute advantage, too?

One hypothesis might be that reducing nutrient availability shifts plants from competing for light to competing for nutrients. Blumenthal observed greater light at the soil surface with reductions in nutrient availability, which might support the idea that reducing nutrient availability favored plants that were better competitors for nutrients over those that are better competitors for light. It might also be hypothesized that species differ in their minimum nutrient supply requirements. If plants differ in the minimum nutrient supply required for growth, then, as nutrient supplies decline, species with lower minimum nutrient supply requirements might gain an advantage as plants with higher nutrient supply requirements perish. Interestingly, there has been no significant research on this topic, and there is little information with which to evaluate whether species differ in the minimum nutrient supply required to grow and reproduce.

Separating the relative importance of supply reduction from supply preemption as mechanisms of displacement is an important component of understanding the traits of plants. For example, species such as the North American C_4 grass *Schizachyrium scoparium* not only produce a high root length density, they can also reduce N supplies by increasing microbial immobilization through litter feedbacks. If *Schizachyrium* has a lower minimum nitrogen supply requirement than other species that *Schizachyrium* displaces, it is possible that the reduction of supply contributes to, if it is not responsible for, the displacement of the other species.

COMPETITION FOR NUTRIENTS UNDER HETEROGENEOUS SUPPLIES

The previous section considered the mechanisms by which plants compete for nutrients when nutrients are supplied uniformly in space and time. With only one notable exception, the major selection pressures on plants that dominate low-nutrient environments have been to acquire nutrients that are supplied uniformly, but at a low rate. Nitrogen supplies, however, are presumed not to be distributed uniformly, even if the spatial and temporal scales of heterogeneity of the nitrogen supply have not been well characterized (Robertson and Gross 1994). Nutrient supplies may be locally high (patches) and may be supplied at higher rates at some times than others—that is, in pulses. Although there is little evidence that any species requires patches or pulses of nutrients to maintain itself in low-nutrient ecosystems, this does not mean that competition for heterogeneous supplies does not occur, or that it would not be advantageous for plants to utilize these supplies if they were present. This section reviews the basic mechanisms by which plants compete for heterogeneous nutrient supplies. In addition to understanding how competition for nutrients works under a regime of heterogeneous supplies, it is important to know the traits associated with such competition, if only to distinguish this strategy from strategies used by low-nutrient species.

As when nutrient supplies are homogeneous, under regimes of heterogeneous nutrient supply root length dominance is an important component of competition for nutrients. As long as nutrient concentrations do not rise too high (the patch or pulse is not too intense), acquisition is still partitioned among plants according to their root length. Partitioning soil nitrogen supplies in a patch generally requires root proliferation, to achieve root length dominance in the soil volume that has higher supply. When soil solution concentrations remain low, partitioning of the nitrogen supply from a patch is related to the fraction of root length for a plant in the patch (Hodge et al. 1999a; Robinson et al. 1999). To accomplish root length dominance in the patch, local production rates generally increase, but plants can also decrease specific root length or have more dichotomous root branching for finer precision sampling (Farley and Fitter 1999). Mycorrhizal proliferation follows the same patterns, where uptake is related to the fraction of length in soil volume. Thus, there can be proliferation of mycorrhizal length in a patch under competitive conditions (Hodge, Campbell, and Fitter 2001; Hodge 2003).

Whereas under a regime of uniform nutrient supply, a low nitrogen supply is associated with low soil solution concentrations, with a heterogeneous nitrogen supply, nitrogen supply can be limiting to a plant, but soil solution concentrations can be high locally. It appears that when local nitrogen availability increases enough, not only is there root length proliferation, but upregulation of uptake capacity also occurs (Hodge et al. 1999b). Some data suggest that faster growing species proliferate more and have faster induction of uptake (McKane, Grigal, and Russelle 1990), but these patterns need to be confirmed by more direct and comprehensive studies (Kembel and Cahill 2005).

For pulses of nutrients as for patches, total uptake capacity is a product of root surface area and the uptake potential of a given unit of root area. In some cases a plant with a high root biomass with lower uptake capacity could outcompete a smaller root system with higher specific uptake potential. The interactions among root system size and root activity, the postpulse responses of plants in root production and activity, and characteristics of pulses such as size, duration, and frequency is an area that would benefit from more theoretical and empirical research.

That said, pulses of high availability are likely to favor plants that have high uptake kinetics. McKane, Grigal, and Russelle (1990) added ^{15}N-labeled NH_4^+ to a grassland assemblage in a nitrogen-poor soil. The aboveground biomass was dominated by *Schizachyrium scoparium*, a C_4 bunchgrass that is competitively superior for nitrogen over long time scales when the nitrogen supply is uniform. These plants have lower fractions of their biomass in roots and similar if not thicker roots, and so the root length discrepancy was likely greater than the differences in biomass aboveground. Yet as much if not more of the added ^{15}N was acquired by plants with less aboveground biomass, such as *Poa pratensis* and *Artemisia ludoviciana*.

When inorganic nitrogen is added in a pulse, it is likely that plants with high specific rates of nutrient uptake, such as *Poa* or *Artemisia*, are able to acquire a higher fraction of the available nitrogen than their fraction of the total root length. Initially after a pulse, when concentrations are high, these plants are able to acquire nutrients at a higher total rate. The benefit of higher root length does not occur until concentrations are reduced. By then, most of the nutrients from the pulse would have been acquired by the high-uptake species. Pulses would have to be infrequent so as to limit the standing biomass of species with high specific uptake rates, and the pulses would have to be short in duration to limit the benefit of responding to a pulse by growing quickly to benefit species that maintain a large root system with low specific uptake capacity.

COMPETITION FOR LIGHT

When competing for nutrients, the plant that is better able to preempt the supply of nutrients that would otherwise come in contact with the roots of competitors acquires the bulk of the nutrient supply. Within a given soil volume, placing roots closer to the nutrient source sets nutrients to move down the concentration gradients of a given plant's root system. Since nutrients are supplied to a root from all directions, competition is symmetric with respect to size. Larger plants do not necessarily get a disproportionately greater fraction of the nutrient supply. When nutrients are supplied uniformly in a given soil volume, there is no way to get roots closer to the supply besides generally increasing root length density.

In many ways, competition for light is analogous to competition for nutrients. The key to acquiring a large share of the light supply and reducing light availability to other plants is to produce leaves that are between the sun and the leaves of other plants. The major difference between nutrients and light that distinguishes the competition for the two resources is that light is generally supplied directionally relative a given leaf. On a clear day, the greatest portion of the light comes directly from the sun and the highest intensity of light occurs at midday, when the sun is approximately directly above the plants. Other differences between light and belowground resources exist, such as the lack of storage of light in the ecosystem. Nutrients and water that are not immediately acquired remain in the soil for some period of time. Unacquired light is immediately gone. As opposed to reducing nutrient supplies, there is no way for a plant to interfere directly with another plant's acquisition of light other than to intercept the light itself. Compared with the directionality of light, however, these factors play a minor role in distinguishing light and nutrient competition.

With light coming directly from above, competition for light involves placing leaves above other plants. Just as for nutrients and root length dominance, successful competitors for light attain *leaf area dominance*

(Fahey, Battles, and Wilson 1998) by producing a large number of leaves or a high leaf area above competitors, which ensures that the majority of the light supply comes in contact with one's leaves. A given leaf can absorb as much as 80% of the incident light (Chapin, Matson, and Mooney 2002). As such, a plant whose leaves are positioned even slightly above the leaves of another plant reduces light availability substantially to lower plants. Proximally, this requires allocating resources to leaf and stem production, to display the leaves above other plants.

Assuming that light only comes from directly above a plant is a valid starting point for understanding how light competition has shaped different plant strategies. That said, many important details of plant adaptations that arise from light competition come as a result of light not being supplied unidirectionally over the course of the day. On a cloudy day, light intensities at the top of a canopy are approximately equivalent from all directions above the horizontal plane. With diffuse light supplies, placing leaves that were completely opaque above another plant would reduce only a fraction of the total light supply to the subordinant plant. Similarly, light angles are constantly changing over the course of the day, producing many times of day when light is primarily supplied from the side rather than above. In addition to diffuse radiation and changing angles of supply, as one moves poleward on Earth, the angle of the sun's rays becomes more oblique. Even on a clear day at high latitude, most light is coming not from above but from the side. Again, being above another plant or even adjacent to it does little to limit light interception for the shorter plant over the course of the day.

Factors such as diffuse light supplies and oblique light angles weaken the intensity of one plant's effects on another plant, making competition among individuals more diffuse. The interactions between plants become weaker and more numerous than if light were supplied only from above. The changing angles of light over the course of the day and the times when light is supplied diffusely reduce the intensity of competition among individuals. For example, for two isolated plants with narrow canopies that are vertically separated but in the same vertical cylinder, over the course of a day the subordinant canopy can still acquire considerable light. For only a short period of the day does a plant with a superior canopy shade a lower one.

Although obviously of great importance for understanding plant strategies, the consequences of these factors have not been explored in much detail. There is still much work to be done to understand how competition for light among individuals works when light is supplied directly from above. A simplifying approach is to examine competition at the stand level, which effectively negates any importance of light being supplied from oblique angles. At the stand level, there is little consequence for most scenarios as to whether light is supplied directly or diffusely, or whether the angle of light changes over the course of the day. This book largely examines competition for light at the stand level and assumes that most light is supplied directly from above, an approach qualitatively similar to assessing patterns at the stand level. Developing the low-light strategy requires working through some of the consequences of light being supplied diffusely over the course of the day, but there is no need to go much beyond this in order to understand the basic patterns of light competition and its effects on plant strategies.

Asymmetries and Competition for Light

A key question to understanding light competition is whether plants that differ in height and whose canopies do not overlap are even competing for light. By definition, competing plants must both have the potential to reduce resource availability to each another. With light coming directly from above, shorter plants do not reduce the availability of light to taller plants. Therefore, competition is considered to be size-asymmetric. Taller plants reduce light availability to shorter plants, but shorter plants do not reduce light availability to taller plants.

The difficulty with understanding competition for light is the asymmetry of partitioning of the light supply. When canopies are vertically discontinuous, the shorter species has no negative effect on the light acquisition of the taller species. Shorter plants cannot shade taller plants. It is only when the growth rate of the taller species slows that their canopies can mix as the highest leaves of shorter plants emerge above the lowest leaves of the taller plant and reciprocal negative effects are present. Yet in a successional sequence, the taller species often dies before the canopies mix. If one species never has a negative effect on the other, does this mean that the two species never compete for light? The asymmetry of light acquisition is the reason why researchers have characterized the growth of plants in the shade of taller plants in terms of tolerance rather than competition for light.

Determining whether two plants or populations of different species at the stand level are competing for light depends on the time scale over which interactions are integrated. Two hypothetical species growing at a site provide an example. Species A germinates first and begins to raise its canopy upward. Species B germinates after species A and grows more slowly in the shade of species A. At the end of the first growing season, species B has never reduced the light supply to the taller species A. By some strict definitions, the two species could not be considered to be competing, since there was never any reciprocal reduction of light.

Now imagine that at the end of the first year, all of the aboveground biomass of species A dies, but species B retains all of its biomass. At the beginning of the second growing season, species A begins to produce leaves at the ground surface, but species B already has a canopy that is above species A. During the second year, species B begins with complete leaf area dominance; the canopy of species A never catches up. Analyzed over just the second year, the two species are also found never to be competing for light, since their canopies never overlap.

When interactions are integrated at the annual scale, there is never any mutual reduction of light supplies. Shorter plants are effectively "downstream" of taller plants and would not classically be considered to be competing against one another. Yet, if the time scale of integration extends across years, it is clear that there is a reciprocal reduction in light supplies. During the first year, the ability of species A to suppress species B has a strong effect on the amount of light that is available to species A the following year. At the interannual scale, these two species are definitely competing, even though at any one point in time their interactions are asymmetric.

This analogy should be extended a bit further to finish up the logical basis for ascribing to plants competition for light. Imagine the same scenario in which species A initially produces a canopy above species B, and at the end of the first growing season the aboveground biomass of species A is lost, while species B maintains its entire canopy. Instead of species A regrowing from meristems retained in the soils, however, it had produced seeds that fell directly downward. At the beginning of the second season, species A still is producing a new canopy beneath species B, but the second year's plants were not the same plants that were present in the first year and would be considered a new generation of species A, even if the seeds were produced parthogenetically. Will the small step to allow competition to extend across generations be taken? It is unclear how one could argue that the intragenerational scenario was competition and the intergenerational one was not, especially if seeds represent the same genetic individual over time.

Limiting competition to only that occurring between individuals over short time scales produces situations in which competition for light almost rarely occurs. At least for evolutionary time scales, accepting that competition for light can occur across generations broadens the scope of light competition to the scale at which it is often considered—the stand level between species—and improves our understanding of natural selection. Revisiting the working definition of competition—*the process by which two or more individuals differentially capture a potentially common limiting resource supply*—a key here is over what spatial and time scales to apply the word "potential." For example, if dispersal is included

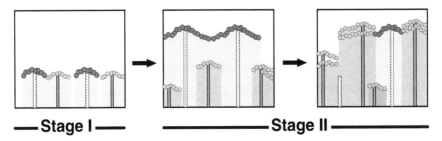

— Stage I —   — Stage II —

Figure 5.5. The two stages of light competition. In stage I, competition for light is largely a race to project leaves above competitors' leaves. In stage II, vertical separation of the canopies has occurred, and competition takes the form of attaining height beneath the canopies of others and reducing light levels in the understory.

in the process of competition, plants could compete for resources at much broader spatial scales than are occupied by individuals.

The Two Stages of Light Competition

Once the assumption that plants in the same vertical cylinder are competing for light is adopted, regardless of whether their canopies mix or not, it becomes clear that there are two stages to competition for light. The first stage of competition for light is a classic race to the top, where plants begin growing at the same height, generally at the ground surface, and at approximately the same time—soon after a severe aboveground disturbance (figure 5.5).

The details of the strategy that is associated with winning the first stage of competition for light are the subject of chapter 8. Briefly, the strategy requires producing leaves rapidly and continuing to produce them above neighboring plants. As such, plants are faced with optimizing allocation to both stem and leaf. The first stage of competition would be quite different if plant stems elongated from the base rather than the apex. With stems elongating at their tips, plants cannot just push the old leaves up; instead, new leaves have to be produced, and old leaves find themselves below the new ones.

After plants have become vertically sorted after the initial race, some plants find themselves completely under the upper canopy where plants are still racing against one another. As growth of the canopy species slows or there is a selective disturbance to canopy species, the species that can maintain leaf area dominance in the shade of others is best positioned to maintain dominance in the new canopy. The key question to focus on for the second stage of light competition is what traits allow plants to attain leaf area dominance in the shade of others, so they can either catch up to a canopy that has slowed in its ascent or dominate after a disturbance to the superior canopy.

Runaway Competition for Light

In a similar manner to how low-nutrient species allocate more resources to root growth than plants that optimize growth in the absence of competition, there is also evidence that high-nutrient plants allocate more resources to leaf production than would be optimal if they were not competing for light. One line of evidence is that new leaves of a plant often shade older leaves, and their production can result in only marginal increases in light acquisition for isolated high-resource plants. Another line of evidence is the high allocation of resources to stem production. Stems that raise new leaves higher do not directly acquire more light. In the absence of competition, plants still might be selected to grow in height to escape ground-based disturbances such as fire or mammalian herbivores, but many species far exceed the height needed to escape them. Only when plants are competing for light does stem allocation lead to greater light acquisition for an individual.

Finally, and most interesting, even when competing for light, many species, including high-resource species, appear to produce leaf canopies that would be suboptimal for maximizing canopy photosynthesis in the absence of competition. In addition to being taller than is optimal, many species that would be competing for light maintain a higher leaf area than would be optimal in the absence of competition, and they also hold their leaves more horizontal than is optimal (Anten 2005). When evaluated using models of light acquisition for isolated plants and plants growing in the presence of neighbors, some species may have twice the leaf area than would be optimal to maximize canopy photosynthesis (figure 5.6). It also would be more optimal for plants to hold their leaves at a higher angle and let more light deeper into the canopy. Yet having lower leaf area, or holding leaves at a higher angle, or being shorter are not evolutionarily stable traits. Plants that hold more than optimal leaf area, have more flatly held leaves, or greater height are competitively superior for acquiring light and are able to displace species that are solely optimizing canopy photosynthesis.

SYNTHESIS

Competition occurs when two or more plants attempt to acquire a potentially common, limiting resource supply. When nutrients are limiting, a

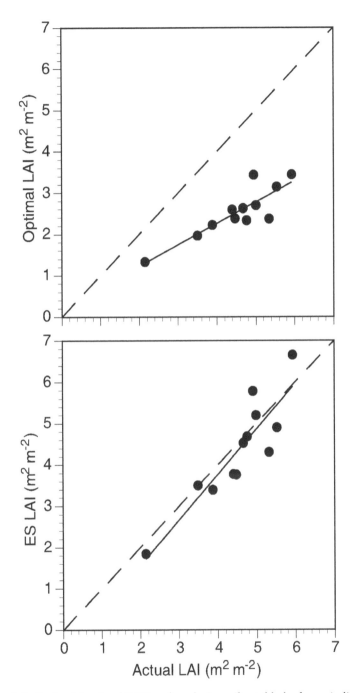

Figure 5.6. Optimal (optimal LAI) and evolutionarily stable leaf area indices (ES LAI) plotted against observed LAI for a number of species. Dashed lines indicate a 1:1 correspondence between variables; solid lines indicate linear regressions.

plant competes by attempting to preempt the nutrient supply from other plants. Owing to the relatively slow diffusion of nutrients in soil, as roots acquire nutrients from the soil solution, nutrient concentrations become depleted around individual roots. Altering uptake kinetics provides little additional uptake once concentrations of nutrients at the root surface become depleted. Instead, nutrient supplies are partitioned among plants based on the relative amount of root length they hold in a particular soil volume. Increasing the fraction of the total root length in the soil returns a greater fraction of the nutrient supply. Thus, the key to acquiring the largest share of a given nutrient supply is root length dominance, which reduces the availability of nutrients to others.

The concentration reduction hypothesis assumed that soil solutions were well mixed and that it was the average soil solution concentration that determined the rate at which a plant grew. It followed that lowering the average soil solution concentration of a limiting nutrient was the key to displacing other species. Although there is no Popperian way to reject the hypothesis, the concentration reduction hypothesis can generate incorrect predictions as a consequence of its assumption of well-mixed soil solutions and the dependence of a plant's growth on average soil solution concentrations. Comparing the average soil solution concentrations between species grown in monoculture at best provides a useful index for estimating the ability of a species to reduce nutrient availability via supply preemption.

One consequence of supply preemption being the mechanism of competition for nutrients and root length dominance the key to preempting nutrient supplies is that plants face an evolutionary tragedy of the commons in their allocation patterns to roots. When the nutrient supply is limiting and a given plant is grown in isolation, a relatively low root length density optimizes growth. In the presence of competitors, however, plants that can maintain higher root length densities than is optimal in the absence of competition are able to acquire a larger fraction of the total nutrient supply, and therefore would have been favored by natural selection. As such, high root length densities are more evolutionarily stable than the lower root length densities that would optimize growth in the absence of competition. Therefore, plants can be expected to allocate a greater fraction of resources to root growth, to have thinner roots, or to have roots that live a longer time than would be expected based on a plant that optimizes growth in the absence of competition.

In addition to competing by acquiring limiting nutrient supplies, a given plant can interfere with the growth of other plants either reducing by their ability to acquire nutrient supplies or by reducing nutrient supplies. Little is known about the prevalence of plants' actual interference with other plants' ability to acquire nutrients, which largely occurs through releasing chemicals in the soil environment. Plants can reduce nutrient supplies by producing litter that inhibits microbial mineralization, both through high C:N and by having secondary compounds that can restrict nitrogen availability. The potential evolutionary significance of this reduction is addressed in chapter 7.

Nutrient supplies in low-nutrient environments are relatively uniform over time, yet nutrients can also be supplied heterogeneously in space and time. When nutrients are supplied in patches, root length dominance is still the key to acquiring the large proportion of nutrient supplied there. This primarily requires the ability to precisely proliferate roots within the patch. When nutrients are supplied in a pulse, concentrations at the root surface are generally high initially, benefiting plants with high uptake capacity.

The supply of light differs fundamentally from nutrient supplies in that it is largely supplied directionally. In a manner analogous to nutrient competition, light competition favors plants that can attain leaf area dominance. With light supplied directionally, this requires the ability to project high leaf area at height. The basic patterns of competition for light suggest there are two strategies associated with light competition, reflecting the two stages of light competition. The first stage of competition for light is a race to project leaf area at height soon after a disturbance. The second stage of light competition involves the ability to maintain leaf area dominance beneath the plants that are involved in the first stage of competition.

The most difficult aspect of light competition to incorporate into concepts of competition is that light competition is inherently asymmetric. Over the short term, plants that have intermingling canopies would classically be considered to be competing. Both reduce the supply of light to one another and reduce each other's growth. With definitions of competition that are restricted to short time scales, once the canopies of plants in the same vertical cylinder become vertically separated, they would no longer be considered to be competing. Over longer time scales, however, it is clear that there is competition for light that either extends across the years, for individuals, or extends across generations.

Just as the most evolutionarily stable strategy for competing for nutrients involves maintaining higher root length density than is optimal in the absence of competition, competition for light can select for plants that have canopies that would be suboptimal in the absence of competition. This includes greater stem production, high leaf area, and more flatly held leaves. For example, shorter plants might be able to allocate more resources to reproduction or to leaf area production but quickly become overtopped by plants that allocate more to leaves. Similarly, plants that are optimizing canopy photosynthesis might hold their leaves at a higher angle to allow more light to penetrate deeper into the canopy, where it can be used more efficiently. Yet plants that hold their leaves more flatly can invade a stand of plants with vertically oriented leaves and displace these species.

CHAPTER 6

Comparing Negative Effects

IN CHARACTERIZING ECOLOGICAL PATTERNS of natural selection, stresses and disturbances are the two main sets of factors that have shaped assemblages and plant strategies. For stresses, it is important to attempt to separate whether the stress is induced as a result of competition or is independent of neighboring plants, as each shapes plants and structures assemblages differently. Additionally, it is important to identify whether a stress agent decreases the availability of a resource, decreases the ability of plants to acquire the resource, or increases the loss of resources. With regard to disturbances, plants can lose biomass as a result of an intense stress, may have biomass removed selectively, or may be disturbed by agents and forces largely independent of specific plant traits and common to all plants in an area. Disturbances may primarily focus on aboveground biomass, belowground biomass, or both.

In weighing the influence of all these factors in modern ecological interactions and natural selection, it is important to begin to rank their absolute and relative influence. On some scales, it is difficult to begin to rank the influence of the availability of different resources on natural selection of the flora of the world. Determining whether low water availability or low nutrient supplies were more important overall in shaping the most species is an exceedingly difficult task. Yet for a given environment with its specific combination of resource supplies, it should be possible to begin comparing the absolute and relative effects of the different factors on growth and reproduction and to interpret the history of natural selection that would have produced the traits of the successful species in the environment. For this reason, there is an emphasis on describing the characteristics of a habitat that are important for assembly, as well as the traits of plant species in the habitat, which largely are the products of natural selection for growing in similar habitats.

This chapter begins by reviewing concepts of the contribution of different factors to ecological interactions and natural selection. This is followed by a discussion on how to measure and evaluate the importance of different factors that influence the growth of plants, the assembly of communities, and the evolution of plant species. Thereafter the factors likely to have a large influence on different kinds of habitats with regard to growth, community assembly, and evolution are evaluated. Environments vary in nutrient supply and stand-resetting disturbance, and different factors come into play as influential. Environments with a low nutrient supply that have not had soil disturbance are discussed first, followed by ones with a high nutrient supply both a short and a long time after nonselective aboveground biomass disturbances.

Comparing Negative Effects

Since Darwin first began his long argument in the *Origin of Species*, differential reproduction among members of a species has been understood to shape the species over time. Natural selection operates on variation in a species, with the fittest surviving and the least fit perishing. The action of a given factor might push the genetic structure of a species in one direction by differentially removing plants with a given trait, while another factor might push it in another direction by removing plants with a different trait. The final evolutionary path depends on the interplay between trait variation and the strength of selection by different factors.

Attempting to quantify the relative influences of different negative effects on the natural selection of plants relies on understanding the reduction in reproduction for a species that can be attributed to a given factor relative to all other factors. For the evolution of species, the absolute value of reduction in reproduction from a given factor or from all factors has little meaning. Natural selection integrates over such long time scales that functionally, all species are equally at steady state relative to their potential growth. Differences in reduction thus might only describe some hypothetical difference among species in potential growth rate over millions of years. As we know from Malthus, it doesn't take long before even the slowest reproducers attain ridiculously high numbers.

If we turn our attention from characterizing natural selection to the relative importance of agents in determining the relative abundance of species in modern plant communities, then not only is the relative influence of different factors important, but also the absolute importance. For example, a plant that suffers an equal amount of reduction in growth from nutrient stress and herbivory but is increasing in abundance in a given habitat is qualitatively different from a plant that is also suffering equally from the two factors but is more affected by them, and as a result is declining in abundance.

Defining the Influence of Negative Effects

The definitions and terminology usually used to describe the influences of negative effects come from Welden and Slauson (1986). In characterizing competition, Welden and Slauson offered terminology for the absolute and relative influences of effects. They defined the intensity of competition as "the amount of strain competition induces in an organism." The importance of competition was defined as "the relative degree to which competition contributes to the overall decrease in growth rate, metabolism, fecundity, survival, or fitness of that organism below its optimal condition." The difference between the two? Welden and Slauson stated that intensity qualifies the "*process* of competition," whereas importance concerns the "*products* of competition." When assessed quantitatively using growth as the metric, intensity is the total reduction in growth caused by a factor, while importance is the reduction in growth caused by the factor relative to all other factors that reduce growth. The units on intensity might be in grams of biomass per day, while importance is unitless and is constrained between 0 and 1. Other metrics have been offered, such as those that are specific to competition, but these generally have analogs in Welden and Slauson. For example, the relative competitive index (RCI) is analogous to the importance of competition but standardized to plant biomass attained in the absence of competition (Choler, Michalet, and Callaway 2001).

Although the concepts that Welden and Slauson highlight are relevant, their choice of the words "intensity" and "importance" was poor. First, the terms are confusing. There are studies in which researchers purportedly measured intensity but actually measured importance. For example, Sammul et al. (2000) carried out an experiment in which they clipped all plants in a grassland except those of a target species. The response of the target species to the removal of all competitors was considered to be an index of *importance sensu* Welden and Slauson. In reality, the removal of competition yielded only the *intensity* of competition *sensu* Welden and Slauson. Multiple factors need to be assessed in order to quantify the importance of competition, and Sammul et al. measured only the influence of one factor, competition, on growth.

Second, the distinction between intensity modifying a process and importance modifying the product is functionally false. As used by Welden and Slauson, intensity denotes the reduction in growth of an individual as a consequence of competition. It, too, is measured as the product of competition and reveals little about the process of competition. Third, in the vernacular, intensity is calculated per unit of something. *Merriam-Webster's Collegiate Dictionary* defines intensity as "the magnitude of a quantity (as force or energy) per unit (as of area, charge, mass, or time)." Welden and Slauson restrict intensity to being scaled to the individual. There are many problems with relying on individuals, such as determining the limits of physiological integration. A given factor may be more "intense" for an individual with a high biomass than for a small individual, but the reduction on a ground area basis may be the same. Likewise, if one were to calculate the reduction in growth on a clonal plant due to a given factor and then physiologically separate the plant into individual ramets, the intensity of the factor would necessarily decline, while remaining the same at the stand level. Fourth, in the vernacular, an agent or process may have a high importance relative to other factors but be "unimportant" in the vernacular sense. With the Welden and Slauson terminology, one would state that the agent had high importance but low intensity.

A much better terminology would use the term *absolute importance* (or just *importance*) to designate an absolute reduction in growth (or induction of strain). The same definition as Welden and Slauson used for intensity could be used for absolute importance without requiring that it be calculated per individual, and have the units stated. Hence, importance is the reduction in biomass (or other performance metric) per individual or per unit of ground area relative to the performance of plants growing in the absence of factors that reduce biomass. With importance defined as the absolute reduction in biomass caused by a given factor, *relative importance* would then be defined as the importance of one factor relative to all other processes that reduce biomass. Relative importance would still be unitless and ranked from zero to one when comparing negative effects only (see below). The relative importance would not have to be relative to the importance of all other processes, but it would be necessary to state whether the importance was relative to all other factors or the factors to which it was being compared. "Absolute importance" (or more commonly "importance") will be used here to represent an absolute reduction in growth. "Relative importance" (or "importance of x relative to y") will be used to standardize an agent or process relative to other agents or processes.

Finally, although the speed of displacement or reduction in growth has not been investigated, "intensity" could be reserved to represent the rate at which a process reduces growth, or the rate at which resources are removed from the environment by competing plants. As such, intensity would truly characterize an aspect of the process of competition, as originally intended by Welden and Slauson.

How to Measure the Importance of Stress and Disturbance in Environments

As mentioned earlier, the relative importance of factors affecting the growth and reproduction of different species in a given environment does not necessarily mirror the relative importance of those factors in the evolution of the species. This section discusses how to quantify the importance of factors in a given habitat and a later section discusses how to assess the importance for the factors in shaping the evolution of a plant species.

With regard to the performance of species in habitats, Welden and Slauson stated that calculating the importance and relative importance of factors in the performance of plants in an environment is as simple as quantifying the state of a plant in the absence of a factor and the state of the plant with the factor. There are two general approaches to making these comparisons. In one approach, the plant is examined under "ideal" conditions and factors that negatively affect growth are individually added. In the other approach, the plant is examined under actual conditions and factors that should be negatively affecting growth are individually removed. For example, with the first approach, in assessing the importance of competition in a habitat, plants in monocultures (the condition without the negative effect of competition) are compared with plants that grow in the presence of competitors (negative effect added) (Wedin and Tilman 1993). In contrast, the importance of competition for a species can be quantified by starting with an assemblage where plants are likely competing (actual conditions) and remove the neighboring plants (negative effect removed) (Diaz et al. 2003). Although these approaches seem straightforward, there are technical and strategic problems with these approaches.

Technical Questions

Among the technical questions, as Welden and Slauson suggested, importance is quantified as a reduction in the value of a given metric, such as the growth rate of a species, in the presence of a factor. Later, they stated that the relative importance can also be compared using sums of squares (SS) of the total variation from an analysis of variance (ANOVA). This is incorrect, for two reasons. First, in an ANOVA model, the total SS includes the model SS and error SS. Error SS can include unmeasured factors as well as measurement error. If the importance of a factor is calculated relative to the total SS, which includes measurement error, the relative importance is affected by how well something can be measured. If measurement error increases, the relative importance appears to decrease.

Second, the relative importance values as calculated with SS are not necessarily equivalent to those calculated with the effects. For example, if plots are compared that manipulate competition and a stress in factorial and the effects are considered to be additive, the biomass of a target species might follow the hypothetical progression in table 6.1. For this example, competition is responsible for a reduction of biomass of 5 (from 10 to 5). Stress is responsible for a reduction in biomass of 2 (from 10 to 8).

TABLE 6.1

Competition	Stress	Biomass
Absent	Absent	10
Present	Absent	5
Absent	Present	8
Present	Present	3

The effects of stress and competition are additive and reduce biomass 7 units when present together. The relative importance of competition is 5/7 (0.71). The relative importance of stress is 2/7 (0.29).

If the SS approach is used, the SS of competition is 25, the SS of stress is 4, and the total SS is 29. Using the SS approach to calculate relative importance, the relative importance of competition is 0.86 (25/29), compared to 0.71 when effects are used. The relative importance of stress using the SS approach is 0.14 (4/29), compared to 0.29 using the effects. The SS approach does not always inflate the importance of the more important factor relative to using the effects test as it can be altered by the presence of statistical interactions. In all, it is best not to use the SS approach when determining importance. Importance should be calculated with effects.

Strategic Questions

Strategic questions about assessing the importance of different factors' influence on the performance of species in an environment follow the technical questions. Again, strategically, the importance of different factors is assessed to understand the determinants of plant performance, the assembly of communities, and natural selection. In the past, many of the assumptions the underlie strategic approaches were left implicit, but some assumptions are explicit here, most specifically those regarding (1) the potential interactions among factors in their effects, (2) the potential of factors that positively affect growth relative, (3) how manipulations or comparisons are carried out in order to assess effects, and (4) the species of an assemblage that are used to represent the characteristics of an environment.

First, it is relatively simple to manipulate a single factor or multiple factors individually. Yet the approach of Welden and Slauson and many others assumes that the effects of the factors are additive. For example, if nutrient stress reduces growth by 25% and herbivory by 50%, then plants that are subjected to nutrient stress and herbivores should have their growth reduced by 75%. If the factors interact, such that their combined effects are greater than the sum of the individual effects, or are redundant, such that their combined effects are less than the sum of the individual effects, then assuming that effects are additive in their influence on plant performance can be misleading.

As an example of redundant effects, Wedin and Tilman (1993) used the approach of comparing the growth of a species (*Agropyron repens*) in monoculture at high nutrient supply with (1) the species in competition with another species (*Schizachyrium scoparium*) at high nutrient supply, (2) the species in competition with *Schizachyrium* at low nutrient supply, and (3) the species in the absence of competition at low nutrient supply (figure 6.1). In monocultures at high nutrient supply, *Agropyron* had a biomass of approximately 125 g m^{-2} after five years. In soils with low nitrogen content, the biomass *Agropyron* reached only approximately 30 g m^{-2} after five years, but was extirpated when grown in competition at low nutrient supply with *Schizachyrium*. In this comparison, the importance of stress from a low nutrient supply would be 95 g m^{-2} and the importance of competition would be 30 g m^{-2}, leading to relative importance values of approximately 0.8 and 0.2 for low nutrient supply and competition, respectively. Although these results could legitimately be interpreted as indicating that low nutrient supplies are four times more important than competition in determining the relative abundance of the two species, analyzing the importance of competition before low nutrient supply yields a different story. In the same experiment, at higher soil nitrogen content, *Schizachyrium* eliminated *Agropyron*. If the effects are ordered differently such that the effect of competition is determined first, followed by the effects of low nutrient supply, then the relative importance of competition would be 1.0, and reductions in nutrient supply would have no further importance.

Depending on the comparisons that are used, one could state that the presence of competition had little impact on the growth of *Agropyron* when compared with nutrient supply by assigning preeminence to low nutrient supplies arbitrarily. By the same logic, one could also state that reductions in nutrient supply are unimportant. Competition is enough to remove *Agropyron* at the higher nutrient supply, and further reductions in nutrient supply contribute nothing to its extirpation.

By ordering the effects, one can eliminate the complications of interactions. For example, Grime has stated that soil infertility is of preeminent importance, followed by competition (Grime 2007). Although Welden and Slauson inveighed against invoking preeminence of one factor over another a priori, their additive approach is unable to incorporate nonadditive effects among factors. Effects should not be ordered in this manner even if it means that it might be impossible to separate the importance of

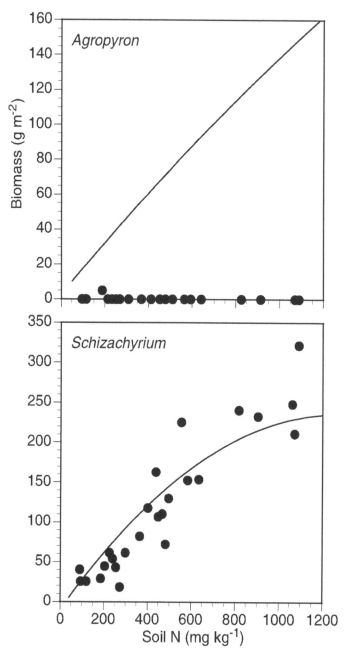

Figure 6.1. Aboveground biomass of *Agropyron repens* and *Schizachyrium scoparium* after five years of growth on a gradient of soils with increasing total soil nitrogen. Species were planted at the same time from seed. Solid line is biomass of species in monoculture. Points represent the biomass of each species when grown together. Data from Wedin and Tilman 1993.

factors in situations where there is the equivalent of a statistical interaction between factors. In these cases, simple manipulations or comparisons might not be able to completely separate the relative importance of interactive factors without making assumptions about the relative importance of interacting factors ahead of time.

The second potential problem with the approach of quantifying the importance of different factors is that not all factors negatively affect plants. With the Welden and Slauson approach, it is assumed that factors can only negatively affect the production of plants, since the reference condition is the plant growing under ideal conditions. Since this is rarely feasible, the reference condition is often less than ideal. If one uses monocultures as the reference condition and then adds factors, plants might perform better than they do in monoculture. For example, comparing the growth of a species in monoculture on low-nutrient soils with the species in a mixture of species would normally lead to a decline in biomass as other species competed with the target species for nutrients. Yet the presence of other species could lead to increases in growth if the other species were able to increase nutrient availability. In a similar vein, subtracting factors from extant conditions might lead to a decrease in performance.

The potential for positive interactions has begun to be incorporated into the metrics. For example, rectifying a technical shortcoming of assuming that all effects of neighboring species are negative, Armas, Ordiales, and Pugnaire (2004) had suggested accommodating the potential for positive effects of neighbors on performance with their relative interaction intensity (RII) measure. When plots with and without interspecific interactions are compared, if the target plant cannot grow without another neighboring species, the RII is +1. If the target plant cannot grow with another species, the RII is −1.

In general, the manner in which positive effects are incorporated is dictated by the specific comparisons being undertaken. However, it is important to investigate the presence of positive effects when comparing factors to be sure that the eventual pattern that is described is not an artifact of ignoring positive effects.

The third problem in quantifying the effects of factors arises when factors are removed from habitats or monocultures are constructed for reference status of species. If factors that are assumed to have an effect on plant growth are removed, the short- and long-term responses of the remaining species might not be the same. For example, at 11 alpine sites around the world, Ray Callaway and others (2002) compared the growth of species of alpine plants in intact communities and with neighbors removed (figure 6.2). After two growing seasons, the removal of plants in high-elevation sites led to less growth in the remaining plants, presumably as a result of increased exposure to a harsh environment. Although the short-term

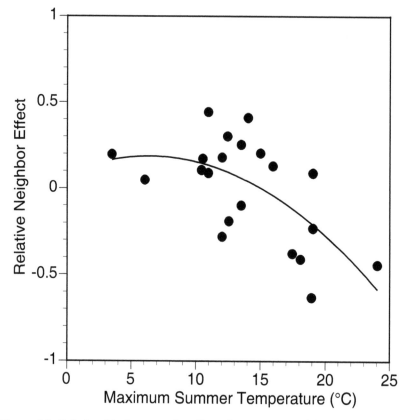

Figure 6.2. Relationship between the effect of removing neighboring plants (relative neighbor effect) and the maximum temperature in early summer for 22 alpine sites. Points above zero on the *y*-axis indicate facilitation; points below indicate competition. Data from Callaway et al. 2002

interactions among plants were positive overall, over longer time scales species more than likely will have had negative effects on one another. The species should have been functionally redundant when it came to shielding neighbors from harsh environments, and the presence of one species should probably reduce the ability of individuals of other species to recruit and grow. Similar issues arise regarding the use of monocultures as a reference. As discussed more in detail in the next chapter, plants affect their growing environment, which alters the utility of monocultures to represent optimal growing conditions. In addition, there are likely factors that are important for the growth of plants but whose effects occur in low intensity. As such, short-term experiments are likely to underestimate their importance.

Last, and most important, the importance of factors that are supposed to characterize the environment is not independent of the species on which the effects of the factors are being measured. Whether the effects of factors are measured directly or natural selection is inferred through the traits of species, there is no way to determine the importance of nutrient stress or disturbance without deciding which species to elevate in importance (Chapin, Vitousek, and Van Cleve 1986). For example, if one asked whether at a given nutrient supply, competition for nutrients or disturbance was more important, the answer would depend on the identity of the plant species. For the dominant plant, competition from other species might not be important. Removing other species might have no positive effect on the plant. Yet for a competitively inferior plant, competition might be very important. When faced with differences among species in the importance of a factor, how can importance of a factor in an environment even be described?

Implicit assumptions regarding which species to target when describing the importance of factors in an environment have been the cause of some of the apparent differences of opinions about environments among ecologists. For example, Grime's characterization of the importance of competition in ecosystems around Sheffield, England was restricted to the modern factors that affected the local pool of plant species, all of which were herbaceous. While Grime characterized Sheffield based on the local plant species pool under the current disturbance regime, Tilman admonished Grime for not considering a regional species pool under a past disturbance regime:

> Before neolithic clearing and grazing began, Grime's richer pastures contained closed canopy forests and forests will still eventually return to these areas if grazers are excluded (Tansley, 1949). Thus, in the absence of unnaturally high densities of herbivores and thus unnaturally high rates of herbivore-caused disturbance, most areas in which Grime has worked would be forest. (Tilman 1987a, p. 312)

In general, the importance of factors in habitats can be characterized by the dominant species, rare species, or excluded species. Focusing on dominant species when assessing the importance of factors concentrates on understanding what restricts the dominant species from growing more. It does not determine what factors allow them to dominate. Alternatively, the growth of rare species is likely restricted by different factors than is the growth of dominant species. For example, removal experiments often show increases in the abundance of rare species, suggesting that competition for resources with dominants is important in reducing the abundance of rare species. There are separate questions about the factors that allow rare species to coexist with dominant species; they will not be addressed here. Finally, factors that have no impact on dominant and rare species could be excluding other species, increasing the importance of a novel set of factors. For example, Grime suggests that high-fertility species might be excluded from calcareous soils as a consequence of selective herbivory or differential susceptibility to drought (Grime 1963; Grime, MacPherson-Stewart, and Dearman 1968). Likewise, freezing events are likely to be important for eliminating some species from cold environments while having little effect on the dominant and rare species that withstand freezing.

Assuming that it is possible to assess the relative importance of different factors in a given environment for a given species, novel issues arise when attempting to compare importance across environments. A major question is the selection of species to compare when comparing environments. Although it would seem consistent to use the same species across different environments, using a single species for comparison might not effectively characterize the importance of factors for a given environment. For example, a given species might dominate one environment but be excluded from another. Although a given factor might be relatively more important in the environment where the species is excluded, the relative importance of different factors might be the same for dominant species in each environment. The presence of a specialized herbivore in one environment might exclude one species, and the presence of another specialized herbivore in the other environment might exclude a second species. This does not mean, however, that herbivory is more important in one environment than in the other.

No set of species is necessarily the correct set of species to choose for understanding the importance of factors in a given environment, much less for comparing multiple environments. Each approach reveals something different about the functioning of ecosystems and the assembly of communities. As the relative importance of different factors in environments that differ in nutrient supply and time since a general disturbance is investigated, what restricts the abundance of dominant and rare species as well as what likely excludes other species both needs to be addressed. Before attempting that, it is important to comment on how to measure the importance of stresses and disturbances in the natural selection of species.

How to Measure the Importance of Stress and Disturbance in the Natural Selection of a Species

Even if one can determine the relative importance of factors for the relative abundance of species in a given environment, there are difficulties in translating ecological importance into evolutionary importance or independently determining the relative importance of different factors in the natural selection that has shaped a given species over evolutionary time.

Of the major issues, the most important one is that the relative importance of a given factor in modern times is a consequence of natural selection in the past. As such, there is no reason that the two are necessarily positively related, and in fact they might be inversely related. Most famously, the importance of competition in the past—that is, the ghost of competition past (Connell 1980)—has been cited as a reason for the relative unimportance of competition in determining the relative abundance of two species in modern times. In this case, as a consequence of species competing for a given resource in the past, one or both species have been selected in a manner that minimizes competition. As such, competition would have low relative importance in modern times but high importance on evolutionary time scales. This same line of reasoning regarding the limits of uniformitarianism could apply to almost any factor. Herbivory might not be important today in limiting the biomass of a given species, but only because herbivory had been important over long time scales, causing the evolution of more effective defense strategies.

The performance of individuals in a given environment may or may not be a good way to evaluate past importance of different factors. The "ghost of competition past" example would support an inverse relationship between the modern and evolutionary importance of factors, or between their importance for dominant species and for rare species. A particular stress might not negatively affect a species today only because it has long been a major part of natural selection for a species over evolutionary time. Similarly, that a plant has been selected to compete well for nutrients only becomes apparent when it is compared with a plant that has not been selected to compete well for nutrients.

Regardless of whether a given species succeeds or fails in a particular environment, the performance of the species in the environment might be completely unrelated to the environments that had the most impact on its natural selection. For example, a plant might be successful in an environment today, but that environment might be a novel combination of factors, and the success serendipitous. Or a given factor that consistently kills plants in a given environment might have killed plants for millions of years, yet that source of mortality might have had little effect on the evolution of the species. For example, propagules of a coastal species whose seeds are intolerant of salinity might have been losing seeds to the ocean for millions of years, but this consistent source of mortality need not have materially affected the evolution of the species.

Another approach to assessing the relative importance of factors over evolutionary time is to examine the patterns of traits for a given species. Natural selection causes changes in the genetic structure of species, which is evident in the traits they express. Much of the discussion in the rest of this chapter and in the following chapters focuses on the traits of different species in different environments. There are important questions about which traits are best indicators of past selective pressures, which species should be compared, and under what conditions traits should be assessed. These questions are best addressed as they arise.

IMPORTANCE OF FACTORS AT LOW NUTRIENT SUPPLY

As described in chapter 4, in low-nutrient ecosystems, nutrients that plants eventually acquire are generally supplied at a low, uniform rate over the course of a growing season. Grime and Chapin had generally assumed that nutrient supplies predominantly came in pulses, followed by intervening periods of low rates of supply. This assumption greatly influenced their assumptions about the relative importance of factors such as competition in low-nutrient ecosystems.

For low-nutrient ecosystems experiencing a low, uniform nutrient supply, the relative importance of nutrient stress, resource competition, and disturbance is assessed for dominant, rare, or excluded species. A low-nutrient ecosystem generally has high light and water availability and experiences little general disturbance. Here, questions about the importance of other stresses, such as cold temperatures in some ecosystems, while generalizing for low-nutrient environments are set aside. Also, there are important questions about how low the nutrient supply has to be before the ecosystem can be characterized as low nutrient. This is a subjective question that cannot be quantified at this point but is discussed further in the next chapter.

Importance of Stress from Low Nutrient Supply

A low nutrient supply—nutrients supplied at a uniform rate that is low relative to demands—induces stress in almost all species, and competition for nutrients among species further reduces the availability of nutrients to plants. But has the stress of low nutrient supplies in the absence of competition from other species and in the absence of disturbance agents been important? Can low nutrient supply alone explain the absence of some species (Thompson 1987)?

Although an important conceptual question, the minimum nutrient supply required for a plant to grow and reproduce is largely unknown. Certainly, reducing nutrient supplies reduces plant growth, but no studies have varied the nutrient supply rate over a given soil volume (or per individual in hydroponics) and assessed at what nutrient supply (or nutrient supply density) plants are unable to maintain growth or to reproduce.

Thus, it is unknown whether low nutrient supplies alone could be responsible for the absence of some species in low-nutrient environments.

In the absence of hard evidence, it is likely that species differ in their requirements for nutrient supplies for growth and reproduction. Just as others have done (e.g., Chapin 1980), I have observed high-resource species growing in monoculture in low-nutrient soils that appeared to be unable even to flower, much less reproduce. For example, *Asclepias tuberosa* (butterfly milkweed) plants growing in monoculture in low-nutrient soils in Minnesota were able to produce leaves at the beginning of the growing season. As the growing season progressed, however, the size of newly produced leaves and the longevity of old leaves both decreased. Halfway through the growing season, the *Asclepias* shoots had died, whereas plants of other species in adjacent plots were continuing to grow well.

Although these observations did not isolate plants from other stress or disturbance agents or from intraspecific competition, these plants likely had nutrient demands that exceeded the effective supply rates. Meristems must produce leaves at a minimum rate to remain viable. With a minimum nutrient content to leaves, there is a minimum nutrient supply that plants require in order to maintain leaf production. As such, there is some minimum rate at which nutrients must be supplied to meristems for the plant to continue to produce leaves, or the meristematic tissue dies. Although low-nutrient stress alone might be able to remove some species from low-nutrient environments, carefully designed experiments should be able to test the hypothesis that nutrient stress alone in the absence of interspecific competition and disturbance agents is enough to remove species from a low-nutrient environment.

Importance of Competition

If we assume that some species are able to maintain populations at a low nutrient supply, the next hypothesis to test is whether competition is important for removing some species from low-nutrient environments or to make them rare. There seems to be little dispute that in some low-nutrient ecosystems, light competition is not important. Although this basic assumption is adjusted later, only the importance of nutrient competition is addressed in this section.

Grime contended that competition (for light or nutrients) was unimportant in habitats where nutrient supply was low. Grime stated, "although competition, especially that for water and mineral nutrients, is not restricted to productive habitats, its importance in unproductive habitats is small relative to the ability to conserve the resources which have been captured and to resist the severe hazards to survival (e.g., herbivory, extreme climatic events) which characterize many infertile environments" (Grime 2001). Tilman countered Grime's hypothesis and proposed that competition was just as important as when nutrient supply was high, with the difference that the competition was just for belowground resources (Tilman 1988).

The evidence for Grime's assertion of the lack of importance of competition can be traced to an experiment in which plants of the slow-growing *Festuca* and the faster growing *Arrhenatherum* were grown together in sand (Mahmoud and Grime 1976). Nutrients were supplied in solution every three weeks and then washed out after three days. In the experiment, the concentrations of nutrients were varied to test the effect of nutrient supply on competitive interactions. After 12 months at low nitrogen supply, where total biomass was just 1% of the biomass of plants in the high-nitrogen treatment, *Festuca* still did not dominate *Arrhenatherum* or reduce its growth significantly. The faster growing species acquired a greater fraction of the nutrient supply at low and high nutrient supply. This was offered as proof that *Festuca* was an inferior competitor to *Arrhenatherum* for nutrients at low nutrient supply, and as such, greater competitive abilities could not explain the dominance of *Festuca* in low-nutrient-supply environments.

Although the results of this experiment could be considered to reject the prediction that competition in low-nutrient environments is important, there are critical questions to ask about aspects of the experiment that might have influenced the outcome. First, the experiment followed the view that nutrients are supplied in pulses with intervening periods of low nutrient availability. What if nutrients were supplied uniformly over time? Would *Arrhenatherum* still have dominated? Although discussed more in chapter 7, high-resource species like *Arrhenatherum* likely have greater uptake capacity and are better at getting pulses, whereas species like *Festuca* might be better at competing for slow bleeds of nutrients. Second, what if competition were allowed to progress for longer? The faster growing *Arrhenatherum* likely could preempt nutrient supplies better initially but might not be able to compete as well against *Festuca* on longer time scales, even in the absence of disturbance. *Festuca* might have a lower rate of root production initially but over long time scales might be able to maintain a higher root length density than *Arrhenatherum*. Should the eventual dominance by *Festuca* be considered a product of stress tolerance or better competitive ability for nutrients?

In low-nutrient environments, competition from dominants can extirpate species or reduce their abundance drastically. At Cedar Creek, the presence of *Schizachyrium* caused the extirpation of *Agropyron* at low nutrient supply (see chapter 5). But is competition important for the species that dominate low-nutrient environments? From the Wedin and Tilman experiments, competition can clearly have importance at low nutrient supply, at least for nondominant species. In a setting of low nutrient supply, species that are less proficient at maintaining root length at low nutrient supply are likely to be diminished if not extirpated when competing for nutrients. Although interspecific competition does not reduce the biomass of dominant species much at low nutrient supply, intraspecific competition likely does. Because of the manner by which nutrient supplies are partitioned, if nutrient supply is too low for competition to exist, it is likely too low to be important in the natural selection of a species. For nutrient supplies to be too low for competition to exist implies that plants are unable to grow dense enough for their roots to overlap. Although this might be true for a short while for stands at low density, the only way that it can be maintained is if nutrient supplies are too low for reproduction. If nutrient supplies are too low for any reproduction, then the environment would have little selective pressure on the species, since the environment would not allow any differential survival.

Selective Disturbance

In contrast to the nutrient stress hypothesis or the nutrient competition hypothesis, the disturbance resistance hypothesis states that low-nutrient species dominate low-nutrient environments as a result of their low susceptibility to herbivory or disease. For example, according to the disturbance resistance hypothesis, in the absence of competition, when plants are grown at low nutrient supply, herbivores preferentially consume high-resource species over low-nutrient species. This reduces the relative abundance of high-resource species, allowing low-nutrient species to dominate.

The disturbance resistance hypothesis has been a point of intellectual tension in the theories of Grime and Tilman. Grime states (2001, p. 34) that Tilman underestimates the importance of resource loss rates to herbivores and pathogens incurred by fast-growing species on resource-poor soils. Tilman characterized disturbance as being nonselective, and differential resistance to disturbance was never a central part of his theories.

The basis for the disturbance resistance hypothesis is that low-nutrient species would be better defended than high-resource species. The basis of Grime's assertion that low-fertility species were less palatable than high-fertility species came from laboratory experiments in which leaves of different species were offered to a species of snail (Grime, MacPherson-Stewart, and Dearman 1968). Of the 52 species that were examined, only a small fraction were considered palatable to the snail, and "a high proportion were plants associated with disturbed habitats and fertile soils." Other feeding trial studies have supported the conjecture that high-

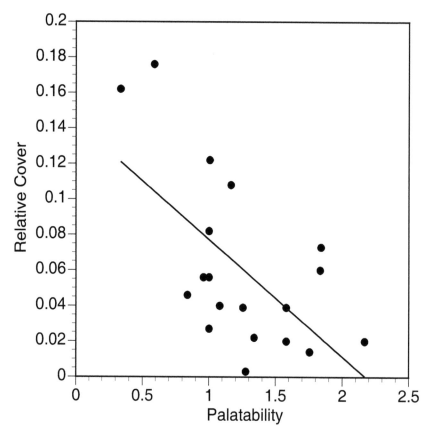

Figure 6.3. Palatability indices for species in an experimental diverse assemblage and their relative cover in the assemblage. Data from Burt-Smith et al. 2003.

resource species are preferred by herbivores over low-nutrient species. For example, Burt-Smith, Grime, and Tilman (2003) showed that among 24 prairie species at Cedar Creek, the palatability of species to the domestic cricket (*Acheta domestica*) correlated negatively with their abundance in plots on low-nitrogen soils (figure 6.3).

Feeding trials can only support a potential link between resistance to herbivory and relative abundance. Experiments that manipulate the relative abundance of herbivores are needed to show that the presence of herbivores reduces the relative abundance of high-resource species in low-nutrient environments. For example, Lauchlan Fraser and Phil Grime (1999) grew 24 grassland species for two years in mixture at three nutrient supplies with either no herbivores or four generalist herbivores (three species of snail and one species of aphid). Nutrient levels were modulated by varying the amount of nutrient solution periodically added to each mesocosm, with the lowest fertility level receiving no external nutrients.

At the lowest fertility level, there was no relationship between the RGR_{max} of species and the reduction in biomass caused by herbivores. Herbivores reduced fast-growing ruderals and competitors as well as stress tolerators such as *Leontodon hispidus,* although there were no significant differences between treatments for any one species. The one species that tended to increase in abundance with herbivory was *Holcus lanatus,* a relatively fast-growing pasture grass.

The lack of differential response to herbivory does not support the differential disturbance hypothesis. After two years, species that are rare at low nutrient supply were not extirpated at low nutrient supply, or even reduced in abundance to a greater degree than species that dominate at low nutrient supply. Although Fraser and Grime might seem to have refuted importance of selective herbivory at low nutrient supplies, they used a restricted set of herbivores, which in aggregate apparently did not eat what is considered to be a very palatable species, *Holcus lanatus.* Yet in their study many species were excluded as a result of selective herbivory, and there was competitive release for species like *Festuca ovina* that are considered to be dominants of low-nutrient grasslands. It is axiomatic that more research is needed on the topic, but it is interesting that Fraser and Grime had replicated the experiment at different nutrient supplies. At intermediate fertility, there did seem to be support for the disturbance resistance hypothesis. At this fertility level, there actually was an inverse relationship between RGR_{max} and a reduction in biomass due to herbivores. Fast-growing species were reduced in biomass, while slow-growing species were more likely to increase in biomass.

Field experiments that exclude herbivores also show the importance of selective herbivory. For example, at Cedar Creek, excluding deer for 13 years from a regularly burned savanna doubled productivity (Knops, Ritchie, and Tilman 2000). Deer selectively feed on a legume, *Lathyrus venosus,* that reaches high abundance inside exclosures and fixes high amounts of nitrogen. Herbivore exclosures in other ecosystems have shown differential herbivory on species that are more common at higher nutrient supply (Carson and Root 2000; Howe, Brown, and Zorn-Arnold 2002; Fine, Mesones, and Coley 2004; Olofsson 2006).

Like herbivory, pathogens can specialize on individual species at many points in the life history of plants, thus differentially impacting some species (Gilbert 2002). At low nutrient supply, experiments in which disease is experimentally removed by spraying plants with fungicide reveal that pathogens can be important in reducing the productivity and biomass of plants (Mitchell 2003). Yet whether pathogens are a consistent source of differential mortality that contributes to the general patterns of relative abundance in low nutrient ecosystems is still an open question. More experiments are necessary that examine the consequences of removing pathogens in determining the performance of plants in the absence of competitors, as well as in mixed assemblages.

It should be noted that manipulations of the abundance of herbivores or disease at low nutrient supply cannot separate out the effects of competitive ability and differential disturbance. For example, the lack of effect of herbivores at low nutrient supply in Fraser and Grime's work could have reflected the greater competitive ability of low-nutrient species. The lack of effect on plant species composition of pesticide application to mixed assemblages of prairies that Tilman reported as a personal communication (Burt-Smith, Grime, and Tilman 2003) does not rule out the possibility that had fast-growing species been present, they would have been differentially consumed by herbivores. Monocultures of different plant species at low nutrient supply in factorial with herbivore abundance are needed to test whether differential disturbance would potentially reduce the biomass of species that are less abundant at low nutrient supply more than those species that are dominant.

Although selective herbivory is an important component of low-nutrient ecosystems, it is commonly misconceived that herbivory pressure is constant across terrestrial ecosystems and would be just as high in a low-nutrient ecosystem as in a high-nutrient ecosystem, all other things equal. East (1984) examined the relationship between herbivore biomass from African grasslands and precipitation. With increasing precipitation associated with increasing aboveground net primary productivity (ANPP), East showed that herbivore biomass increased proportionally with rainfall for grasslands on low-, medium-, and high-fertility soils. East's review became the basis for a subsequent review by Fritz and Duncan (1994) that carried forward the idea of a constant herbivore pressure across ecosystems (figure 6.4). McNaughton et al. (1989) broadened the comparison beyond grasslands and upheld the conclusion that herbivory closely paralleled ANPP.

Although there is a long history of herbivory being a constant fraction of ANPP on a continental to global scale, on reexamination, East's (1984) data show that this relationship might hold for high-fertility soils, but that herbivory is proportionally lower on low-fertility soils. East had divided up the African grasslands based on soil fertility and examined the patterns of biomass of arid savanna and moist savanna herbivores with increasing precipitation. He stated, "arid savanna herbivores, which dominate total herbivore biomass, . . . decline at higher levels of rainfall on low nutrient status soils. . . . Moist savanna species . . . biomasses are usually low and show a positive correlation with rainfall on soils of low nutrient status" (East 1984, p. 245). On reexamination, East's data clearly show that total herbivore biomass for African savannas peaks at

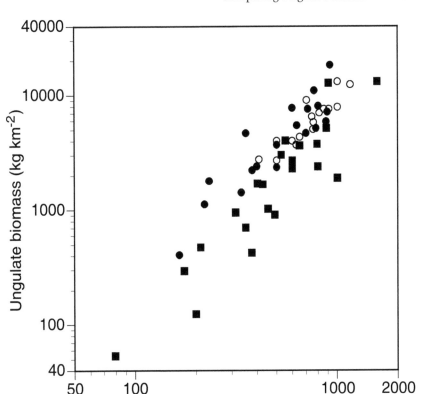

Figure 6.4. Relationship across sites between precipitation and ungulate biomass. Data are for high-fertility (closed circle), medium-fertility (open circle), and low-fertility (closed square) sites. Note the log scale for ungulate biomass. Data from Fritz and Duncan 1994.

intermediate precipitation and declines with increasing precipitation on low-nutrient soils (figure 6.5). In low-nutrient ecosystems, a small fraction of biomass is removed by herbivores, although the relative importance of herbivory for some plant species can still be high.

IMPORTANCE OF FACTORS AT HIGH NUTRIENT SUPPLY

Much as in environments with low nutrient availability, plants in environments with high resource availability can be in competition for light and are subject to disturbance agents such as herbivory and disease. High nutrient supply leads to high nutrient availability, and as a consequence, light levels can be rapidly lowered near the soil surface as a dense leaf

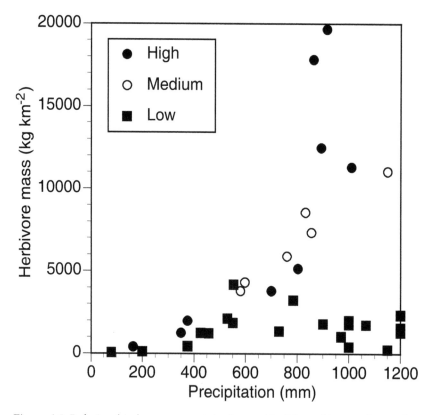

Figure 6.5. Relationship between precipitation and herbivore biomass from a data set that preceded the review by Fritz and Duncan. Data from East 1984. The herbivore biomass is not log-transformed.

canopy is produced and then begins to rise upward. Disturbance agents are also present in high-resource environments, with herbivores and pathogens again having the potential to remove plant biomass.

The first and second stages of competition are associated with different mechanisms that lead to success and different traits that allow for success. Yet the hypotheses associated with the importance of factors associated with success soon and long after an aboveground disturbance in high-nutrient environments are similar. As such, these hypotheses are addressed concurrently in this section.

As with low-nutrient environments, there are three hypotheses to explain the relative abundance of species in high-resource environments. First, a variant of the nutrient stress hypothesis states that some species are made rare in high-nutrient environments as a direct consequence of nutrient availability being too high. Second, the resource competition hypothesis states that species can be excluded from high-nutrient environments as a consequence of competition for light in the absence of selective disturbance agents. Light competition reduces light levels, and it is possible that in the absence of agents of selective disturbance, low light levels alone can kill plants. Third, according to the disturbance resistance hypothesis, species can be excluded from high-nutrient environments as a consequence of differential disturbance by factors such as herbivory and pathogens.

This section separates the importance of differential disturbance for plants with leaves in the upper canopy (first stage of competition) and for plants growing in the understory (second stage of competition). The next section addresses how to determine the relative importance of factors deemed to be important at each stage of competition.

Nutrient Stress Hypothesis

In contrast to the potential for nutrient stress from low nutrient availability in low-nutrient ecosystems, Grime hypothesized that stress tolerators can be excluded from high-resource environments as a consequence of high levels of nutrients (Grime 2001, p. 59). This hypothesis echoes Liebig's characterization of nitrophilic species that are able to tolerate the high nitrate concentrations in some soils. For Grime, as a consequence of a slow growth rate, toxic levels of nutrients could accumulate in tissues of stress tolerators.

For phosphorus, high phosphorus availability can cause toxic levels of phosphorus to accumulate in tissues of plants adapted to low phosphorus availability. For example, members of the Proteaceae family, which often dominate in low-phosphorus soils, can be killed by phosphorus availabilities that are fine for most plants (Shane and Lambers 2006). Proximally, these plants are unable to downregulate phosphorus acquisition at moderate phosphorus availabilities, causing the toxic levels of accumulation (Shane, Szota, and Lambers 2004). There are important questions as to whether it is the high phosphorus availability alone or the combination of high phosphorus availability with low availability of other nutrients that proves lethal, but it is clear that high phosphorus availability can exclude some species from some environments.

For nitrogen, NH_4^+ is more toxic to plants than NO_3^-. NH_4^+ concentrations in the cell can alter cell pH and are energy intensive to efflux, resulting in symptoms such as leaf chlorosis (Miller and Cramer 2005). Sensitivity to NH_4^+ has been offered as an explanation for some successional patterns (Kronzucker et al. 2003), but in general, the conditions that lead to high inorganic nitrogen availability in soils are rare in the natural world. With so many mechanisms by which nitrogen can be lost from soils, toxic levels of accumulation seem to be rare. Certainly, at some artificially high nutrient supply rate or in localized areas like rhino middens, species might die from toxicity, and there are likely to be different abilities to grow with potentially toxic availabilities of nutrients. Yet it is hard to know whether for most environments that are considered to have a high nutrient supply, toxicity would set in for plants. Just as with the nutrient stress hypothesis for low-nutrient environments, the appropriate experiments have not been carried out to evaluate this hypothesis for high-nitrogen environments.

On the flip side, Grime (2001) hypothesized that shade-tolerant plants are actually stressed for nutrients. The low light levels of the understory reduce carbon availability to roots, indirectly causing nutrient stress. The rationale for the hypothesis was based on a flawed assumption of very low diffusion rates of nutrients, along with a poor conceptualization of the process of nutrient mineralization that would continue to supply nutrients to roots. There is little direct evidence for this hypothesis, and it is unlikely that plants that are excluded from understory environments are excluded as a consequence of the stress of low nutrient availability.

Competition

Competition among plants for nutrients in an ecosystem with a high nutrient supply is unlikely to be very important. With high nutrient supplies, adjacent plants are unlikely to be able to reduce nutrient availability to adjacent plants via uptake. This should be true both for recently disturbed vegetation and for plants in the understory. Aside from first principles, vegetation in many ecosystems shows little response to fertilization or trenching around plants in the understory. It has also long been understood that fertilization in agronomic systems shows diminishing returns in terms of aboveground biomass. In these systems, if increasing nutrient availability does not increase the growth of individuals, they are unlikely to be competing for nutrients.

It is true that there is a gradient of nutrient availabilities, and that overstory plants can compete for nutrients with understory plants. For example, Coomes and Grubb (2000) reported that many understory plants respond positively to trenching around their root systems, which eliminates competition from larger trees. At the highest nutrient supply rates, however, there is unlikely to be any competition for belowground resources. For example, Jack Putz and Charlie Canham (1992) showed that understory plants did not respond to trenching when nitrogen supply was high. Under the same conditions, however, growth was greatly increased when the canopy was tied back to increase light levels to the understory. Canham et al. (1996) also showed that at low light, variation in nutrient availability had little effect on seedling shoot growth across a range of tree species.

As shown by Putz and Canham's work, in contrast to competition for nutrients, competition for light is clearly important at high nutrient supply, both relatively soon after a disturbance and long after a disturbance. Very soon after soil or aboveground biomass is disturbed, leaves of adjacent individuals are unlikely to overlap significantly initially. If disturbances are frequent and intense enough, it is possible that competition for light would never set in. Yet leaf canopies develop quickly, and plants begin to reduce the light availability to other plants as the race to leaf area dominance occurs. Although competition for light is asymmetric, growth in the understory can be thought of as part of competition for light. Hence, understory plants are heavily affected by light competition.

The major question with light competition and the reduction of light levels is whether low light levels in and of themselves are enough to remove species from the understory. As described in more detail in chapter 9, there has been much investigation of differences in minimum light levels among species required for positive net photosynthesis at the light level. Givnish (1988) argued that an understanding of adaptations to low light must progress beyond the leaf level and incorporate a whole-plant carbon analysis. Givnish showed that at the leaf level for *Liriodendron tulipifera*, its photosynthesis was carbon-neutral at light levels of 13 μmol m^{-2} s^{-1}. Yet leaves had to experience light levels that were twice as high to balance nighttime respiration, and seven times higher to pay back the carbon invested in the leaf. Echoing Warming more than 75 years earlier, as plants increase in size, resources must be provided for a proportionally larger support systems, and a 5-m tree requires light levels of 355 μmol m^{-2} s^{-1}, 20 times greater than the light levels required just for photosynthesis to equal respiration during the day.

Species comparisons of whole-plant light compensation points have not been carried out. The key for these studies (and for interpreting past studies) is not to ask what minimum light level is required for a species to grow. It is clear that even high-resource species can grow at relatively low light levels. Instead, the question to ask is how large a size can species attain at low irradiance, and what happens to plants when they approach their maximum size at low light. Are fast-growing plants at low light able to maintain an equilibrium biomass, or do they begin to decrease in size soon after reaching maximum biomass, even in the absence of agents of disturbance? Unfortunately, long-term comparative studies of different species grown at low light have not been carried out, and it is unknown whether the low light levels caused by overstory plants are enough to remove high-resource species from low-light environments.

Importance of Disturbance

By definition, high-resource environments are consequences of severe, general aboveground disturbances. The frequency with which these disturbances return can vary among environments even as the importance of the first stage of competition is upheld, as long as fast-growing species maintain leaf area dominance. Repeated grazing or fires can keep herbaceous vegetation at a low height and maintain high nutrient availability. Many perennial grasslands are maintained by frequent aboveground disturbances. Repeated physical disturbances can maintain high light levels and dominance by fast-growing species over other species. Severe droughts of annual grasslands or annual scouring near the edges of lakes can maintain populations of annuals. In some cases, disturbances are intense enough and frequent enough that light competition does not become important, but these situations are rare and inherently unstable. For example, areas that are grazed heavily such that plant density is low generally soon show increases in well-defended plants, which increase in abundance enough for light competition to become important.

Insofar as high-resource environments are dependent on disturbance, high-resource species are also dependent on disturbance to some degree, and the importance of disturbance is inseparable from the importance of the environment itself. Once a major disturbance creates a high-resource environment, how important are different types of disturbance for determining the relative abundance of species? In some cases, selective disturbance aboveground appears to be very important in these environments. Although data on this are rare, many of the plants that dominate high-resource environments are well defended, and specialist herbivores can quickly reduce the abundance of species that are poorly defended with respect to the herbivore. Aboveground disturbance keeps vegetation near the ground and subject to herbivory by ground-based mammals. High-resource savannas are dominated by fine-leafed trees with thorns, whereas low-resource savannas have larger leaves that are defended constitutively. In grasslands, the abundance of individual species can be periodically reduced by outbreaks of specialist herbivores. For example, Fraser and Grime (1999) found that selective herbivory was important at high nutrient supply, selectively removing some species from their grassland mesocosms. In all, after a major general disturbance has created high-resource conditions, the dominant species might not be reduced much by selective disturbance, but their presence is often dependent on the presence of agents of selective disturbance that reduce the abundance of rarer species.

The Relative Importance of Factors

In the face of all the research on what can be important in different ecosystems, is it possible to begin to erect a hierarchy of importance of the different factors in different habitats? For example, is competition of more relative importance in ecosystems with low nutrient supply than in those with high nutrient supply? Is selective disturbance more important for reducing the relative abundance of species in the understory of a dense forest than in a low-nutrient grassland? To move to an evolutionary time scale, have the species that now dominate low-nutrient ecosystems been shaped more by competition or by disturbance?

Although it is uncertain whether low nutrient supplies in the absence of competition are enough to exclude some species in the absence of competition and herbivory, when nutrient supplies are low, competition for nutrients certainly can be important for reducing the relative abundance of some species. Likewise, as many experiments have shown, selective herbivory can be important for reducing the relative abundance of non-dominant species. Although both are important, is it possible to rank one higher than the other with regard to the relative abundance of species?

For a dominant species in a low-nutrient ecosystem, neither interspecific competition nor herbivory might significantly affect the growth of low-nutrient species. For example, if a grass species were to attain 90% of the biomass in a stand, the removal of other species might have little positive effect on dominant species (Smith et al. 2004). Herbivores might remove only a small fraction of the annual production of the dominant species, and there might not be a species that would increase significantly if herbivores were removed. Yet in the same environment, competition and herbivory could be limiting the abundance of a rare species. Remove the dominant species and exclude herbivores, and a rare species could have greater biomass. For example, some forb species in grasslands can attain high biomass if grasses are removed and specialist herbivores are excluded. With the presence of either, the forb species are greatly reduced. Dominant species, on the other hand, are likely limited only in the short term by low nutrient availability, with individuals secondarily limited by intraspecific competition.

In the above example, whether competition is more or less important than herbivory cannot be determined for either the dominant grass species or the rarer forb species. Other examples show that for some species, competition is more important, whereas for others species herbivory would be important. For example, many forbs attain high biomass when grasses are selectively eaten by grazers, implying that competition primarily limits the forb's biomass (del-Val and Crawley 2005). Alternatively, many introduced plants dominate assemblages until specialist pests or pathogens are also introduced.

In short, there are too few experiments that adequately assess the relative importance of selective disturbance and competition in different environments to allow generalizations about their relative importance for different species when nutrient supplies are low. The relative importance of different factors over evolutionary time scales is also difficult to assess. As the patterns of traits among species are assessed, it is clear that both have shaped the plants that dominate low-nutrient habitats, but it is uncertain which has been more important as a component of natural selection.

Similar logic regarding the ability to assess the relative importance of major factors applies to high-resource-supply environments. It seems clear that if nutrient competition is important at low nutrient supply, then it would likely be relatively unimportant when nutrients are supplied at a high rate. There are currently no reliable data sets that distinguish the importance of competition for light from that of susceptibility to disturbance, and there is no way to separate their evolutionary influence. Soon after a disturbance, the biomass of many species is reduced as a consequence of suppression from species that can quickly produce tall canopies, while other species are preferentially eaten or attacked by pathogens. In the understory of a dense canopy, other species can be excluded as a consequence of the dense shade, as well as by being eaten, by disease, or from the damage sustained from a consistent rain of woody debris.

In the early stages of investigating the traits of species from different habitats, different factors can be understood as important in a given environment without having to be ranked in importance. In part, the relative importance of the factors changes with the species that are assessed.

SYNTHESIS

Factors differ in their absolute importance in reducing the productivity of species in a given environment, as well as in their importance relative to other factors. Little is known about differences among environments in the intensity of factors.

Comparing the magnitude of negative effects of factors on different species in a given environment is a complicated endeavor. First, factors can interact in their effects on species, and their relative importance might not be easily determined. Second, not all factors negatively affect plants, making it difficult to calculate importance values or to know what conditions to use as reference conditions when assessing the importance of factors. Third, there is no clear best way to alter the presence of factors, and the importance of factors can differ depending on the time scale over which importance is assessed. Fourth, the importance of factors is not solely a characteristic of an environment. The importance of factors can differ among dominant, rare, and excluded species.

In addition to patterns among similar environments, a fundamental ecological question is how the importance of different factors changes across environments that differ in the availabilities of resources. Comparing the relative importance of different factors across environments, however, is more complicated than assessing the importance of factors in just one environment. For example, the importance of factors in a given environment is dependent on the species examined. Yet the same species might not be present in the different environments, and standardization of species for the sake of comparison can be difficult.

In examining the basic patterns of importance of different factors when nutrient supplies are low, it becomes evident that competition for light can be unimportant in ecosystems with low nutrient availability. However, it would be wrong to assume that light competition is by definition unimportant when nutrient supplies are low, for its importance depends on the traits of the species that are present, as well as on the disturbance regimes. When nutrient supplies are low and competition for light is low, individuals of species that dominate low-nutrient environments are affected most by intraspecific competition for nutrients and the low nutrient supply. Selective disturbance agents such as herbivory, however, could be restricting other species that would be more competitive in the absence of herbivores.

There are three alternative hypotheses for explaining the relative abundance of rare and excluded plants under low nutrient availability. First, with the nutrient stress hypothesis, plants could be made rare or excluded solely by the low nutrient supplies, in the absence of competition and agents that selectively disturb plants. Unfortunately, this hypothesis has been little researched, and it is unknown whether low nutrient supplies alone could explain the rarity or absence of some species from low-nutrient environments. Second, with the nutrient competition hypothesis, species can be made rare as a result of interspecific competition for nutrients. Third, with the selective disturbance hypothesis, agents such as herbivory and disease can disproportionately reduce the biomass of less abundant species. Assessing the relative importance of these factors is problematic. As laid out, competition and low nutrient supplies can both independently remove some species while having interactive effects for others.

When nutrient supplies are high, nutrient availability is high, and there is the untested potential for species to be reduced in biomass as a result of nutrient toxicity. At high nutrient supply, whether soon or long after the general disturbance of aboveground biomass, light levels are reduced near the soil surface. The reduction in light certainly reduces the growth of most species, although some species are inhibited by high light availability. No species likely experiences optimal growth at the lowest light levels occurring in the deepest shade, and as such, competition for light and the subsequent reduction in light levels certainly are important in high-nutrient environments. Finally, with the disturbance resistance hypothesis, some species can be excluded from high-resource environments as a consequence of the differential susceptibility to agents of disturbance such as herbivores and pathogens. More than likely, there is an interaction between light availability and susceptibility for species, with some species more susceptible to herbivory or pathogens at low light than other species.

Assessing the relative importance of different factors on evolutionary time scales can be difficult, with little in the way of standardized methodology. Ecological importance cannot simply be extrapolated to evolutionary importance. In some cases the relative importance of a factor on ecological time scales might be inversely related to its importance on evolutionary time scales. Trait analysis is another approach to determining evolutionary importance. In this approach, derived traits are likely to have been the result of selection in the past for factors that had been important.

CHAPTER 7

The Low-Nutrient Strategy

DIFFERENT REGIONS of the world exhibit many similarities in the adaptations of plant species that allow the plants to grow and reproduce successfully in low-nutrient ecosystems. The traits observed in plants with the low-nutrient strategy are associated with (1) increasing the acquisition of nutrients, (2) decreasing the requirements for nutrients, and (3) decreasing the losses of nutrients, with the specific traits spanning physiological, whole-plant, and ecosystem effects properties.

An ecosystem may have one or more inherent characteristics that predispose it to provide an inadequate supply of nutrients to a plant. When soil moisture is high, nutrients are more likely to be limiting than water. If decomposition is retarded, mineralization by microbes might be low. This can happen in water-saturated soils, cold ecosystems, or when soils become too acidic. Other factors can limit the accumulation of nutrients; an example is coarse-textured soils, which limit the accumulation of soil organic matter and hence soil nitrogen. In other cases, factors can favor the reduction of available nutrients. Some soils strongly bind phosphorus, partly as a result of the types of minerals present in the soil and how long weathering has occurred, with more phosphorus becoming occluded over time. In some ecosystems the ability of plants to increase nutrient supplies is limited. N_2-fixing plants are best suited for soils with circum-neutral pH and can be selectively eaten.

In ecosystems where nutrients are in short supply, the dominant plants have been selected to increase their ability to acquire limiting nutrients. One manner in which this can occur is by increasing the supplies of the limiting nutrient. Species that can increase supplies so that they are no longer effectively limited by the nutrient are not considered to have the low-nutrient strategy, even though they are successful in ecosystems where other species (in their absence) would experience a low availability of nutrients. Although the definition is somewhat circular, low-nutrient species are defined as those that can be successful in ecosystems with a low supply of at least one nutrient, even as their growth is still strongly limited by that nutrient.

In addition to potentially increasing nutrient supplies, dominant plants of low-nutrient ecosystems have been selected to compete well for nutrient supplies. As discussed in chapter 5, although there can be heterogeneity in space and time in nutrient supplies, pulses and patches of nutrients have not been important selective forces for the species that dominate low-nutrient ecosystems. Proximally, being a successful competitor for a low, uniform supply of nutrient requires the ability to produce and maintain a high root length density. As described in chapter 5, the root traits associated with the low-nutrient strategy reflect the importance of high root length (or its equivalent in mycorrhizal fungi).

Second, natural selection has acted to decrease the nutrient requirements of plants as part of a low-nutrient strategy. This has not necessarily made plants small, which would decrease the nutrients required per plant, but rather has decreased the nutrients required to produce a given unit of biomass. Reducing specific nutrient requirements is apparent in how plants construct their leaves and roots. Species with the low-nutrient strategy are generally considered to have low nutrient concentrations and restricted use of the limiting nutrient for purposes not considered of primary importance to growth, such as defense against herbivores.

Third, in addition to increasing their access to nutrients and reducing nutrient requirements, species with the low-nutrient strategy have been selected for decreased rates of loss. Major pathways of nutrient loss include loss through biomass turnover and herbivory. Low-nutrient species reduce the loss rates of biomass in ways that are compatible with a high value of nutrients relative to carbon.

In describing the low-nutrient strategy, the chapter first reviews the traits considered to be typically associated with success in ecosystems with low nutrient supplies. The specific advantages conferred by each trait are discussed later in the chapter. As this theme is developed, the low-nutrient strategy is discussed in general, with occasional identification of traits that are associated specifically with low nitrogen availability as opposed to those associated with low phosphorus availability.

The physiological and structural adaptations of plant organs—leaves, roots, and stems—that are included in the low-nutrient strategy are reviewed first, followed by an analysis of those traits assessed at the whole-plant level, such as biomass allocation among organs and RGR. How species that dominate low-nutrient ecosystems can affect nutrient cycling is then described. In general, plasticity of traits as a potentially advantageous character in and of itself is not discussed, although the controls over some of the intraspecific variation in traits are. After the low-nutrient plant strategy is described, the mechanisms that underlie the correlations of traits are investigated, and common errors in understanding the low-nutrient strategy are discussed. Finally, the major extant explanations for the correlations of traits are reviewed, along with a description of the major ways that the low-nutrient strategy allows plants to be successful in ecosystems with low nutrient supplies. The chapter concludes by revisiting how relaxing some basic assumptions about the nature of nutrient limitation reveals that co-limitation by light should extend to ecosystems with low nutrient supplies, too. Central to these arguments is understanding the placement of some species of trees in the low-nutrient strategy and identifying hidden aboveground disturbances that have colored the view of the low-nutrient strategy.

PHYSIOLOGICAL TRAITS

The general set of traits associated with the low-nitrogen strategy should be geared toward increasing the availability of nitrogen in the face of competition while decreasing demands and losses. The set of physiological traits associated with the low-nutrient strategy includes having long-lived leaves, having a low initial and final investment of nitrogen in tissues relative to the investment of structural carbon, low rates of photosynthesis and respiration, and growing auxiliary structures that reduce light interception. Roots have been selected for an analogous set of traits. The low-nitrogen strategy includes having roots that live a long time, a high structural investment, low nitrogen concentrations, and low rates of activity. Low-nutrient species are more likely to be infected by mycorrhizal fungi, but not necessarily so, while average fine root diameter depends on whether nitrogen or phosphorus is more limiting. Defensive chemicals for both leaves and roots are more likely to be nitrogen-free chemicals, whereas structural defenses such as thorns are rare.

Leaves

LONGEVITY

Leaf longevity can be constrained by external agents that cause leaves to die, such as fire or herbivory. Alternatively, leaves can be actively shed by plants, for two reasons. First, nutrients are required to maintain meristem growth, and old leaves serve as the source of nutrients for new leaves when nutrient availability is low (Chapin and Moilanen 1991). Second, leaves are shed when they are unable to meet their own carbon requirements, which includes adjacent branches (Sprugel, Hinckley, and Schaap 1991; Lacointe et al. 2004). A small reduction in light can cause a leaf (and associated support tissues) to respire more carbon than it fixes, which induces the leaf, if not the branch, to be shed.

Empirically, the dominant species of plants in ecosystems with low nutrient supplies have leaves that live a long time. For example, leaf longevity for trees in low-nutrient ecosystems can be as long as 30 years for gymnosperms, four years for dicotyledonous angiosperms, and three years for grasses (Williams 1977; Ewers 1982; Rogers and Clifford 1993). Although leaf longevity varies continuously among species, a basic categorical difference recognized among trees regarding leaf longevity is that between "evergreens" and "deciduous" species. Evergreens have leaves that persist through at least one entire year and deciduous species have leaves that live less than one year.

The evergreen classification is often used to categorically classify low-nutrient species. Evergreen trees such as pines and spruces are more common than deciduous trees in low-nitrogen soils, and their greater leaf longevity holds in common gardens (Withington et al. 2006). When comparisons of species are constrained to a given region or taxonomically constrained, the predominance of high-leaf-longevity species in low-nutrient environments holds. For example, leaf longevity was compared among temperate grassland species in a common garden experiment conducted on low-nitrogen soils at Cedar Creek Natural History Area, Minnesota. Even among this restricted set of species, leaf longevity varied by a factor of three (4–14 weeks), with species associated with low nutrient availability, such as *Schizachyrium scoparium*, having high leaf longevity and other species, such as *Lupinus perennis*, having low leaf longevity (Craine et al. 1999, 2001).

STRUCTURAL INVESTMENT

The greater leaf longevity of low-nutrient species is associated with greater investment in leaf structure. In species with greater structural investment, leaf tissue density (dry mass per unit of volume) is greater. Among Cedar Creek prairie species, leaf tissue density can be five times greater for high-leaf-longevity species such as *Schizachyrium* than for low-longevity leaves of species such as *Lupinus* (Craine et al. 2001). High leaf tissue density comes as a result of a having higher proportion of leaf mass in cell walls, owing either to having small cells or to having thick cell walls, and can also include thick cuticles (Turner 1994). Consequently, low-nutrient species have leaves that have a low proportion of their volume filled by water or air, which increases tissue density.

In general, the greater investment in structure is represented by some as specific leaf area (SLA), which is the ratio of leaf surface area and plant mass. Often this ratio is expressed inversely as the ratio of mass to surface area and called leaf mass area (LMA). Plant leaves with greater structural investment have a lower SLA, implying more mass per unit of leaf area. Yet SLA is a composite metric generated by leaf thickness and leaf tissue density (mass per unit volume), whereas thickness and tissue density can vary independently of one another (Wilson, Thompson, and Hodgson 1999; Craine et al. 2001) and are of different significance to plants. The low SLA of species with the low-nutrient strategy is driven by greater

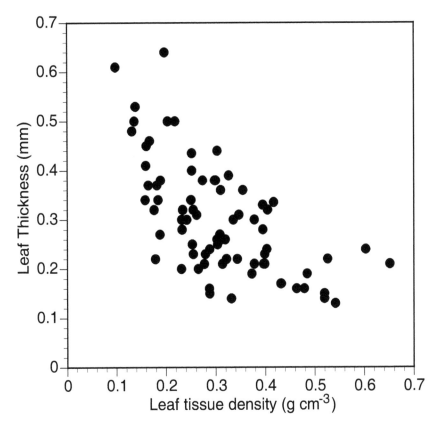

Figure 7.1. Relationship between leaf tissue density and leaf thickness among 76 herbaceous species at Cedar Creek Natural History Area. Data from Craine et al. 2001.

tissue density, not greater leaf thickness. For example, among 76 prairie species in the Cedar Creek region, those species with the highest tissue density actually had leaves that were the least thick (figure 7.1) (Craine et al. 2001).

NUTRIENT CONCENTRATIONS

In addition to having high leaf longevity and high tissue density, species with the low-nutrient strategy have low nutrient concentrations in their leaves. Nitrogen in leaves is primarily contained in proteins, but it also occurs in other important compounds associated with cellular metabolism, such as RNA and DNA (Sterner and Elser 2002). Leaf nitrogen concentrations of both C_3 and C_4 grasses, as well as of dicotyledonous angiosperm species such as those in the Proteaceae family, can be below 5 mg N g^{-1}; by comparison, other species highlighted in subsequent chapters have leaf nitrogen concentrations that can exceed 60 mg N g^{-1} (Wright et al. 2004). As it has long been known that different nutrients such as nitrogen, phosphorus, and potassium are positively correlated across plants (Liebig 1843; Garten 1976), low-nutrient species have lower concentrations of many nutrients (Grime et al. 1997).

The lower investment of nutrient per unit leaf mass is in part associated with the dilution of nutrients by other elements as a result of greater investment in cell walls. Interestingly, the low-nutrient strategy apparently does not necessarily involve reducing the amount of nutrient per unit of leaf area (Wright et al. 2004). Because the standard by which species are compared is flexible, it is difficult to separate whether low-nutrient species have lower tissue nutrient concentrations as a result of greater investment in cell walls or secondary compounds, as opposed to less investment in primary metabolites such as protein, DNA, and RNA.

NUTRIENT RATIOS

Nutrient limitation per se is not supposed to affect the N:P ratio in leaves. Yet plants of ecosystems with low nitrogen availability (relative to phosphorus availability) are generally considered to have low N:P (Koerselman and Meuleman 1996; Tessier and Raynal 2003). For example, Koerselman and Meulemans (1996) analyzed the responses of wetland vegetation to fertilization with nitrogen and phosphorus in sites primarily located in northern Europe. When the ratio of N:P on a mass basis of unfertilized vegetation was less than 14, aboveground biomass increased with fertilization with nitrogen. When the biomass of unfertilized vegetation had an N:P greater than 16, aboveground biomass increased with fertilization with phosphorus. When N:P was between 14 and 16, vegetation responded to the addition of both nitrogen and phosphorus. As opposed to the wetland studies of Koerselman and Meulemans, Tessier and Raynal (2003) reviewed fertilization studies in upland ecosystems along with their own results from fertilizing forest understory plants in the northeast United States. From their review, the authors supported the use of the Koerselman ratios in indexing the relative limitation of nitrogen and phosphorus.

Although the general concept of N:P empirically predicting relative limitation by nitrogen and phosphorus has not been questioned to date, there have been some adjustments to the specific thresholds that define limitation by a given nutrient. Güsewell (2004) proposed a broader range of N:P for co-limitation (N:P = 10–20) than Koerselman and Meuleman (1996), while Tessier and Raynal (2003) noted that the threshold for nitrogen limitation in upland ecosystems might be lower than what Koerselman suggested. It has also been suggested that absolute concentrations of nutrients should be considered in tandem with nutrient ratios to gauge whether plants are likely to be limited by nutrients at all (Wassen,

Veterink, and Deswart 1995), but there has been little broad support for this approach (Güsewell et al. 2003).

Although there seems to be strong support for plants from ecosystems with relatively low nitrogen availability (relative to phosphorus) having universally low ratios of N:P, a critical analysis of extant data calls this into question. First, the data used by Koerselman and Meuleman (1996) were restricted to wetland vegetation, largely in northern Europe, much of which also is subject to high levels of nitrogen deposition. Their data do not necessarily apply to upland ecosystems in other parts of the world. Second, in assessing limitation by nitrogen or phosphorus in upland ecosystems, Tessier and Raynal (2003) made no distinction between studies that reported increases in nutrient concentrations and those that reported increases in productivity. Having nutrient concentrations increase with fertilization is not the same as having productivity increase, and many of the instances in which vegetation was considered to be "limited" by nitrogen or phosphorus were found to exhibit increases in nutrient concentrations but no productivity response. Even in their own study, which purported to support N:P reflecting the relative limitation by nitrogen and phosphorus, only one of the five species Tessier and Raynal investigated increased in biomass with fertilization, and their conclusions relied largely on increases in nutrient concentrations. Increased nutrient concentrations could just as well be considered luxury consumption and need not be associated with long-term increases in growth (Rastetter and Shaver 1992). Finally, in a review of grassland fertilization studies, many of which were published after Tessier and Raynal's review appeared, Craine, Morrow, and Stock (2008) found little support for N:P reflecting limitation. Co-limitation of aboveground production by nitrogen and phosphorus occurs over a much broader range of N:P than would have been expected from the Koerselman thresholds (or the more relaxed thresholds of Güsewell), with co-limitation by nitrogen and phosphorus occurring at N:P as low as 3 (Craine, Morrow, and Stock 2008).

At this point, the claim that the strategy for succeeding specifically when nitrogen is strongly limiting necessarily involves species with a low N:P is tenuous. From first principles, when nitrogen availability is low, species that did not use nitrogen for secondary purposes (see below) would be favored, and this should lower their N:P. Yet too little is known about the chemical makeup of plants at different ratios of supplies of nitrogen and phosphorus. For example, grasses of Kruger National Park in South Africa often have an N:P of 3, five times lower than what is considered to occur under optimum ratios of supplies (Grant and Scholes 2006; Craine, Morrow, and Stock 2008). This occurs so consistently that the low N:P is unlikely to be driven by luxury consumption of phosphorus. It is unknown whether phosphorus is being used for some other secondary purpose such as strengthening cell walls in these low N:P species or whether grasses with the C_4 photosynthetic pathway have lower nitrogen requirements.

For extreme cases such as the South African grasses that have a low N:P, no less generally, there are not enough data on the major chemical constituents of biomass, such as primary versus secondary metabolites or how much of the nitrogen or phosphorus is in storage compounds. The use of N:P in predicting limitation is more likely to be subject to Bayesian principles and assessed on its utility rather than its nonfalsifiability (Hilborn and Mangel 1997). Yet the current analyses (1) have been restricted in their geographic extent, (2) did not separate changes in nutrient concentrations and biomass in assessing limitation, (3) are contradicted by empirical results in grasslands, and (4) are hampered by too little research on the chemical makeup of biomass of different species.

PHOTOSYNTHESIS AND RESPIRATION RATES

With lower specific investment of nitrogen in metabolites, the activity rates of leaves are also lower. Approximately half the nitrogen of a leaf is invested in proteins associated with photosynthesis (Evans 1989). Thus, the lower nitrogen concentrations of the low-nutrient strategy cause plants to have lower maximum photosynthetic rates. For example, the maximum mass-based photosynthetic rates for many low-nutrient trees such as pines and junipers can be less than 2 μmol g^{-1} s^{-1} (Wright et al. 2004). Across plants, foliar respiration rates also scale with foliar nitrogen concentrations (Wright et al. 2004), since a large proportion of the respiration of a leaf is associated with protein turnover. Leaves of low-nutrient species do not necessarily have significantly higher specific respiratory costs to produce their leaves (Chapin 1989) or to unload resources from the xylem or load them to the phloem. As such, along with low-nutrient species having low maximal rates of photosynthesis, rates of respiration are also low, often below 0.5 μmol g^{-1} s^{-1}. The ratio of photosynthesis to nitrogen concentrations is higher for low-nutrient species, but not markedly so (Wright et al. 2004).

Low-nutrient species, even though they can have low respiration rates, can have high light requirements for net photosynthesis. The light flux at which net photosynthesis is equal to zero is considered the leaf-level light compensation point. For example, two low-nutrient trees, *Auracaria angustifolium* and *Quercus coccifera*, have been measured to have a leaf-level light compensation point of approximately 40 μmol m^{-2} s^{-1}, 10–40 times greater than that of other species that do not perform well in low-nutrient habitats. For reference, full sunlight can range from 1,500 to 2,000 μmol m^{-2} s^{-1}.

In addition to differences at the cellular level, leaves of low-nutrient species often have traits that serve to reduce absorption of incident light. With low nitrogen concentrations and often high light levels, high incident light can overwhelm the capacity of leaves to transform absorbed radiation into chemical energy and can cause leaf temperature to rise to the point where proteins are denatured. Absorption of light in excess of the capacity to convert it to chemical energy or reradiate it can damage photosynthetic membranes and possibly degrade chlorophyll (Krause and Weis 1991). As such, excess light absorption is a stress that is detrimental to growth.

To reduce the incident light, leaves are often held at a high angle (Craine et al. 2001), reducing light interception at midday when light levels are the highest. For example, among Cedar Creek species growing in field, low-nutrient species such as *Schizachyrium scoparium* and *Solidago rigida* had leaf angles of more than 70 degrees—nearly vertical. These leaves of low-nutrient species are often coated in a reflective wax or leaf hairs, which also serve to reduce light absorption (Ehleringer, Bjorkman, and Mooney 1976).

NUTRIENT RESORPTION

Upon senescence, nutrients are resorbed from leaves. Nutrient resorption is an active process by which plants spend energy breaking down structures within the cell and loading the resultant free nitrogen-containing compounds into the phloem so that they can be stored or used for immediate growth elsewhere (Aerts 1996). Resorption is an important process in the resource budgets of plants and likely to be under strong selection. Approximately half of the nitrogen in the leaf canopy is resorbed with each turning over of the canopy (Aerts 1996), which is the equivalent of approximately a third of the nitrogen acquired from the soil each year. There has been some debate as to whether low-nitrogen species are better at resorbing nutrients in leaves than other species.

Some of the earliest debates regarding nutrient resorption centered on the most accurate metrics for resorption and how to account for mass loss during senescence. Other debates surrounded whether the fraction of a nutrient removed during senescence (resorption efficiency) or the amount of nutrient remaining after senescence (resorption proficiency) was a better index of how well a plant had resorbed the nutrient (Killingbeck 1996). Other researchers improved the statistical approaches to analyzing resorption data. For example, Craine and Mack (1998) focused on comparing lower bounds of data sets rather than averages, while Knops, Koenig, and Nash (1997) began to address autocorrelation among resorption metrics.

More recent reviews are improvements on the past but are still lacking in a few critical areas. Aerts (1996) compared the resorption efficiency of plants fertilized with nitrogen with that of their unfertilized counterparts. In 63% of the studies there was no change in resorption efficiency, while in 32% resorption efficiency decreased. Although it seems logical from these comparisons that unfertilized plants should be considered more likely to resorb a higher fraction of nutrients, it was concluded that nutrient supply had little impact on resorption efficiency, presumably since the majority of studies showed no significant response in efficiency. Aerts and Chapin (2000) compared the resorption efficiency of evergreens and deciduous woody species and found that both the median efficiency as well as the overall ranges were similar for the two groups. From this, they felt that low-nutrient species did not necessarily have greater resorption efficiencies.

In the best statistical analysis of resorption data to date, Kobe, Lepczyk, and Iyer (2005) reanalyzed the patterns of resorption using log-transformed data on green and senesced tissue nutrient concentrations. After comparing green and senesced nitrogen concentrations, Kobe, Lepczyk, and Iyer concluded that resorption efficiency declined with increasing initial nutrient concentrations, which suggests that low-nutrient species have greater resorption efficiency. Echoing the conclusions of Aerts and Chapin's (2000) analysis, Kobe, Lepczyk, and Iyer reported that evergreen and deciduous species have similar relationships, differing only in their green nitrogen concentrations, not in their resorption efficiency at a given nitrogen concentration.

Although the analysis by Kobe, Lepczyk, and Iyer (2005) is the best statistical analysis to date, the conclusions are still limited by deficiencies in the way that individual studies were conducted. For example, most studies show poor understanding of the identity and magnitude of the limiting resource for a given plant. Further, examining patterns of resorption across sites does not allow complete discrimination of what is a trait of a species and what is a function of the environment the species grows in. The understanding of resorption is limited less by statistical techniques, but better experiments are still needed that allow determination of whether species, independent of environment, differ in their ability to resorb nutrients. With the continued development of the understanding of nutrient resorption during senescence, low-nutrient species are recognized as having not only lower initial nutrient concentrations but also lower final nutrient concentrations and greater resorption efficiency. Whether they also have greater proficiency remains an unanswered question that could benefit from better statistical analyses and experiments.

Roots and Mycorrhizal Fungi

For dominant species in low-nutrient-supply environments, the set of traits observed for roots parallels the set seen for leaves. Like leaves, roots are responsible for acquiring resources, but unlike leaves they also transport resources along their length. The fine roots of plants are often defined somewhat arbitrarily as those less than 1 mm (sometimes 2 mm) in diameter. Fine roots are the most analogous to leaves, as they are produced primarily for the acquisition of nutrients and water. Coarser roots are more important for resource transport and support, and functionally are more analogous to stems. Even when the 1-mm threshold is used, many plants have only fine roots, while others have mostly coarse roots, with mycorrhizal fungi serving the acquisition functions that are performed by other species' fine roots.

Although superficially similar in their purpose, roots are not completely analogous to leaves in their function, as roots are under different constraints than leaves as a result of nutrient limitation. As such, there are unique aspects of roots of low-nutrient species that warrant special attention.

LONGEVITY

Although the greater longevity of leaves in low-nutrient species seems clear, there is still considerable uncertainty as to the relative importance of internal and external factors causing root mortality in different environments and whether greater root longevity should be considered part of the low-nutrient strategy. Unlike leaves, roots do not appear to have a programmed senescence. Instead, death might come as a result of disturbances, such as soil movement that severs roots or herbivory, or as a result of long-term degradation consequent on the activity of microbial exoenzymes, which can slowly break down root biomass.

The little data on root longevity that are available suggest that just as leaves of low-nutrient species live a long time, the roots of low-nutrient species also have a high longevity. For example, at Cedar Creek, grasses that dominate low-nitrogen habitats have fine roots that live as long as three years (Craine et al. 2002). In contrast, other grasses that are associated with habitats with higher nutrient supply have roots that live a few months, while the roots of *Lupinus perennis*, a fast-growing N_2-fixing legume, live just a few weeks (Craine et al. 2002).

Other patterns of root longevity have been observed that suggest that the low-nutrient strategy might involve lower root longevity, if there is any pattern at all. For example, when locally restricted pulses of nitrogen are added to the root environment, roots adjacent to the patch live longer (Pregitzer, Hendrick, and Fogel 1993), but these intraplant patterns do not necessarily apply across species. Across species, it has also been observed that some species with long leaf longevity, which would seem to point to high root longevity as part of the low-nutrient strategy, actually have relatively low root longevity. For example, Ruess, Hendrick, and Bryant (1998) measured the root longevity of black spruce (*Picea mariana*), which has needles that live more than a decade, and found that the roots lived less than a year. From these data, the authors suggested that root and leaf longevity might be inversely correlated among species or ecosystems. Additionally, among trees in a common garden in low-nitrogen soils (Withington et al. 2006), root longevity ranged from 0.5 to 2.5 years, but there was little relationship between leaf traits and root longevity. Roots that lived longer were distinguished only by their low root nitrogen concentrations, something expected as part of the low-nutrient strategy, but there was little linkage between leaves and root longevity that would suggest that root longevity was part of the low-nutrient strategy.

With so little data on root longevity, it is difficult to statistically determine the basic patterns and separate out the myriad influences on root longevity. It can also be difficult to compare roots fairly across species, as root systems differ in their average diameter and individual roots differ in the relative importance of their roles in nutrient acquisition and resource transport, as well as relationships with mycorrhizal fungi. Yet some of the confusing patterns are determined by natural selection to exist in environments with high belowground disturbance, namely, the freezing soils of the high northern latitudes. Each winter, soil freezing causes frost heaving, which is strong enough to push large rocks to the soil surface, no less kill the fine roots of trees. This is discussed a bit more later when the determinants of plant biomass ratios are covered, but the belowground disturbance sets an upper limit to average root longevity that obscures the patterns of longevity seen among some sets of species. Species such as black spruce do not have roots built to live a long time because the extra resources required for greater longevity would be wasted in most years, with severe disturbance causing fine root mortality every winter, regardless of the level of investment. Even plants that were built to have roots that lived a long time in a different environment would experience lower root longevity in these soils.

A better test of role of root longevity in the low-nutrient strategy is in more temperate ecosystems where soil freezing is less severe. There, low-nutrient species have longer root longevity than other species. Many of the traits of plants with the low-nutrient strategy rest on this assumption, but the selection of roots to live longer in low-nutrient environments is a logical consequence of how roots acquire nutrients and of the importance of competition in low-nutrient environments.

STRUCTURAL INVESTMENT

For species with roots that live a long time, there is also greater investment in root structure. Analogous to leaves and SLA, root structural investment is generally measured as specific root length (SRL), the ratio of root length to mass. Species that have a high structural investment in roots are considered to have a low SRL, or little length per unit mass. Yet, like SLA, SRL is a composite of root diameter and tissue density. SRL can be low as a result of thick roots or dense roots. Thick roots are thick primarily because of a greater amount of stele tissue (xylem and phloem), but there is little need for high capacity to transport resources for low-nutrient species. Instead, in low-nitrogen ecosystems, dominant species have roots with a higher tissue density. Although multiple factors besides root tissue density can affect longevity, the Cedar Creek species such as *Schizachyrium scoparium*, whose roots live approximately two years, have a root tissue density five times greater than that of species such as *Rudbeckia serotina* and *Lupinus perennis* (Craine et al. 2001), whose roots live approximately one month. Similar to what is seen with leaves, the greater root tissue density apparently comes as a result of thicker cell walls, potentially both in the cortex and in the stele (Wahl and Ryser 2000).

Many of the differences from species adapted to low phosphorus availability follow from the lower diffusion rates of phosphorus than of nitrogen in soil, as well as the different ways that phosphorus supplies can be increased. One set of adaptations to low phosphorus availability reflect the slow diffusion of phosphorus in soil. Plants can rely on diffusion less to deliver phosphorus to root surfaces and therefore must bring the root surface closer to the phosphorus. One way this occurs is through the production of fine root hairs, elongated epidermal cells that extend up to 0.2 cm away from the root surface. Root hairs are redundant for nitrogen acquisition, generally residing within the nitrogen depletion zone of a given root, but they extend outside the phosphorus depletion zone of a root and therefore can be useful for acquiring phosphorus.

As a consequence of greater phosphorus limitation, the grasses of tropical grasslands have thicker roots than the grasses of temperate grasslands. In temperate ecosystems, grasses often form dense root systems (high root length per unit soil volume), whereas the root systems of grasses from tropical ecosystems are more sparse, resembling chow mein noodles more than the fine grass root systems of temperate environments (Craine et al. 2005). The root systems of tropical grasses often have an average diameter four times greater than that of the root systems of temperate grasses, such as 0.06 versus 0.015 mm (Craine et al. 2005). As discussed below, the greater root diameter is associated with a greater reliance on mycorrhizal fungi.

NUTRIENT CONCENTRATIONS

Roots that live a long time and have high tissue density also have lower nutrient concentrations (Craine et al. 2002). As in leaves, the nitrogen in roots is primarily in proteins in cells, but unlike in leaves, there is not a large pool of protein that is used for resource acquisition analogous to the pool of nitrogen incorporated into enzymes and pigments associated with photosynthesis in leaves.

Nutrient concentrations might be lower in low-nutrient species simply because of dilution by structural investment. If this were the case, then low-nutrient species would have the same nitrogen per unit of root volume but less nitrogen per unit of mass, since there is greater mass per unit root volume. Data on root nitrogen concentrations and tissue density from a common garden study (Craine et al. 2002) and a cross-continental comparison of roots of grasses (Craine et al. 2005) suggest that the lower nitrogen concentrations of plants can be only partly explained by dilution by cell wall material. Species with low nitrogen concentrations have less nitrogen per unit of root volume than would have been expected if the low nitrogen concentrations were driven solely by dilution by cell wall materials (figure 7.2). As such, only some of the lower nitrogen concentrations come as a result of dilution, and the rest is due to having lower nitrogen concentrations in cells.

Without a large mobile pool of nitrogen not tied to primary metabolism in roots, there appears to be little nitrogen that can be resorbed without shutting down cellular function, which would prevent the active process of resorption. As such, it is presumed that there is no resorption of nitrogen during the lifetime of a root (Nambiar 1987). In support of resorption being tied to mobile pools of nutrients not recruited for primary metabolism, across species, roots have about half the nitrogen concentration of leaves, and both senesced leaves and roots have about the same nitrogen concentrations (Craine et al. 2002, 2005).

RESPIRATION RATES

Like leaf respiration rates, specific rates of root respiration scale with nitrogen concentrations (Tjoelker et al. 2005). Because the roots of low-nutrient species have low nitrogen concentrations, they also have low specific respiration rates. As with leaves, much of this respiration is associated with the maintenance of proteins. Yet there are additional costs for maintaining the ion gradients that allow nutrients to be brought in against an electrochemical gradient, and these costs are often greater for low-nutrient species, which would experience the lowest soil nutrient concentrations at their root surface (Poorter et al. 1991).

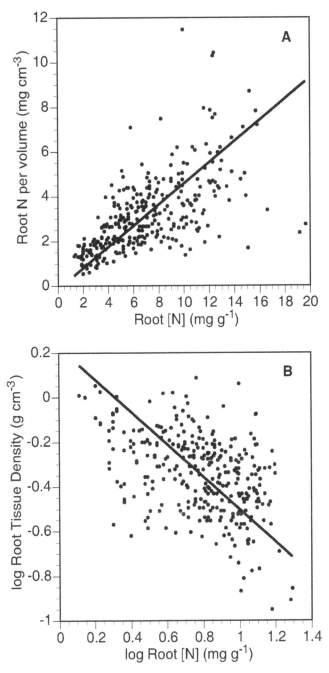

Figure 7.2. Relationship between root nitrogen concentration and root nitrogen per unit volume (A) and log-transformed root nitrogen concentrations and root tissue density (B). Data from various published sources.

UPTAKE KINETICS

The five-part trait analogy can now be extended from leaves to roots. Just as the leaves of low-nutrient species have low photosynthetic rates, roots of low-nutrient species have low maximum rates of nutrient uptake. In general, data on the uptake kinetics of plants are exceedingly sparse, but what little work has been done shows that low-nutrient species have lower V_{max} (Chapin 1988). The minimum concentrations at which nutrients are acquired (C_{min}) appear to be very low for all species, but again, good data on these measurements are rare (Lambers, Chapin, and Pons 1998).

The last parameter of the Michaelis-Menten formulation of nutrient uptake across a nutrient concentration gradient is K_m, the concentration at which uptake is half the maximum rate. Although Chapin had focused on K_m as an important parameter to describe the affinity of roots for nutrients, it helps describe the relationship between external concentrations and nutrient uptake well, but in and of itself has little significance. For example, a plant with a high V_{max} and a high K_m can have the same rate of uptake at an intermediate nutrient concentration as one with a low V_{max} and a low K_m. Plants also have a secondary low-affinity uptake mechanism that becomes important at high external soil solution nutrient concentrations, but little is known about the patterns across species. It is unlikely that low-nutrient species can be induced to have high uptake rates.

MYCORRHIZAL FUNGI

Symbioses with mycorrhizal fungi are generally thought to be adaptations to low nutrient supply (Read 1991). Mycorrhizal fungi aid plants in the acquisition of nutrients that generally have low diffusion rates, such as $H_2PO_4^-$ (see below) or NH_4^+. Many mycorrhizal fungi also have the ability to mine for nitrogen or to acquire organic nitrogen (see chapter 4). The thinness of mycorrhizal fungi allows the functional equivalent of root length to be produced at a lower cost, which is a major reason for subcontracting nutrient acquisition of low-diffusion ions to mycorrhizal fungi.

One question is whether low-nutrient species are more likely to depend on mycorrhizal fungi than other plants. On the one hand, plants of high-nutrient-supply environments, such as Chenopodiaceae species and the species of the legume genera *Lupinus*, are nonmycorrhizal. With declining nutrient availability, species that form associations with ericoid and ectomycorrhizal fungi become more common. As another example of the importance of mycorrhizal fungi when nutrient availability is low, individual plants often respond to increasing nutrient supply by reducing mycorrhizal infection.

Although many species of plants that are abundant in low-nutrient-supply environments utilize mycorrhizal fungi, many other species abundant in the same environments are nonmycorrhizal. For example, in tundra assemblages with ectomycorrhizal *Betula* species and the ericoid *Vaccinium* speices, nonmycorrhizal species of the sedge family are also abundant. Sedge family species such as *Eriophorum vaginatum* are not nonmycorrhizal because they are reliant on high nutrient availability but instead because they can acquire amino acids directly and grow in soils where nitrogen uptake is dominated by organic nitrogen. Amino acids likely become soluble without the activity of mycorrhizal fungi (or become available with activity of mycorrhizal fungi associated with other species) and diffuse readily in soils, so there would be little benefit to a symbiosis with fine-diameter, proteolytic mycorrhizal fungi for sedges. It should be noted that in the genus *Carex*, there appear to have been some compensatory morphological changes in these nonmycorrhizal roots, as *Carex* species have some of the finest average root diameters among vascular plants (40 μm), approaching the diameter of mycorrhizal hyphae (<10 μm).

Within certain taxonomic groupings, plants that dominate low-phosphorus environments rely more on mycorrhizal fungi than plants of low-nitrogen environments. The thick-rooted grasses of tropical grasslands are likely more dependent on arbuscular mycorrhizae. Like root hairs, mycorrhizal fungi extend the depletion zone of an individual at low cost, owing to their inherently lower diameter. Mycorrhizal fungi can also increase the availability of phosphorus through exudation of phosphatases and organic acids, as is evident from the many nonmycorrhizal species that are dominant in low-phosphorus environments.

Although within some taxonomic constraints, there is greater reliance on mycorrhizal fungi when phosphorus availability is low, many species of low-phosphorus ecosystems are nonmycorrhizal. Many of these plants do not rely on mycorrhizal fungi to acquire low-diffusion phosphorus but instead increase phosphorus availability directly. Much of the phosphate in many soils is present as organic phosphorus. It is unlikely that plants can acquire organic phosphorus directly, but its mineralization is enhanced by the release of phosphatases by plants themselves. In other soils, the greatest phosphate pools are inorganic, and instead of releasing phosphatases to increase phosphate supply, plants can decrease the pH of soils, which can increase phosphate availability. As discussed in chapter 4, low-phosphorus plants can release chelating agents that preferentially bind to cations such as calcium or iron and release phosphate from the cation-phosphate complexes. Often the dynamics of phosphorus release have selected for plants that have unique structures that increase the ability of plants to make phosphorus available locally and increase the probability that the plant acquires the phosphate that it made available. For example, species such as sedges can have "dauciform" roots, localized areas of high-density root hairs from which organic acids are released into the surrounding soil (Shane, Dixon, and Lambers 2005).

Defense

Both leaves and roots are defended structurally and chemically, but not all types of defenses are equally likely to be found when nutrients are limiting. Low-nutrient species generally have low tissue quality that is of limited nutrition to herbivores, and the plants are generally defended with greater cell wall allocation (if that can be thought of as a defense). Structural defenses such as thorns are rare, as are nitrogen-containing chemical defenses when nitrogen is limiting to plant growth.

LOW TISSUE QUALITY

Plants that are abundant in low-nutrient ecosystems are often of too poor quality to support herbivores that digest cell walls. For example, in humid African grasslands, average nitrogen concentrations of shoots are below the critical threshold of 10 mg N g^{-1} (see chapter 3) for all but a few weeks a year (Breman and de Wit 1983). If low-nutrient species are utilized by herbivores, it is often during a brief period when concentrations are relatively high, or during an unfavorable season as a source of energy, and not for protein after other, higher quality plants in other areas have been eaten. In other low-nutrient ecosystems, such as tundra, fynbos, kwongan heathlands, and other humid grasslands such as the tallgrass prairies of North America, only a small fraction of biomass would allow most herbivores to maintain weight, even if there were no defensive chemicals.

DEFENSIVE CHEMICALS

Although the average nitrogen concentrations in many of these ecosystems are generally below levels needed for herbivore maintenance, no less growth and reproduction, plants allocate significant resources to defensive chemicals. The leaves of low-nitrogen species often contain high levels of constitutive nitrogen-free compounds, such as tannins and phenolics. For example, although tannins are hypothesized to have other direct and indirect benefits (see below), tannins are generally considered to be defensive chemicals that reduce protein availability. Low-nutrient species such as Labrador tea (*Ledum palustre*) may have more than 25% of their leaf biomass and 10% of their root biomass as condensed tannin (Kraus, Zasoski, and Dahlgren 2004).

In ecosystems with termites, the low nitrogen concentrations of biomass are little impediment to termite consumption. In these areas, termites can achieve high biomass and acquire a large fraction of aboveground productivity. It is no surprise that in these ecosystems, plants such as grasses are more likely to be defended chemically than grasses in similar environments but without termites. For example, species such as those of the genera *Cymbopogon*, which yields culinary lemongrass and the insect repellant citronella, are common in tropical humid grasslands and can have high levels of essential oils with monoterpenes. Other species of humid grasslands such as *Bothriochloa ischaemum* (common name, stinkgrass) have high levels of monoterpenes.

In addition to how phosphorus is acquired, plants that are adapted to low phosphorus availability use nitrogen differently than plants adapted to low nitrogen availability. In general, when phosphorus is limiting, nitrogen is likely to be more available and to have a lower relative value for the plant. Although nitrogen and phosphorus are tightly correlated for primary metabolic function, having an excess of nitrogen frees up nitrogen for allocation to secondary functions such as defense. Although the relative amounts of different defenses along natural nutrient supply gradients as well as among species are poorly known, there are examples of plants with low nutrient concentrations that use nitrogen for defense. For example, in *Eucalyptus cladocalyx*, up to 20% of leaf nitrogen is in the form of cyanogenic glycoside (Gleadow and Woodrow 2000), even though its leaf nitrogen concentrations could be below 10 mg g^{-1}, a result of strong phosphorus limitation. Interestingly enough, the contrary scenario, in which phosphorus is used for defensive purposes, is not apparent in low-nitrogen plants.

For the most part, phosphorus is not used in any naturally produced chemical defense, even though phosphorus can be part of some of the precursors to active chemical defenses. Some storage compounds of phosphorus (inositol hexaphosphate) also have the ability to chelate iron in insect herbivores, which interferes with their ability to detoxify defensive chemicals (Green, Zangerl, and Berenbaum 2001).

Failure to incorporate the relative values of carbon and nitrogen may explain why some analyses have contradicted the prediction that along a gradient of increasing nitrogen supply, carbon-based defenses should become more expensive and nitrogen-based defenses less expensive. For example, Skogsmyr and Fagerström (1992) calculated the cost of the carbon and energy directly associated with production and maintenance of nicotine, an alkaloid that contains nitrogen and confers resistance to herbivores. The authors calculated that nicotine should be cheap even at low nitrogen availability, but their calculations did not incorporate the high cost of nitrogen in the cost of the defense. The only cost of nitrogen was the energy required to reduce it from NO_3^-.

STRUCTURAL DEFENSES

Thorn-type and wire plant structural defenses are rare in low-nitrogen ecosystems. In the setting of low overall quality, which reduces the ability of herbivores to digest entire biomass, sucking insects still can be important agents of stress to plants. Hairs that reflect away light, however, also diminish the ability of sucking insects to tap into vascular tissues.

Support

If nutrients are in short supply and nutrient stress is the predominant factor reducing growth, there would seem to be little advantage to producing stems. For example, Grime associated low stature with the stress tolerator syndrome, as taller plants were associated with greater nutrient supplies (Grime 1979). Although low-nutrient species might be short in stature, they can still allocate a large proportion of their annual aboveground biomass to stems (Gleeson and Tilman 1994). These stems are not necessarily for raising canopies (Craine et al. 2001) but serve to project flowers at height. Any leaves on the stem are often small and diminish in size with distance from the ground.

Although low-nutrient species do not necessarily allocate significantly less biomass to stems than other plants do, stem biomass in some species can be retained over the years, allowing plants to grow into shrubs or trees. Many low-nutrient ecosystems are dominated by trees, some very tall, that have the suite of leaf traits, for example, of shorter low-nutrient species. From the first principles covered in chapter 5, low-nutrient-supply ecosystems should not be dominated by trees, since light competition should be relatively unimportant when nutrients are limiting. Yet many species of trees should truly be considered low-nutrient species, and as such, the low-nutrient strategy could lead to tall plants (and light competition can become important in low nutrient ecosystems).

Storage

In contradistinction to water and carbohydrates, there is little evidence of consistent significant storage of nutrients in low-nutrient species. In response to occasional pulses of nutrient availability, nutrients may accumulate in tissues (Millard 1988). At the end of a growing season, low-nutrient species store nutrients that have been resorbed from leaves for the next growing season. Yet there is little evidence that low-nutrient species store appreciable amounts of nutrients while the plants are actively growing.

WHOLE-PLANT TRAITS

Biomass Ratios

Another trait that has long been considered part of the foundation of the low-nutrient strategy is the allocation of a greater fraction of a plant's resources belowground, which generates a high ratio of root biomass to shoot biomass, or a high root weight ratio (RWR). RWR is not necessarily determined by differences in allocation. The evolutionary-scale controls over RWR are discussed later in the chapter.

Herbaceous plants that are abundant in low-nutrient ecosystems often have a high fraction of biomass in roots. For example, among the Cedar Creek flora, 90% of the biomass can be in roots for *Schizachyrium scoparium* mid-season, when leaf biomass is highest, as opposed to just 30% for species such as *Rudbeckia hirta* (Craine et al. 2002).

The greater RWR of plants has often been considered to be caused by higher allocation to roots, which is coincident with the direction of plastic responses of individual plants to lower nutrient availability. With declining nutrient availability, individual plants increase their allocation of biomass to roots (Reynolds and Pacala 1993). In the simplest models of plant growth, RWR is generated by differences in allocation rates between roots and shoots. Plants that allocate a higher fraction of biomass belowground generate a higher RWR. This generalization, however, is not supported by the results of usually short-term experiments that show that the seedlings of low-nutrient species with high RWR do not necessarily allocate a high proportion of their biomass belowground (Gleeson and Tilman 1994).

The causes of the differences in RWR between young and old plants have led to confusion. For example, Gleeson and Tilman attempted to rectify the lack of differences in allocation among species as seedlings and the greater RWR of more established plants by suggesting there was plasticity in allocation, with older plants allocating more biomass belowground (Gleeson and Tilman 1994). A more parsimonious possible explanation is that low-nutrient species that have a high RWR do not allocate more biomass belowground but instead have roots that live a long time compared to their leaves, causing biomass to accumulate preferentially belowground over time.

For example, Craine et al. (2002) measured belowground productivity with root ingrowth cores for different species that were grown in monoculture on soils with low nitrogen content for five year. The belowground production of biomass could be compared to aboveground productivity to generate relative allocation rates of biomass belowground. In this experiment, low-nutrient species had high RWR, but not high relative allocation rates belowground. Instead, the ratio of longevities of fine roots to leaves was high for low-nutrient species. For example, the fine roots of *Schizachyrium* lived ten times longer than its leaves. For *Rudbeckia*, which has an RWR one-third that of *Schizachyrium*, roots and leaves both lived about 45 days. Comparisons like these suggest that low-nutrient species with a high RWR do not necessarily allocate a greater fraction of biomass belowground, but rather a high RWR is generated over time as biomass preferentially accumulates belowground owing to the greater longevity of roots relative to leaves.

Relative Growth Rates

Relative growth rates can be measured when resources are abundant, which represents the RGR_{max} of the plants. RGR can also be measured when a given nutrient is limiting, which is an index of the ability of a species to produce biomass when under nutrient stress. When resources are abundant, plants with the low-nutrient strategy have a low RGR_{max}. As noted by Grime (2001), these observations date back more than 50 years, to Arthur Kruckeberg's analyses of the growth of serpentine specialists in nonserpentine soils (Kruckeberg 1954). In comparing the growth of serpentine endemics with those that were excluded from serpentine soils, Kruckeberg found it was not the low nutrient availability of serpentine soils that was slowing the growth of serpentine species. Even in high-nutrient, nonserpentine soils, serpentine endemics grew slowly.

Recent measurements have confirmed the generalization that arose from Kruckeberg's early observations of low-nutrient species having a lower capacity for growth. For example, Grime and Hunt (1975) measured the RGR_{max} of a number of species near Sheffield, England. Species that were more common in low-nutrient habitats had an RGR_{max} just one-fourth that of species that were more abundant in areas with higher nutrient supply.

If low-nutrient species have a lower RGR under high resource availability, they might have a higher RGR when nitrogen supplies are low. A few studies have attempted to compare the RGR values of different species across a range of nutrient supplies (Reich, Buschena, et al. 2003). Although the conclusions of the studies are potentially limited by the range and values of nutrient supplies examined, as well as the length of time over which RGR was evaluated, in general, RGR values at high and low nutrient supplies are correlated. Yet species with low RGR_{max} occasionally have a higher RGR at low nutrient supplies (Raaimakers and Lambers 1996). It is unknown whether this is an indication that low-nutrient species are better able to grow under regimes of low nutrient supplies and might have a lower minimum supply requirement or whether it is an anomalous result.

Whether these results that show low-nutrient species growing better than other species at low nutrient supplies are experimental anomalies or reflect a general trade-off between maintaining growth at low nutrient supply and having fast growth at high nutrient supply remains to be seen. Without studies that examine plant growth at a low enough nutrient supply to determine the nutrient supply at which RGR is zero or the minimum nutrient supply requirements for reproduction, it is difficult to discern whether the positive correlations between RGR_{max} and RGR at low nutrient supply are limited to a range of nutrient supplies or a subset of species. Although there is solid evidence that low-nutrient species have lower RGR_{max}, the ability of low-nutrient species to better maintain positive growth at low nutrient supplies in the absence of competition, other stresses, or disturbances is poorly known. RGR values should decline proportionally with decreasing nutrient supplies, but it is still possible that low-nutrient species, at some time scale, can actually grow better at low nutrient supplies than species adapted to higher nutrient supplies.

Effects on Nitrogen Cycling

Decreases in Nitrogen Supply

The rate of mineralization of nutrients from litter while it is being decomposed by microbes is generally considered to be a function of the relative availability of carbon and nutrients in the litter (see chapter 4). Because species that are abundant in low-nutrient habitats have low nitrogen concentrations of live biomass and, if anything, higher nitrogen resorption rates from leaves at senescence, the C:N of the biomass entering the decomposition cycle tends to be high. For example, typical values of C:N of senesced leaves seen in decomposition experiments range from greater than 70 for the tundra sedge *Eriophorum vaginatum* (Hobbie 1996) to 110 for *Schizachyrium scoparium* (Wedin and Tilman 1990) and 100 for Proteaceae species (Mitchell et al. 1986). By comparison, microbes are co-limited by carbon and nitrogen when the C:N of substrates is 25 and all the carbon is labile (Chapin, Matson, and Mooney 2002). Insofar as many species have *live* leaves with an equivalent C:N, as seen in the examples just given of senesced leaves, the C:N of litter of many low-nutrient species can be very low.

In addition to producing litter with a high C:N ratio, plants can reduce nitrogen mineralization through their production of secondary compounds, such as tannins (Kraus, Dahlgren, and Zasoski 2003). As described in chapter 4, not only do tannins complex with protein in the digestive systems of herbivores, they also do so in the soil, which can lower nitrogen mineralization. Although there is no doubt that low-nutrient species decrease nitrogen supplies through their production of low-quality litter, it is important to ask in what environments plants can reduce nitrogen supplies long term, and under what conditions it would be advantageous to do so.

Increases in Nitrogen Supply

In addition to decreasing nitrogen supply, plants can also increase nitrogen supplies by influencing N_2 fixation rates and the rate of solubilization of organic nitrogen. It has long been known that plants can increase nitrogen supply via symbioses with bacteria capable of fixing atmospheric N_2 to organic nitrogen. Plants like legumes and *Alnus* species have associations with N_2-fixing bacteria in root nodules. Other species might encourage free-living N_2-fixing bacteria to fix nitrogen through exudation of labile carbon (Bormann et al. 1993), but substantial rates of fixation have been difficult to confirm (Barkmann and Schwintzer 1998).

Although high N_2-fixation rates can confer success to some species growing in low-nitrogen soils, when N_2-fixation rates are very high, the plants are no longer effectively limited by nitrogen and are not considered to have the low-nutrient strategy. For example, plots with the cool-season legume *Lupinus perennis* accumulated enough nitrogen over five years that plants were acquiring 35 g N m^{-2} each year (as opposed to just 2–3 g N $m^{-2} y^{-1}$ for other nonlegumes) (Craine et al. 2002). The greater nitrogen uptake of *Lupinus* was associated with high nitrogen concentrations and low longevity for both leaves and roots, traits that are not associated with the low-nutrient strategy.

Another method for increasing nitrogen supplies is to encourage microbial nitrogen mining of organic matter. As discussed in chapter 4, some microbes can use labile carbon to produce enzymes that decompose recalcitrant organic molecules, which releases any nitrogen that might have been part of the recalcitrant molecules. Both ectomycorrhizal and ericoid fungi have the ability to mine nitrogen from recalcitrant organic matter. The increased likelihood of symbiosis of low-nutrient species with these mycorrhizal fungi supports the idea that nitrogen mining is associated with the low-nutrient strategy. There has been little investigation into differences among species in their influence of nitrogen mining by free-living microorganisms. Although low-nitrogen species also encourage nitrogen mining through release of labile carbon, research is needed to specifically investigate this point. There must be some constraints on the ability of species to increase nitrogen supplies through nitrogen mining or N_2 fixation from free-living bacteria, or else nitrogen limitation would not be so common.

REVISING THE LOW-NUTRIENT STRATEGY

Some of the revisions to the low-nutrient strategy have already been covered, such as the importance of steady nutrient supplies to low-nutrient species (chapter 5) and differential biomass turnover in determining RWR. Of equal significance are some fundamental questions regarding the causes for the linkages among traits in the low-nutrient strategy. First, many different traits are tightly correlated across species, such as leaf nitrogen concentrations and leaf longevity, yet it is difficult to determine whether the traits have been selected for individually (but in a coordinated fashion), or whether the coordination is driven by common underlying mechanisms.

Second, in describing the trait set commonly associated with low-nutrient strategy, it is implicit that all the traits have a strong genetic basis, contribute to success in low nutrient environments, and are a result of natural selection. In general, the set of traits that are associated with a given strategy are derived from correlations of traits among species, either across natural gradients or in common-garden-type experiments. Even in common gardens and especially along gradients, measuring differences among species can never completely separate environment and genetics since plants are growing in environments that they modify. As such, the genetic basis of many traits is uncertain. Determining the proximal and distal mechanisms requires partitioning environmental influences on the expression of traits. Separating traits and nutrient availability is of central importance to understanding the bases of the low-nutrient strategy.

The last point to cover is that, at one level, biomass ratios are determined by relative turnover rates of leaves and roots, but the environmental and evolutionary controls on tissue longevity raise questions about the nature of nutrient limitation. One reason why it is difficult to understand the influence of low nutrient availability on the evolution of plants is that many low-nutrient environments are also affected by disturbances or other stress agents. The influence of these other factors is difficult to detect among regional comparisons of species, and they often cannot be pulled out experimentally. The effects of these factors are imprinted on the traits via natural selection and they remain even in their absence.

Physiological Traits, Growth Rate, and Nutrient Availability

Although low-nutrient species generally differ from other species in having traits such as lower tissue nutrient concentrations and higher organ longevity, this does not necessarily mean that natural selection has selected for each trait independently of one another or that each trait can be considered an adaptation that is under strict independent control. Although it has long been understood that there is plasticity in many physiological traits such as nutrient concentrations, as the mechanisms of trait expression become increasingly better understood, it is clear that many traits are consequences of underlying traits and determined by environmental conditions. To a certain degree, this is true for almost all traits that are measured, since the direct products of gene expression are not being measured. Yet, on examining the results of different experiments, it becomes evident that growth rate and nutrient availability are determining plant traits, and traits such as low nutrient concentrations are consequences of low-nutrient species growing in low nutrient environments and/or the plants themselves reducing nutrient availability through litter feedbacks.

The interconnectedness among traits and nutrient availability along with a failure to understand the mechanisms that produce the correlations among traits became clear in comparing the traits of prairie species grown in field monocultures in two different experiments at Cedar Creek Natural History Area. In one experiment (E111, which has been referred to above), prairie species were started from seed and grown in monoculture on soils with low nitrogen content for five years. After five years of growth in E111, low-nutrient grasses like *Schizachyrium scoparium* and *Andropogon gerardii*, which often dominate grasslands with low nutrient supply, had lower nitrogen concentrations than other grasses like *Agropyron repens* that dominate when nutrient supplies are higher (Craine et al. 2002; Tjoelker et al. 2005). The low nutrient concentrations of the C_4 grasses supported the idea that low nutrient concentrations were part of the low-nutrient strategy. In contrast, in another experiment (BioCON) at Cedar Creek, many of the same species were also grown in monoculture, but the soils of BioCON had greater nitrogen content (and greater nitrogen mineralization rates) and plants were measured after just three growing seasons rather than five (Craine and Reich 2001). After three years of growth in BioCON, species such as *Schizachyrium* and *Andropogon* did not have lower leaf nitrogen concentrations than *Agropyron* but instead had leaf nitrogen concentrations that were 50% higher.

Between E111 and BioCON, there were changes in the ranking of species not only in leaf nitrogen concentrations but also in leaf longevity. In BioCON, after three years, species such as *Andropogon* not only had higher leaf nutrient concentrations than *Agropyron*, they also had lower leaf longevity (Craine and Reich 2001) (figure 7.3). By the fifth year of growth in E111, not only were nutrient concentrations approximately 50% lower for the low-nutrient C_4 grasses, but leaf longevity had nearly doubled. As such, although it was true that plants that had low leaf nitrogen concentrations also had high leaf longevity, species that were domi-

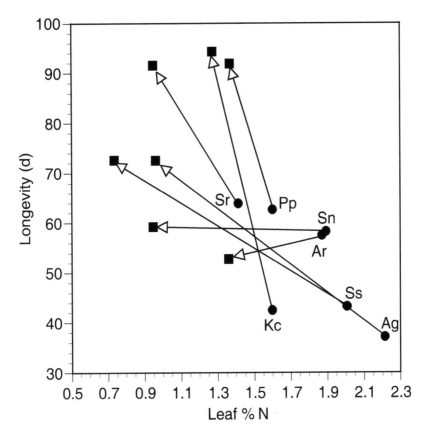

Figure 7.3. Relationship between leaf longevity and leaf nitrogen concentrations in two experiments. In one experiment, plants were measured after two years in soils with high nitrogen content (closed circles). In the other experiment, plants were measured after five years in soils with low nitrogen content (closed squares). Data from Craine et al. 2001.

nant in low-nutrient habitats could not be counted on consistently to have these traits.

Between the two experiments, not only was there variation in the absolute value of leaf nitrogen concentrations and leaf longevity, but the ranking of species had switched. In a meta-analysis of experiments these results might be considered outliers and ignored, or they might raise the question of whether the C4 grasses were good examples of the low-nutrient strategy. Yet, as other traits were examined under other conditions, it became clear that there was a logical explanation for the switch. Although it might be tempting to discard the results of the BioCON experiment as an anomaly, the change in ranking of the species is an important clue to the underlying mechanisms that generate patterns of traits associated with nutrient concentrations.

Traits such as tissue nutrient concentrations are influenced by the environmental consequences of other traits. Three lines of evidence reveal that complex interactions among physiological traits, growth rates, and nutrient supplies generate much of the patterns of expression that have led to a reevaluation of aspects of the low-nutrient strategy.

First, when young plants are compared at the same time after being under initially identical conditions, low-nutrient species can have higher tissue nutrient concentrations. As low-nutrient species have inherently low RGR_{max}, the inherently slow growth rate causes plants to experience higher nutrient availability initially. If supplies are the same but nutrient uptake is lower for the low RGR_{max} species, soil solution nutrient concentrations would be higher at the root surface or the supply of nutrients relative to demand would greater for a while than for fast-growing plants. As a result of the greater nutrient availability or lower growth rates (or both), nutrient concentrations are greater in tissues of slow-growing plants than in tissues of faster growing plants.

For example, as mentioned in chapter 2, when Chapin compared nutrient concentrations of grasses from New Zealand, he found that the slower growing species actually had higher nutrient concentrations (Chapin, Follett, and O'Connor 1982). When considered in isolation, these results led him to suggest that the storage of nutrients causes plants to have slow growth rates. Yet, because the plants grew more slowly, as a result of internal constraints on growth, nitrogen that was acquired was not used to produce biomass but accumulated in extant tissue. Hence, under equal supplies, nutrient concentrations are in part determined by the demand for nutrients, which can depend on the plant's growth rate.

Second, nutrient availability is in part a function of the effects of plants on nutrient supplies. Under some conditions, faster growing species can cause a greater reduction in nutrient supplies than slow-growing species. As a consequence of their initially greater demand for nutrients, faster growing plants can initially have lower nutrient concentrations than slow-growing species and also can return more biomass to the soil for microbes to decompose. Taken together, over short time scales (say, a few months to a few years), nutrient availability is lower in plots dominated by fast-growing species than in plots dominated by slow-growing species. The lower nutrient supplies can reinforce the initially lower nutrient concentrations in reducing the tissue nutrient concentrations of the faster growing species.

Third, although fast-growing species reduce nutrient supplies to a greater extent in the short term, low-nutrient species reduce nutrient supplies to a greater extent over longer time scales. This causes the low-nutrient species to eventually have lower nutrient concentrations. In the fifth year of E111, *Andropogon* and *Schizachyrium* had lower leaf

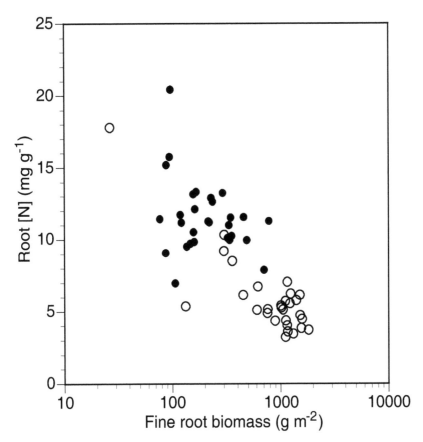

Figure 7.4. Root nitrogen concentrations versus fine root biomass for *Agropyron repens* (closed circles) and *Andropogon gerardii* (open circles) measured over three growing seasons. Data from Craine et al. 2003.

nitrogen concentrations than *Agropyron* (Craine et al. 2002). In addition, net nitrogen mineralization rates were lower in C_4 grass plots than in plots with *Agropyron*, likely reflecting sustained negative feedbacks to the nitrogen supply.

Although in E111, the changes in tissue nutrient concentrations and nitrogen supplies were not tracked over time, in a separate experiment the coincident decline of tissue nitrogen concentrations and nitrogen availability are well illustrated. Craine, Wedin, et al. (2003) grew a number of prairie species and measured root nitrogen concentrations over a three-year period. When plants were small, *Andropogon* and *Agropyron* had similar root nitrogen concentrations at low biomass (figure 7.4). Only after time, as *Andropogon* accumulated biomass, did the differences in nitrogen concentrations develop. The declines in tissue nutrient concentrations for *Andropogon* are less likely to be ontogenetic and a function of plant age per se as opposed to being consequences of sustained feedbacks to nitrogen availability. As plants increased in size, not only did root nitrogen concentrations decline, but so did NO_3^- concentrations in the soil solution (Craine, Wedin, et al. 2003) (figure 7.5). Although there are a couple of alternative explanations for declining soil solution nitrogen concentrations, declining nitrogen supply rates to plants over time could explain this and would be consistent with the lower nitrogen supplies seen in E111 for low-nutrient species.

The specifics of species effects on nutrient cycling depend on initial conditions as well as on the traits of the species, and do not to show the same trajectory over time in all experiments. The traits of the low-nutrient species that eventually allow them to attain a larger size or allow them to subsist with lower nutrient supplies more than other species are poorly understood. What it is clear is that strong interactions among physiological traits, growth rates, and nutrient supplies generate the differences among species in traits such as nutrient concentrations and tissue longevity (figure 7.6). This conceptual framework stands in stark contrast to the previous static approaches, in which low-nutrient species were considered to have inherently lower nutrient concentrations and therefore to reduce nutrient availability to a greater extent. For example, in a review of the effects plants have on nutrient cycling, Hobbie (1992) stated that "species from low-nutrient environments produce poor-quality litter that decomposes slowly, further reducing nutrient availability." Instead, for many important ecological contrasts it might be just as correct to state that species from low-nutrient environments reduce nutrient availability to a greater extent, which causes them to produce poor-quality litter.

An important remaining question is not whether low-nutrient species have inherently lower nutrient concentrations than other plants (they do not), but what other traits unique to low-nutrient species cause them to eventually have lower nutrient concentrations. At this point, from measuring plants over time in initially identical conditions, it is not necessarily tissue nutrient concentrations or organ longevity that differentiates low-nutrient species. Whether other traits such as tissue density or photosynthetic rates are also governed by species effects on nutrient availability remains to be shown conclusively, but it is quite likely.

Until the mechanisms underlying the expression of some traits are understood, care should be taken in assuming that all the traits that appear to be consistently part of the low-nutrient strategy have been selected for directly. Traits such as tissue nutrient concentration, tissue longevity, RGR, and nutrient supplies are closely intertwined, not only in experiments but also across sites. With the currently limited understanding of the contribution of plant traits to differences in nutrient supplies across

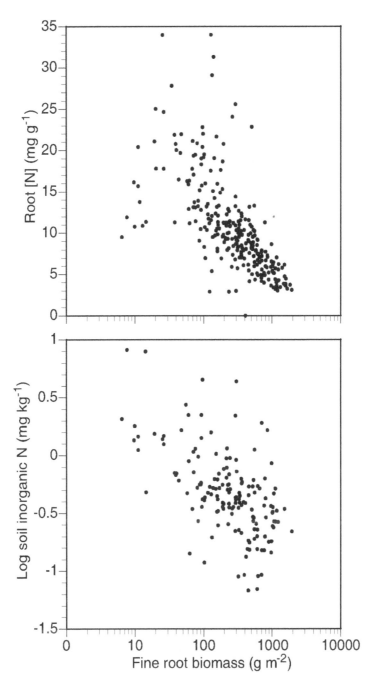

Figure 7.5. Root nitrogen concentrations and available inorganic nitrogen across 12 grassland species over three growing seasons as root systems developed over time. Data from Craine et al. 2003.

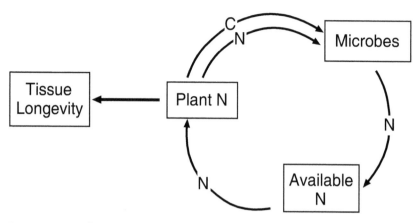

Figure 7.6. Feedbacks to the nitrogen cycle can determine plant nitrogen concentrations, which then influence tissue longevity.

sites, it can be difficult to separate low nutrient supplies in a given site from the species that occupy the site. If traits such as low nutrient concentrations and high leaf longevity arise by feedbacks to nutrient cycling, it is fair to question whether they are also necessarily advantageous, since they might be correlated with the low-nutrient strategy but might also simply be a consequence of other advantageous traits.

Although it is unlikely that feedbacks to nutrient cycling are what separate the leaf and root traits of a boreal evergreen tree from a high-fertility pasture grass, too few comparative experiments have done that have held nutrient availability among species constant over time and too little genetic testing has been done for us to understand the genetic basis of many of these traits. It is still possible that low-nutrient species do differ inherently in their nutrient concentrations, for example, once nutrient supplies and plant size have been standardized, or that low-nutrient species are able to maintain functionality at a lower tissue nutrient concentration.

Until the mechanisms that underlie differences in RGR and effects on nutrient cycling are better understood, traits such as low nutrient concentrations and high tissue longevity can be considered to be associated with the set of traits that is considered the low-nutrient strategy, but more research is required to identify which traits are central to the strategy. Even though low-nutrient species might not have lower nutrient concentrations, all other things equal, selection could have been acting on the low nutrient concentrations of low-nutrient species, even though the low nutrient concentrations result from other traits. In the meantime, it might be helpful to think of the low-nutrient strategy not as a strategy in which low nutrient concentrations are central but instead as a strategy for success in low-nutrient environments.

Longevity and Biomass Ratios

Across species, biomass ratios are determined as much by the relative longevity of tissues as by the relative allocation of resources among tissues. Yet on broad spatial scales, biomass ratios are ultimately constrained by disturbance regimes, and it is the evolutionary-scale frequency of disturbance that determines the potential longevity of roots and leaves. Moreover, disturbance regimes ultimately determine the relative importance of nutrient limitation, as the lack of aboveground disturbance favors plants with long-lived leaves that can cause plants to be more co-limited by light and decrease the relative importance of competition for nutrients.

On a global scale, grasses in nutrient-limited, fire-prone temperate systems can have a high RWR, which fits with the generalization that low-nutrient species have a high RWR. In contrast to most temperate grasslands, in native grasslands of New Zealand, the RWR of grasses is often less than 0.5 (equal biomass of roots and leaves), which is much lower than the ratio seen in other temperate ecosystems (Lee et al. 2000). These ecosystems have all the conditions that should lead to strong nutrient limitation in other parts of the world—low temperatures, high precipitation, low rates of herbivory, and few N_2-fixing plants—and productivity does respond strongly to nutrient addition.

What is unique about these grasslands relative to other temperate grasslands is that there is little evolutionary-scale history of aboveground biomass removal. New Zealand has no evolutionary history of grazers. Herbivorous mammals were not present until Europeans introduced them (Lee et al. 2000). More important, the wet, highly dissected landscape ensured that fire was rare (Bond, Dickinson, and Mark 2004; Craine, Lee, and Walker 2006). Although it is possible that the uniquely low RWR of the New Zealand grasses can be explained by the habitats having a more balanced ratio of nutrient and light supplies, it is more likely that the lack of aboveground biomass removal removes a constraint on leaf longevity that allows plant biomass to accumulate more aboveground than in other temperate grasslands. The leaves of the tussock grasses of New Zealand can have a remarkable longevity that is as long as three years in species such as *Chionochloa rigida* (Williams 1977).

The same tension between interpretations of RWR arises when some taxonomic constraints are relaxed and allow one life form to replaced by another. For example, on the Great Plains of North America, if fire is removed from the landscape, high RWR grasses can be replaced with trees (Briggs et al. 2005). These trees have a lower RWR than the grasses, even if stems are excluded from the calculation of RWR. Trees such as Eastern red cedar (*Juniperus virginiana*) have leaves that live multiple years, which allows leaf biomass to accumulate, generating a lower RWR at the same allocation rates to roots and leaves. Additionally, the greater leaf longevity increases leaf area development and likely increases the relative importance of competition for light (see the next two chapters). Whereas with leaves that live a short time, there is little overlap of leaves in the canopy, with greater leaf longevity leaves begin to shade one another and light competition increases in importance.

If it is evolutionary-scale frequencies of disturbance that ultimately shape the relative amounts of biomass of different plants, then to a degree it is true that RWR represents the relative constraints of above- and belowground disturbance, but it does not necessarily preclude RWR from representing the relative limitation of light and nutrients. The *Chionochloa* and *Juniperus* examples only go to show that relative limitation is as much a function of the species growing in an ecosystem as the characteristics of the ecosystem itself. Just as an N_2-fixing plant and a non-N_2-fixing plant are limited to different amounts by nitrogen availability, plants with different leaf longevities are limited to different degrees by nutrients. High-leaf-longevity plants still experience low nutrient supplies, but their high leaf longevity allows leaf biomass to accumulate and light limitation to become more important.

The costs of building leaves to live longer than the return interval for disturbance are poorly worked out. To begin to understand the constraints on longevity, the marginal benefits and costs to greater leaf longevity in an environment with aboveground disturbance should be quantified, as well as one without aboveground disturbance. A quick way to begin to understand the magnitude of the economics of disturbance and leaf longevity becomes clear when examining the consequences of defoliation for the New Zealand tussock grasses. Following a single defoliation event, a plant can take decades to recover the nutrients lost (Lee et al. 2000). In contrast, in other grasslands that regularly experience fire, there are few negative effects of biomass removal, especially if the biomass is removed during the unfavorable season during which plants are dormant, since less is invested in leaves and the nutrient losses are decreased by preemptive senescence.

Trees and the Low-Nutrient Strategy

The most difficult functional group of species to incorporate into plant strategy theory has been trees. Tilman hypothesized that in a world defined by competition for belowground resources and light, competition for light required high allocation of biomass to stems (Tilman 1988). By this definition, trees should be good competitors for light and characterized as occupying sites of low disturbance and high belowground resource supplies. According to Grime, trees were intermediate in strategy between a competitor and a stress tolerator, since they had characteristics of both (Grime 2001). For Grime, trees had low RGR_{max} and could have low leaf nutrient concentrations, warranting them the characteristics of a stress tolerator. Trees also are tall, and height was the central characteristic of a competitor.

Some trees clearly are good competitors for light when nutrient supplies are high soon after a disturbance, while others are good competitors for light when nutrient supplies are high, but long after disturbance. Others would have strategies that are intermediate between the two. A number of species of trees, however, would be considered to have a low-nutrient strategy, based on their leaf or root traits. Some of the longest lived leaves on record are from trees, and not necessarily short trees. The tallest tree ever measured was a *Eucalyptus regnans*, whose leaves often live two years (Ashton 1975), while *Eucalyptus globulus*, which makes up the tallest stand of hardwoods in North America (just outside the biology building at the University of California, Berkeley) reaches heights of more than 60 m and has leaves that live up to three years (Cannell 1989). The tree with the longest living needles (*Pinus longaeva*, bristlecone pine; 30+ years) (Ewers 1982), still can attain heights of 18 m. In contrast to Grime's approach, it is not appropriate to average the height and organ-level traits; instead, one should recognize there is something unique about these tall plants with long-lived leaves.

Although there are many similarities between shade-tolerant species and low-nutrient species, these tall species with long-lived leaves are clearly not shade tolerant. Shade-tolerant species also have leaves with low nutrient concentrations but they can be differentiated in their light compensation points. Many trees have low nutrient concentrations but are not shade tolerant, instead demanding high light. These are trees that are adapted to low nutrient supplies.

The logical conundrum with trees with long-lived leaves is that long-lived leaves are supposed to be associated with nutrient limitation. Nutrient limitation is not supposed to be associated with a high importance of light competition. Height is supposed to be an evolutionary response to light competition. In trees with long-lived leaves, there are indications that nutrient limitation and light competition are important at the same time. These two are not supposed to go together.

If some trees are to be considered low-nutrient species, it is important to learn how they grow tall and why they grow tall. Contrary to the preliminary assumptions made by Tilman regarding relative allocation rates, research he was associated with was instrumental in showing that trees do not necessarily grow tall as a consequence of allocating more biomass to stems than other species. Gleeson and Tilman (1994) grew 28 prairie and savanna species from seed and measured relative allocation rates. The trees of the three tree species they grew did not differ significantly from grasses or forbs in their allocation of biomass to stems, allocating approximately 20% of their biomass to stems. If anything, grasses tended to allocate more biomass to stem (33%) than trees did. These results do not appear to be erroneous. For example, in the Cedar Creek experiment in which species were grown for five years in low-nitrogen soils (Craine et al. 2002), two of the species measured were woody (*Quercus macrocarpa* and *Corylus americana*). For these species, relative allocation of biomass to stems was higher than most species, but as high as many forbs and the herbaceous legumes of the study with about 15% of the biomass production in stems. There is no evidence that trees grow tall as a consequence of allocating a greater fraction of their biomass to stems.

If trees do not allocate more biomass to stems, then how do low-nutrient trees get big, especially when grown in low-nutrient soils that provide little nutrients for growth? First, just as with the importance of root longevity and RWR, trees end up with larger stems because their stems are retained as functional biomass for longer, often as long as the life of the plant. The stems of herbaceous species die back each year, but the stems of trees remain to support the next year's stem production. Second, trees have the ability to grow not only tall but also wide. The same growth structure that allows them to maintain a broad leaf canopy allows them to produce and maintain a broad root system. As such, it is true that low-nutrient trees grow in soils that have low nutrient supplies, but these supplies are low per unit of ground area. Plants that can effectively acquire nutrients from a large area of ground can increase the nutrient supply they can potentially acquire.

The key unresolved questions regarding how trees can acquire enough nutrients to grow tall have to do with self-thinning. In stands where plant density is high, some plants die as individual plants increase in size, reducing the density of plants per unit of ground area via self-thinning. In low-nutrient ecosystems, self-thinning occurs early in stand development and results in widely spaced trees. Following this line of reasoning, it is not apparent why a plant would benefit from height if plants are widely spaced, even if their long leaf longevity allows plants to develop relatively high leaf area. Although, these low-nutrient species might not self-shade too much, a little bit of shading can reduce leaf longevity and cause plants to have to shed leaves and lose nutrients. And a short low-nutrient plant could still suffer from shading by a tall low-nutrient plant that had leaves that lived long enough to build a canopy with high leaf area.

With trees definitely exhibiting the low-nutrient strategy, the most likely factor determining whether short or tall low-nutrient species would dominate a site is the site's disturbance regime. As long as there is enough water and no aboveground disturbance, species in low-nutrient ecosystems should be selected to grow tall. Consistent aboveground disturbances shorten leaf longevity over evolutionary time scales and consequently reduce competition for light. In the absence of aboveground disturbance, leaf longevity can increase and plants can become co-limited for nutrient and light, which drives selection for trees to become tall. Hence, the idea of a species with the low-nutrient strategy not allocating to stem or having stems that die back ignores a hidden aboveground disturbance that has been constraining the advantages of long-lived stems.

New Zealand grasses such as *Chionochloa* sp. have high leaf longevity and greater leaf longevity can allow for lower RWR. Yet these *Chionochloa* grasslands also exemplify the advantages of low-nutrient trees. Many of these grasses are found in alpine areas, which by definition are above the elevation at which trees can grow. Although these environments are often considered too nutrient limited or too stressful for trees, the grasses would be replaced by trees if trees could grow there, because non-native trees can grow at elevations above native trees. Pines like *Pinus contorta*, whose needle longevity can be greater than 13 years (Schoettle 1990), have recently been invading New Zealand alpine grasslands, displacing grasses with high leaf longevity (ca. 3 years) and raising the treeline by hundreds of meters (Richardson, Williams, and Hobbs 1994; Craine, Lee, and Walker 2006). The elevation at which alpine grasslands start in New Zealand is actually below the elevation at which the pine can grow in other regions of the world, as New Zealand's history has left it depauperate of cold-tolerant trees (see chapter 11). As these pines invade, they shade out the long-lived grasses, which increases the importance of light competition in an environment that originally might have been considered too nutrient limited for light competition to develop.

In other grasslands of the world, trees are also increasing in abundance, displacing herbaceous species that were thought to be present largely because of low nutrient availability. For example, juniper species (*Juniperus* sp.) have needle longevity that can exceed 8 years (Reich et al. 1999), and the trees can invade grasslands with the removal of aboveground disturbance. For example, in the United Kingdom, the common juniper (*Juniperus communis*) has been invading both acidic and calcareous grasslands. Although its spread is potentially associated with elevated atmospheric CO_2, juniper is known to invade grasslands that experience reduced grazing intensity (Vedel 1961). Similarly, *Juniperus virginiana* has been increasing in abundance throughout the central grassland region of North America, often associated with a decline in herbivory or with fire.

Relative Growth Rates

The latest authoritative word on RGR and low-nutrient ecosystems can be found in the textbook, *Plant Physiological Ecology* (Lambers, Chapin, and Pons 1998). The authors write, "Having scrutinized the various hypotheses accounting for variation in growth potential, we conclude that a low potential growth rate per se does *not* confer ecological advantage" (p. 342). Although this statement is likely true, there is still intellectual tension over whether low-nutrient plants are first selected to grow slowly and the slow growth influences other traits or whether low-nutrient plants allocate resources away from primary growth, which then causes the plants to grow slowly. For example, Chapin had suggested different hypotheses regarding the nature of low RGR (see chapter 2), and among these hypotheses he suggested it was possible that low-nutrient species had higher abscisic acid (ABA) expression that slowed growth, independent of resource availability (Chapin 1991). Alternatively, he also put forward the hypothesis that low-nutrient species grow slowly because they allocate more resources to storage and away from immediate resource acquisition (Chapin 1991).

It is true that some low-nutrient species have high allocation to secondary functions. Living in a low-nutrient environment is associated with additional costs that have been cataloged above, such as redundant nutrient acquisition potential in root systems, as well as a high investment in structure and defensive chemicals. Allocating resources to these secondary costs diverts resources from immediate resource acquisition. Yet the presence of these additional costs is not evidence against selection for slow growth, or against the hypothesis that slow growth is controlled independently of preferential allocation of resources away from primary growth. In the end, analyzing the interspecific or intraspecific correlation of traits does not resolve the differences between these two hypotheses. For example, Coley (1986) found that seedlings of tropical trees that had higher levels of tannins in their leaves had slower growth rates (figure 2.3), yet this observation is not evidence of the direction of the mechanism. Plants with high tannin concentrations might grow slowly because resources are preferentially diverted to tannin production over primary growth. There might be other physiological controls over growth rate that are associated with greater tannin production but are not necessarily caused by it.

The only way to resolve this question is through experiments that genetically knock out secondary allocation, to see whether there is a full recovery of growth rates (see Roda and Baldwin 2003). If not, then it can be assumed that selection for constitutively slow growth rates is part of the strategy. The slow growth rates might not have any primary advantage, but if they directly influence other traits that provide advantages, then the low growth rates are advantageous, at least indirectly. Unfortunately, even though the list of traits associated with a low growth rate has increased, we are not necessarily closer to understanding the distal and ultimate causes for slow growth rate in low-nutrient species.

SIGNIFICANCE OF TRAITS IN STRATEGY

Progress in the Face of Uncertainty

Although lists of traits that are somewhat consistently associated with low nutrient supplies can be generated, there are questions about the mechanisms that generate the linkages among traits. For example, low-nutrient species generally have low tissue nutrient concentrations, but low tissue nutrient concentrations appear to be associated only indirectly with the low nutrient strategy. Low-nutrient species do not always have low tissue nutrient concentrations across environments, nor are tissue nutrient concentrations always lower than for other species. Moreover, tissue nutrient concentrations can be considered to be consequences of other traits that must be more directly associated with the strategy. Similarly, it is uncertain why low-nutrient species cannot grow fast. The low RGR of low-nutrient species are associated with greater secondary allocation whose additional costs should slow growth rates down, yet this does not preclude species from having been selected for a lower RGR, independent of allocating resources to these secondary functions.

Without resolution of these issues, it could seem tenuous to move forward in understanding the selective advantage of the traits associated with a low-nutrient strategy, without being certain of the traits in the strategy. These issues take time to resolve, however, and it is difficult to know whether traits that are best thought of as consequences of other traits would have been the reason why some plants in a given environment were successful. New techniques such as structural equation modeling have shown promise in testing alternative hypotheses about the potential nature of some linkages among traits (Shipley et al. 2006), but even these latest technique leave many unanswered questions.

In the meantime, it is important to proceed as if the traits cataloged above are primarily associated with the strategy, even though they appear to be so only indirectly. Low-nutrient species might not necessarily always have leaves with lower tissue nutrient concentrations and greater leaf longevity, but it is important to work through the consequences of assuming that they do. The skeptical scientist should consider the following explanations more hypotheses than facts, but recognize that little progress could be made on any issue if complete certainty was a prerequisite for progress.

This section first reviews (with very short summaries) how others have explained the correlation of traits associated with low-nutrient species. The theories of Grime, Tilman, and Chapin are recapitulated, along with the ideas of others. Again, there is no intention to tally up who was right or wrong about any particular issue or to determine who was "most" right about low-nutrient strategies in general. Instead, it is important to recognize the ideas of others in order to better understand the progression of thought on the issues.

Thereafter the two reasons for differential reproduction among species in low-nutrient environments and how the low-nutrient strategy advantages plants come up for discussion. The first reason why some species fail in low-nutrient habitats is that low-nutrient species are superior competitors for nutrients. The traits of low-nutrient species allow them to be successful competitors for nutrients. An important caveat of the generalization that is similar to the exceptions made for legumes on low-nitrogen soils is that some species *can* grow in some soils with a low nutrient supply where others cannot, but this is due to their ability to increase nutrient supplies, not to their ability to grow better at a given inflexible nutrient supply. The second major reason why some species fail in low-nutrient environments is that they suffer disproportionately more from herbivores. The traits of low-nutrient species allow them to succeed in the face of herbivory. Third, some plant traits reduce nutrient supplies in some situations, but it is uncertain whether reduction of nutrient supplies is advantageous to species.

How the Low-Nutrient Strategy Has Been Explained

As discussed in chapter 2, Grime reasoned that low-nutrient species are not better competitors for nitrogen as, in short-term competition experiments, low-nutrient species acquired a smaller fraction of the nutrient supply. Instead, Grime stated that low-nutrient species are better able to maintain biomass under low nutrient supply in the presence of herbivores, as herbivores are less likely to consume biomass that has low nutrient concentrations and high allocation to defense (Grime 2001). Grime also considered nutrients to be supplied in discrete pulses, and low-nutrient species are better able to maintain biomass between pulses in the face of environmental stresses. Therefore, when a pulse of nutrients occurs, low-nutrient species have the roots already in place to acquire them.

In his 1980 paper, Chapin's interpretation of the low-nutrient strategy followed Grime's theories closely. Chapin does not state that competition is important in low-nutrient ecosystems and, like Grime, focuses on the ability of low-nutrient species to maintain physiological function and growth in between pulses. Chapin states that the traits of the low-nutrient strategy "enable the plant to acquire and maintain nutrient reserves and in this way survive periods of exceptionally low availability in soil" (Chapin 1980).

Tilman reasoned that low-nutrient species are better competitors for nutrients. Plants that are better competitors for nutrients long term excel in reducing average soil solution nutrient concentrations. At one point, the ability to reduce average soil solution nutrient concentrations to low levels was held to be determined by a greater allocation of biomass belowground, but other mechanisms were also proposed to explain the greater ability of plants to lower soil solution nutrient concentrations.

Among others, Aerts put forward ideas that seem to be a hybrid of Grime, Chapin, and Tilman. Aerts compared low-nutrient evergreen and high-nutrient deciduous species (Aerts 1995), and reasoned that the advantage evergreens had over deciduous species in low-nutrient environments was their "low loss rates," which were characterized at the tissue level, not the whole-plant level. Aerts wrote that "[models] clearly show the advantages of low nutrient loss rates of evergreens in habitats where plant growth is nutrient-limited: low nutrient loss rates lead to a higher equilibrium biomass . . . and they lead to competitive replacement of species with higher nutrient loss rates" (Aerts 1995, p. 403). Aerts also emphasized the importance of declining nutrient supply rates in advantaging low-nutrient species (Aerts and Chapin 2000).

Others have begun focusing on the correlation of traits among species. For example, Reich, Westoby, Wright, and others have described what they call the leaf economic spectrum (e.g., Wright et al. 2004), which is the general correlation among species at different sites in traits such as leaf nutrient concentrations, SLA, longevity, respiration, and photosynthesis. Although an important part of understanding strategies is first to understand the nature of the relationships among traits, these authors have generally described the trait set of low-nutrient species, with little attention to the proximal and ultimate advantages provided by the traits. For example, they acknowledge that some trait sets do not (or cannot) occur, such as high photosynthetic rates and low leaf nitrogen concentrations, owing to physiological requirements for high protein levels for photosynthesis (Wright et al. 2004). Understanding why it is impossible for some trait groupings to occur is of considerable importance to understanding plant strategies yet sheds little light on why the set of leaf traits associated with low leaf nutrient concentrations would be advantageous in ecosystems with low nutrient supplies or why having alternative sets of traits causes plants to fail to grow and reproduce.

Stepping back from the potential explanations that have been offered, it is crucial to move from what amounts to correlations among traits to the reasons why trait sets have been selected. If framed as a dichotomy, it is important to answer the question of why low-nutrient species do not die in a low-nutrient environment before reproducing and why other species do. There are a few ways to answer this question with proximal explanations to which traits can be related, although the elevation of approaches is somewhat arbitrary. One approach to analyzing the growth of plants in low-nutrient environments is to recognize that plants die either because they cannot acquire sufficient resources to support growth in low-nutrient ecosystems or because they lose resources too quickly in such environments. With this initial dichotomy, it then becomes helpful to ask which forces are most restricting the uptake of nutrients and causing death—competition with other plant species, or the low nutrient supplies in the absence of competition—and to ask what factors cause some species to lose resources at an elevated rate—external stresses and disturbances, or their inherent characteristics. With the statement of these proximal explanations for the differential success of low-nutrient species, how the traits of low-nutrient species serve as mechanisms for these different hypothetical explanations for differential success must be analyzed.

Acquisition of Nutrients

As described in chapter 5, when the majority of nutrients are supplied slowly and steadily, a high root length density allows plants to compete strongly for nutrients. Many of the traits associated with the low-nutrient strategy are important for producing and maintaining high root length and therefore are associated with selection for an ability to compete well for nutrients.

For example, having roots that are long-lived allows root length to accumulate and be maintained at a greater level for a given level of allocation. There are costs to producing roots that are likely to live a long time, such as the extra resources needed to produce more cell wall material associated with greater tissue density as well as the maintenance costs during any unfavorable period. Yet these costs must be outweighed by the costs required to produce new roots.

Having low nutrient concentrations in the roots allows greater root length to be produced per unit of nutrient acquired, which would be advantageous when nutrients are limiting. As noted earlier, the low nutrient concentrations are a result not just of dilution with cell wall but also of reduced nutrient content per unit of root volume. From another perspective, there would be little benefit to the higher nutrient uptake capacity that comes with greater allocation of nitrogen per unit of length. In addition, the low amount of nitrogen per unit of root length comes in part as a consequence of high allocation to cell walls, which likely is necessary to increase root longevity in the face of environmental stresses or disturbance agents.

As discussed in chapter 5, plants competing for nutrients can become involved in runaway selection that favors plants that allocate a higher fraction of their resources to root production than would be optimal in the absence of competition (Craine 2006). Although from first principles it would seem that low-nutrient species should allocate more biomass belowground than other species, there is little evidence that they do. Measurements of relative production of leaves and roots might be incorrect, but measurements of both seedlings and mature plants reveal the same patterns.

It is difficult to reconcile the "race for fish" principle, according to which plants should allocate a high fraction of their biomass to root production when competing for nutrients (Craine 2006), with the "balanced nutrition" principle (Bloom, Chapin, and Mooney 1985), which holds that plants should allocate internal resources so that resources are equally limiting to growth. The theory and the empirical data could be rectified if the belowground production of low-nutrient species has been underestimated, since mycorrhizal fungi production is not typically measured. Most likely, low-nutrient species do not allocate a greater fraction of their biomass belowground but instead allocate their biomass to producing roots of greater longevity, which in the long run would result in overallocation. That way, although low-nutrient species do not allocate more biomass belowground than other plants, they do eventually allocate more biomass belowground than would be optimal if there were no competition.

Many low-nutrient species have roots that are thin, which allows them to produce more root length per unit of biomass than plants with thick roots. Thick roots generally have a greater ability to transport water and nutrients, but for plants with a high root length, much of the transport capacity would be redundant. Individual roots in a low-nutrient environment do not acquire nutrients and water at a high rate.

Within some contrasts, low-nutrient species are more dependent on mycorrhizal fungi than other species, but there are notable exceptions to this generalization. In some respects, the contribution of mycorrhizal fungi to the low-nutrient strategy is clear. When the diffusion of nutrients in soils is slow, plants that subcontract nutrient uptake to mycorrhizal fungi can produce a high amount of root-equivalent length, owing to the lower diameter of hyphae compared to roots. High allocation of resources to mycorrhizal fungi can also be thought of as an extension of the importance of competition for nutrients, as there would be similar selection pressure for high mycorrhizal length as for root length, as long as it was evenly distributed throughout the soil volume. As the diffusion rate of the limiting nutrient decreased, the advantages of the low diameter of mycorrhizal fungi would become even more important, and the greater reliance on mycorrhizal fungi of grasses growing in soils with lower phosphorus availability would likely explain the greater root diameter of these grasses.

It is also obviously beneficial in some environments to be able to increase nutrient supplies, which is facilitated by associations with some mycorrhizal fungi. When nitrogen is limiting and there are large pools of soil organic nitrogen, some mycorrhizal fungi can increase the supply of nitrogen to plants by producing proteases. As long as the nitrogen that is released is likely to be eventually acquired by the plant that is supplying the carbon to the mycorrhizal fungi (without increasing nitrogen supplies so much that the low-nutrient strategy is no longer beneficial), then the advantage of mycorrhizal fungi seems clear.

In the end, mycorrhizal fungi increase the acquisition of limiting nutrients by increasing their supply and their availability, and must be beneficial in some environments. Yet not all plants need to have this strategy to be successful in low-nutrient environments. Although the benefits of mycorrhizal fungi to plants in some low-nutrient ecosystems is clear a posteriori, cost-benefit analyses that allow us to quantify in which environments it is advantageous for a given plant to associate with mycorrhizal fungi have yet to be produced. For example, why are sedge species in the tundra successful without the benefit of mycorrhizal fungi? Is their success facilitated by the presence of other plant species that increase nitrogen supplies by associating with ericoid or ectomycorrhizal fungi? Or do these species occupy a nutritional niche that is independent of the presence of other plants? Likewise, under what conditions (and why) is it beneficial to rely on mycorrhizal fungi for uptake of phosphorus as opposed to increasing phosphorus supplies?

Roots of low-nutrient species cannot take up nutrients at a high specific rate, which, as Chapin (1980) noted, might simply be a consequence of having roots that live a long time, since uptake capacity declines with time. Yet, if it was possible to have a long-lived root with high maximum nutrient uptake rates, there would be little benefit for the high uptake rates in a low-nutrient environment. As described in chapter 4, soil solution nutrient concentrations at the root surface are relatively low, and in the absence of pulses are rarely high enough for uptake rates to approach V_{max}. In contrast to the lack of benefit, if roots did have high V_{max}, there would be greater nitrogen costs to support the greater rates of activity, as well as the carbon costs of respiration of the high nitrogen roots. A plant that produced roots with high V_{max} would not be able to produce as high a root length density and would be competitively inferior. Similarly, the

C_{min} of roots all seem to be very low, but if plants could reduce their C_{min} to an even lower concentration, there would be relatively little increase in uptake for further declines in C_{min}, as uptake is largely determined by supply and the zero net transfer boundary between roots is influenced little by further decreases in C_{min} (Smethurst and Comerford 1993; Craine, Fargione, and Sugita 2005).

In all, there is strong evidence that the root systems of low-nutrient species reflect the importance of competition for nutrients in many low-nutrient ecosystems. Low-nutrient species have root traits that allow them to produce a high root length or mycorrhizal length density (or both) at low nutrient supplies and to have low maximum rates of uptake that reflect the chronically low soil solution concentrations experienced at the root surface.

Stepping back from the focus on nutrients being supplied uniformly at a low rate, there is little evidence that the roots of low-nutrient species are selected to tolerate low-nutrient stress in the absence of competition, since the standing root length is generally much higher than is required for acquisition in the absence of competition. Likewise, there are few examples of plants obviously built to acquire pulsed nutrient supplies. The exceptions to this generalization are plants like those with dauciform roots, which are short-lived with high activity rates. Yet the pulses of nutrient availability are of the plant's own making, not external to the plant. As such, like the exceptions that are made for N_2-fixing plants in low-nitrogen ecosystems, it seems appropriate to think of these plants as exceptions to the generalization rather than as refuting the general characterization of low-nutrient species. In addition to the rarity of low-nutrient species relying on pulsed nutrient supplies, there is little evidence that most low-nutrient species are adapted to exploit relatively small patches of high nutrient availability.

There are few examples of low-nitrogen plants storing nutrients for further growth. In large part this is due to the relatively uniform supplies, which are coincident with good growing conditions. The lack of consistent times when nutrient availability is lower than other times but growth potential is high negates the need to store nutrients during the growing season. When water and light are in high supply, nutrients are also being supplied. In addition, plants that have aboveground biomass disturbed are likely to be more limited by carbon than by nutrients. With the large remaining root system, there is generally excess nitrogen acquisition capacity relative to demand. That said, exceptions exist, and it is possible that nitrogen could be stored in compounds that have other purposes (such as defense) and hence not considered to be stored (Warren and Adams 2004).

Leaves in the Low-Nutrient Strategy

The leaves of low-nutrient species have low nutrient concentrations and low activity rates, and are built to live a long time. There are two alternative hypotheses for why low-nutrient species have such long-lived, low-activity leaves. These hypotheses may not be mutually exclusive.

According to the *lifetime efficiency hypothesis*, in the absence of agents that cause premature death from disturbance (such as by herbivores), the leaves of low-nutrient species might be more efficient with nutrients over their lifetime. Low-nutrient species have low nitrogen concentrations, which allows lower carbon gain per unit of time, but their leaves live longer, which should provide a greater amount of time for carbon gain. If low-nutrient species have greater carbon gain per unit of nitrogen over the lifetime of nitrogen in the leaf, then from an economic perspective, the longer time for which a given unit of nitrogen can provide carbon should outweigh the greater costs of leaf structure, respiration during unfavorable periods, the greater susceptibility to leaching of nutrients, and the decline in photosynthetic capacity of leaves with leaf aging.

As simple as it seems to run lifetime carbon balance models of leaves, there is still no theoretical confirmation of the greater potential lifetime carbon gain of the leaves of low-nutrient species in low-nutrient environments. From the scaling relationships of maximum specific photosynthetic rates, leaf longevity, and nitrogen concentrations across species (Wright et al. 2004), total potential lifetime carbon gain per unit nitrogen in leaves should be marginally greater for low-nitrogen, high-longevity leaves than for high-nitrogen, low-longevity leaves. Low- and high-longevity leaves have the same potential lifetime carbon gain, but there is slightly greater photosynthetic nitrogen use efficiency for low-nitrogen leaves. From this, low-nitrogen leaves should have greater lifetime photosynthetic nitrogen use efficiency. Whether factors such as declining photosynthetic capacity with age, greater structural investment, or the costs of persisting through unfavorable periods compensate for the greater potential lifetime photosynthetic nitrogen use efficiency remains to be seen. In lieu of more sophisticated models, there is little evidence that lifetime carbon gain per unit of nitrogen is markedly different between long-lived and short-lived leaves.

According to the *defense cascade hypothesis*, the leaves of low-nutrient species might have been selected to have low activity rates and high longevity as a result of the potential importance of selective herbivory in low-nutrient ecosystems (see chapter 6). In the absence of herbivores, low-nutrient species might have lifetime carbon gains similar to or even lower than those of other species, but in the presence of herbivores, less well-defended species are preferentially eaten, reducing their realized carbon gain and nitrogen recovery. Among herbivores in low-nutrient environments, there is strong selective pressure to eat leaves with the highest nutrient availability, and herbivores are going to select plants, all other things equal, with the lowest amounts of defense and the highest nutrient concentrations. Consequently, there might be runaway selection to be the plant that is not the least defended, or not the one with the highest nutrient concentrations. The greater allocation to defense slows leaf production and leaf nutrient concentrations, which requires a greater leaf longevity to recoup initial carbon investments. Consequently, plants also allocate more to leaf structure, which further slows growth.

Transplant experiments such as Grime's early work (Grime 1963) support the importance of herbivores in selecting for well-defended leaves in low-nutrient environments, while more recent research supports legumes being excluded from low-nutrient environments by herbivores (Ritchie and Tilman 1995). Although indirectly supporting the importance of herbivores, these experiments do not isolate the consequences of a given set of leaf traits independent of other traits. With better functional response data on the relationship between leaf traits and herbivory, models like the ones needed to assess lifetime carbon balance for leaves can be amended to address questions of the importance of herbivory.

Regardless of whether allocation to defense is causing the greater leaf longevity, low-nutrient plants often are defended well, and they predominantly rely on constitutive, nitrogen-free chemicals. The greater allocation of resources to defense diverts resources away from primary growth, lowering RGR_{max}. As such, herbivores are the agents that are selecting plants to defend their leaves strongly in low-nutrient environments, and therefore cause the leaves to be long-lived. Why do low-nutrient species not use less carbon-intensive defenses? The reason for the predominance of these constitutive defenses is that inducible defenses still sacrifice some leaves, since it is damage that is needed to induce the defense. Likewise, structural defenses sacrifice leaves, too. Any loss of leaves is costly in terms of nutrients; hence, defenses should be there all the time and should defend the leaves themselves.

The economics of plant growth selects against plants that use nitrogen for defense if nitrogen is limiting. When nitrogen is in short supply, plants rarely use nitrogen in defensive compounds, part of a strategy to minimize nitrogen requirements. Another way to consider this pattern is that nitrogen is better used for growth than for defense. As mentioned in chapter 4, in economic terms, the relative value of nitrogen in terms of carbon is too high for nitrogen-limited plants, and it is less expensive in terms of resources to use nitrogen for defense. For example, Craine, Bond, et al. (2003) analyzed the economics of plant defenses assuming the carbon and nitrogen were co-limiting and could be assigned relative values. At low nitrogen supply, plants that used nitrogen for defense, even in small amounts, had a lower economic return than those that allocated carbon to defense and used the nitrogen for photosynthesis. Although the frequency of their occurrence might be underestimated, it is uncertain why nitrogen-based defenses are not more common in low-phosphorus environments. As mentioned in chapter 4, it is possible that plants in low-phosphorus environments also experience low nitrogen availability, or that nitrogen-containing chemical defenses are too easy to circumvent on evolutionary scales to rely on them at high frequency in any low-nutrient environment.

Disturbance

Aboveground disturbance often reinforces the importance of nutrient limitation in low-nutrient environments by limiting the ability of plants to accumulate leaf area. Belowground disturbance, as with the black spruce example in the previous chapter, further limits the ability of plants to acquire nutrients or increases the amount of resources that must be allocated to nutrient acquisition. In ecosystems where nutrient supply is increased by plant action, removal of plant biomass can actually decrease nutrient supply.

The availability of nutrients in a low-nutrient ecosystem can increase after a disturbance. Although the increase in nutrient availability is not without consequence, it is unlikely to be high for very long and likely to have little impact on the evolution of low-nutrient species. There is little evidence that species in low-nutrient ecosystems that (1) colonize after an intense disturbance, (2) persist while other plants are disturbed, or (3) remain through a general above- or belowground disturbance are built much differently from those that dominate long after a disturbance. Because nutrient supplies are low, plants are unlikely to be able to complete their life cycle before nutrient supply declines to the point where competition for nutrients becomes important. In some cases, disturbance in ecosystems with low nutrient availability can favor species besides those considered low-nutrient species. Under some situations, species adapted to high resource availability that can reproduce quickly could dominate for a short period.

The Adaptive Significance of Reducing Nitrogen Supplies

The dominant plants in ecosystems with low nutrient supply eventually have low nitrogen concentrations in their litter and induce nutrient immobilization by microbes. The role of reducing nutrient supplies in affecting the traits of plants and understanding of characteristics of low-nutrient species was discussed earlier. One major question that remains is whether reducing nitrogen supplies, independent of the changes in plant traits, can advantage some plants.

Aerts and Chapin (2000) reviewed this topic and concluded that indeed, if a low-nutrient plant reduces nutrient supplies, even though it is reducing the availability of nutrients for itself, it is advantaged. In support of this statement, they wrote, "Using a simulation model . . . Berendse [(1994)] demonstrated that the plant traits of evergreens . . . can be favourable under nutrient-limited growth conditions. Low litter decomposability and the resulting low rate of nutrient release from that litter, as observed in evergreen species, leads to longer dominance of the evergreen species."

In questioning this issue, the first point to address is whether an increase in nutrient immobilization alters competition for nutrients in favor of low-nutrient species. Berendse's model assumes that the fundamental differences among species are their nitrogen loss rates and competitive abilities for nitrogen. The differences in the performance of the species with nitrogen supply were relatively phenomenological in the model, with evergreen species (low-nitrogen species) losing proportionally less nitrogen than deciduous species, but deciduous species being better competitors for nitrogen. In Berendse's model, as nitrogen supply increases, high-nitrogen plants are favored because of their better competitive ability for nitrogen. Yet low-nitrogen plants are better competitors for nitrogen long term, and reducing the supply of nitrogen without changing the relative importance of competition for nitrogen should not alter the relative abundance of species.

In addition to questioning the mechanism by which a reduction in nitrogen supply would affect the relative abundance of two species, it is uncertain whether plants are actually able to reduce nutrient supplies long term via feedbacks to decomposition. At intermediate time scales, the production of high C:N litter induces immobilization and reduces net nitrogen mineralization in the soil. Over longer time scales, however, nitrogen that is immobilized would be more likely to accumulate in the soil and, although the average turnover rate of soil nitrogen might be low, the greater nitrogen content would lead to similar total net mineralization rates. For nitrogen mineralization rates to decline over long time scales, nitrogen has to be sequestered away from microbes. This is possible if ecosystems are underlain by permanently frozen or anoxic soils, or is lost through periodic disturbance such as intense fire. In ecosystems in which all the nitrogen in the soil profile is eventually available for microbial degradation, nitrogen that is immobilized in the medium term has to become available eventually, which limits the ability of plants to reduce nitrogen availability. As such, the ability of plants to limit nitrogen mineralization long term through litter feedbacks might be restricted to a subset of ecosystems.

With these two issues unsettled, then, starting from first principles, if a species develops a high tissue C:N and increases microbial immobilization, in the medium term net nitrogen mineralization would decline, as has been shown experimentally. Low-nutrient species could benefit from this situation, as the increased immobilization potential of the soil would likely reduce pulses of nutrient availability, which benefit plants with roots that have high potential uptake rates. The reduction in nutrient availability also could be of high importance for nutrient competition by limiting the ability of other species that are better competitors for light to produce leaf area. If there is no change in the temporal heterogeneity of nutrient supplies or in the relative importance of competition for nutrients, then reducing nutrient supplies would only differentially advantage low-nutrient species if they are better able to reproduce at lower nutrient availability than other species, that is, have lower minimum supply requirements, something about which little is currently known. However, the evolutionary advantage of this trait must be weighed against not having the trait. If by not reducing nutrient supplies, low-nutrient species were able to reproduce more (in total), then it would be disadvantageous to reduce nutrient supplies. For example, reducing supplies from low to very low might afford a greater relative advantage to low-nutrient species but ultimately lead to lower reproduction rates than if they did not reduce nutrient supplies. Because the issues surrounding the advantages of lowering nutrient supplies are difficult to work out from first principles, this is an area in which models of plant growth and nutrient cycling are helpful.

If there is a benefit to reducing supplies and if there is a mechanism that sequesters nitrogen (or causes its periodic, catastrophic loss), then the short-term benefit could extend long term. If there is no mechanism by which nitrogen is sequestered from microbial activity, then nitrogen should accumulate in the soil profile and, if anything, become mineralized at a similar rate but over a greater soil volume. For this to favor low-nitrogen species, a given nitrogen supply per unit of ground area that is diluted over a greater soil volume would have to favor low-nitrogen plants.

The prevalence and timing of the reduction in nitrogen mineralization need to be questioned in light of the facts that plants can increase nitrogen solubilization through nitrogen mining and also may have access to nitrogen that is part of gross mineralization but not net mineralization. Much of the confusion over the issue likely resides in our inability to measure nitrogen supplies in some ecosystems and in the lack of long-term experimental data in others. In the end, it is uncertain under what conditions and over what time scales plants reduce nutrient supplies, and whether this is actually an advantageous trait to have.

SYNTHESIS

Natural selection for success in environments where nutrients are in short supply has shaped plants to compete well for a uniform supply of nutrients while minimizing nutrient loss from herbivory. In the face of nutrient stress, conservation of nutrients is an important component of the low-nutrient strategy, but the purpose of conservation is to accumulate biomass in order to better compete for resources.

The roots of low-nutrient species are structured so that the plants are competitive for a slow, even supply of limiting nutrients. In the absence of belowground disturbance, their roots live a long time, have a high structural investment, and have low tissue nutrient concentrations, all of which increase long-term root length density at a given level of allocation of resources belowground. Low-nutrient species often form relationships with mycorrhizal fungi, but under some low-nutrient-supply regimes, mycorrhizal fungi do not benefit plants and nonmycorrhizal plants are predominant. The roots of low-nutrient species do not have high specific uptake rates. With soil solution nutrient concentrations typically low at the root surface in low-nutrient environments, there is little benefit and great cost to having high potential uptake rates. In ecosystems with low nitrogen availability, roots are thin, which increases root length density but has little impact on the ability of the root system to transport water and nutrients to the shoot. Also, if plants are to succeed in low-nitrogen environments, their roots should be defended with defensive chemicals that are nitrogen-free, as nitrogen is better used for primary rather than secondary functions. When phosphorus availability is low, roots are thicker, but this is because of greater reliance on mycorrhizal fungi, not because of a change in the fundamental importance of root length density and/or competition.

The leaves of low-nutrient species either are built to provide a greater return of carbon per unit of nitrogen over the lifetime of nitrogen in the plant or are structured to minimize herbivory, or both. Both hypotheses rely on a high value of nitrogen relative to carbon, and consequently, the leaves of low-nutrient species live a long time, have a high tissue density, have low nutrient concentrations, and have low specific rates of photosynthesis and respiration. During senescence, a greater fraction of the initial nitrogen is likely to be resorbed by low-nutrient species, but not markedly more than is resorbed by other species. If the leaves of low-nutrient species are defended beyond the additional investment in cell walls, these defenses are typically constitutive nitrogen-free chemicals. As with leaves, except when phosphorus is limiting, nitrogen has too high a relative value in these environments to be used for defense rather than growth, or nitrogen-based chemicals are too easy to circumvent by herbivores. There is conflicting evidence as to whether biomass N:P indicates the relative limitation of nitrogen and phosphorus.

Understanding the final form of plants in their ratios of leaf, stem, and root biomass relies on understanding the relationships between disturbance and the relative longevity of different tissues. When viewed on evolutionary time scales, the absence of belowground disturbance allows plants to generate a high RWR, which was often considered to be an adaptation to compete or acquire nutrients better. Yet the high RWR does not necessarily develop because more biomass is allocated belowground but because the relative longevity of roots is greater than that of leaves, causing biomass to accumulate belowground. The roots of plants that evolved in the presence of belowground disturbance, such as severely freezing soils, often have low longevity, which remains even after the belowground disturbance is removed. When nutrient supplies are low but aboveground disturbance is absent, a constraint on leaf longevity is removed, and natural selection selects for plants with greater leaf and stem longevity. As such, leaf and stem biomass can increase at a given allocation rate, evening out the relative amounts of biomass between roots and leaves and allowing for taller plants.

Differences in aboveground and belowground disturbance also determine the relative limitation of belowground resources and light at a given nutrient supply. When there is chronic aboveground disturbance, species are favored that do not accumulate stem biomass and that have shorter leaf longevity. As a consequence of chronic aboveground disturbance, the relative importance of nutrient limitation is high. In the absence of chronic aboveground disturbance, plants are favored that have long leaf life spans. As a consequence of long-lived leaves, even in ecosystems with a low nutrient supply, leaf area accumulates enough for light competition to be important. Consequently, low-nutrient environments that favor long-lived leaves also favor plants to get tall. Hence, trees with long-lived leaves are most common in environments without chronic aboveground disturbance, and in these environments the relative importance of competition for light can be high. Low-nutrient ecosystems can also have chronic belowground disturbance, which likely only increases the importance of nutrient limitation.

Low-nutrient species have low RGR_{max}, although there is little evidence that low RGR_{max} is directly advantageous. Low RGR_{max} has been linked to allocation of resources away from primary growth, although uncertainty remains regarding the proximal controls over RGR. One hypothesis to explain lower RGR_{max} is that for low-nutrient species, maximum growth rates are a direct consequence of a large fraction of resources being preferentially allocated to secondary functions, such as reinforcing cell walls or chemical defenses. Instead of producing new root length in unexplored soil volume or new leaves away from previous leaves, which keeps RGR high, the allocation of resources to secondary purposes constrains the ability of plants to incorporate newly acquired resources into resource acquisition capacity. For low-nutrient species, the genetic or ecophysiological cause of slow growth might be the direct consequence of preferential allocation of resources to secondary purposes, but whether the slow growth itself is constitutive remains an open question. Beyond RGR at high nutrient availability, it is currently unknown whether low-nutrient species have lower supply requirements to maintain a positive RGR or perhaps reproduce at lower nutrient supplies than other species.

As a consequence of their traits, low-nutrient species can decrease the supplies of nutrients in the short term. The ability to affect their environment makes separating genetic determinants of traits from environmental effects difficult, and the genetic basis of many traits, such as low tissue nutrient concentrations, is poorly understood. That aside, lowering nutrient supply likely is more of an advantage for minimizing pulses of nutrient availability than for decreasing the supplies of nutrients to neighboring plants. Without a mechanism for sequestering nitrogen away from microbes, such as permanently frozen soils, plants cannot decrease nitrogen availability long term. Although low-nutrient species are generally considered to lower nutrient supplies, many low-nutrient species spend considerable resources increasing nutrient supplies.

There are still multiple competing hypotheses that need to be separated regarding the low-nutrient strategy. It is clear, however, that the low-nutrient strategy has consequences for growing when nutrient supplies are higher. The next chapter focuses on the selection associated with growth soon after a disturbance when light, water, and nutrients are all highly available, which is the first stage of competition for light.

CHAPTER 8

The High-Resource Strategy

DISTURBANCE reduces the ability of plants to acquire resources in the short term, which generally increases resource availability. Both the type of disturbance and the predisturbance importance of nutrient and light limitation determine which resources increase in availability. When disturbance kills plants, both light and nutrients increase in availability. Aboveground disturbance that removes leaf area increases the amount of light that reaches the ground. Belowground disturbance reduces the ability of plants to acquire nutrients, which generally increases the availability of nutrients in the soil. Some disturbances actually increase the supplies of resources, such as when physical disturbance of the soil increases soil organic matter decomposition rates.

The effects of the disturbance on resource availability can also cross the soil boundary. Disturbance that exclusively removes aboveground biomass can reduce the flow of carbon to roots and decrease their ability to acquire nutrients. In rare situations, aboveground disturbance, because it removes a large pool of nutrients, can also cause nutrient stress in plants. This can lead to greater rates of nutrient uptake (Chapin and McNaughton 1989) and presumably *declines* in nutrient availability. Belowground disturbance can also translate to nutrient stress, which increases light availability. As root mortality decreases the ability of plants to acquire nutrients or increases the amount of resources allocated for nutrient acquisition, the ability of plants to produce leaf area can be reduced.

Although there is a factorial of disturbance types, severities, and environmental conditions to consider, the basic adaptations of vegetative growth to disturbance in low-nutrient and high-nutrient environments are clear. As discussed in the previous chapter, in low-nutrient ecosystems most types of disturbance continue to favor low-nutrient species. In contrast, most types of disturbance in high-nutrient ecosystems (or belowground disturbance that increases nutrient supplies in low-nutrient environments) create a set of resource availabilities distinct from those that have led to selection for low-nutrient plants. These disturbances produce environments with high nutrient availability and high light at the soil surface. When nutrient supply is high and aboveground biomass is disturbed, there should be little change in nutrient availability, since nutrient supplies remain high and were not strongly limiting to begin with. Although the nutrient availability is unlikely to change, light availability increases below any disturbed leaves. With intense disturbances, light levels at the soil surface are at full intensity.

For the relatively isolated plant, this high resource availability allows it to grow at its maximum growth rate (assuming that the resource levels are not so high as to be inhibiting to growth) and maintain exponential growth. When plants are growing exponentially, each new root increases total nutrient uptake proportional to its contribution to total root biomass, and each new leaf increases total light acquisition proportional to its fraction of total leaf biomass.

With high-resource plants having a high maximum rate of exponential growth, it could be hypothesized that disturbance selects for plants that can grow quickly but are poor competitors for resources (Tilman 1988). Yet in the evolutionary history of a given species, growth at RGR_{max} is unlikely to continue for long. For example, the seed of an annual plant might find itself alone in a large bare patch of ground, but it is unlikely that the next generation of annual plants will be quite so lonely. The original plant growing in the absence of competition has likely produced a large number of seeds, leading to crowded conditions for the next generation. Additionally, for plants to continue to grow exponentially at RGR_{max} each additional unit of leaf biomass has to lead to the acquisition of proportionally more light, such that resource acquisition increases exponentially. Roots might overlap without reducing nutrient availability when nutrient supplies are high. Yet exponential growth is generally quickly prevented by self-shading, even for the isolated individual. Once self-shading begins, it might be advantageous to decrease leaf production, as it would not lead to an increase in light capture. Many high-resource species continue to produce new leaves and continue to grow taller long after self-shading has begun.

The reason why plants continue to produce what in some circumstances would be considered redundant leaf area is that, over evolutionary time scales, growth in isolation is rare. Plants might grow to take advantage of times when they are growing without neighbors, but by and large they have been selected to grow in the presence of neighbors. When plants under high resource availability grow in close proximity to one another, their leaf canopies become near enough to reduce light to adjacent plants, and light competition has begun. High-resource species have been selected to compete for light.

It is competition for light that defines the postdisturbance environment of high-nutrient ecosystems. As described in chapter 5, in some ways, competition for light after a disturbance is analogous to competition for nutrients in low-nutrient ecosystems. When nutrients are limiting, plants compete to place their roots closer to the source of the nutrient supply. Nutrients are supplied throughout the soil, and the race to get closer to the source results in a struggle for root length dominance whereby roots are placed evenly throughout the soil. With competition for light, there is also a race to get closer to the source. In contrast to nutrients, light is generally supplied directionally, typically from above the plant. As such, the race for leaf area dominance requires racing to place leaf area above the leaves of potential competitors.

The specifics of the race for light in high-nutrient ecosystems depend on characteristics of the disturbance. With infrequent disturbance or a high-intensity disturbance that kills plants, new individuals are likely to have to establish from seed. In contrast, with frequent disturbance that is localized aboveground, plants regrow from belowground. Each disturbance regime resets competition for light, and though it remains a race, the conditions under which the race begins are different.

THE SCOPE OF THIS CHAPTER

The traits of plants of high-resource environments reflect the importance of the first stage of competition for light. Natural selection has had a strong effect on the way that high-resource plants acquire, allocate, and lose resources, much of which reflects the unique characteristics of the resource environment and the nature of competition for light under these conditions. This chapter first examines the traits of species that dominate after aboveground biomass (with or without belowground disturbance) is disturbed in ecosystems with high nutrient supply. As with low-nutrient species, natural selection for growth in high-resource environments has affected the construction and function of leaves, roots, and support material, how high-resource species defend themselves, their whole-plant characteristics, and their effects on nutrient cycling. As the traits of high-resource species are described, where appropriate, species that are adapted to high-resource environments where aboveground disturbance is frequent are differentiated from those adapted to high-resource environments where aboveground disturbance is infrequent or intense enough to kill the resident plants, such that plants start from seed.

After the traits of high-resource species are cataloged, how these traits contribute to the success of species under high resource availability is described. This section begins with a brief review of the history of hypotheses regarding natural selection in postdisturbance environments. Thereafter the specific contributions of each group of traits, such as the adaptations of aboveground plant parts, to succeeding in high-resource environments are enumerated. It is important to ask how the characteristics of disturbance specifically regulate the initial race for light. The chapter concludes by exploring why the race ends, opening the way for the second stage of competition for light.

PHYSIOLOGICAL TRAITS

The traits that comprise the high-resource strategy are geared to maintaining leaf area dominance in a race against adjacent neighbors for light while nutrient availability is high. Physiological traits include leaves and roots that live a short time, high initial and final investment of nitrogen in tissues relative to structural carbon, and high rates of photosynthesis/nutrient uptake and respiration. For high-resource species, leaves are deployed in a manner that maximizes light interception, and roots rely little on mycorrhizal fungi. For high-resource species, defensive chemicals tend to be inducible or to contain nitrogen, while structural defenses like thorns are also more common.

Leaves

LONGEVITY

The leaves of high-resource plants do not live a long time. The leaves of low-nutrient tree species may live more than a decade. In contrast, the leaves of high-resource trees such as *Cecropia* species last only 80 days (Kitajima et al. 2002). Among herbaceous species, the patterns are the same. When grown long term in monoculture in low-nitrogen soils, low-nutrient species have leaves that live longer than high-resource species. *Schizachyrium* has leaves that live 100 days, whereas *Lupinus perennis* has leaves that live only 30 days, and *Agropyron repens* has leaves that live only 55 days (Craine et al. 1999).

STRUCTURAL INVESTMENT

Leaves of high-resource species have low tissue density. As described in the previous chapter, in contrast to low-nutrient species, high-resource species may have a leaf tissue density only 20% that of low-nutrient species (Craine et al. 2001). Mirroring low-nutrient species, the low tissue density of high-resource species comes as a result of low total investment in cell walls (Turner 1994).

NUTRIENT CONCENTRATIONS

High-resource species have high nitrogen concentrations in their leaves. As with low-nutrient species, approximately half of the foliar nitrogen is associated with photosynthesis. Maximum photosynthetic rates occur at approximately 40 mg N g^{-1}, but leaves can have more than 60 mg N g^{-1}. Beyond 40 mg N g^{-1} N, the increase in leaf nitrogen concentrations tend to come as a result of accumulation of nitrogen that is associated with secondary rather than primary purposes. Often leaves that have high nitrogen concentrations have accumulated NO_3^- in the vacuole or nitrogen-containing secondary compounds (see below). As discussed in the previous chapter, there are generally positive correlations among all the major nutrients. As such, high-resource species also have high concentrations of phosphorus, potassium, calcium, and other nutrients.

NUTRIENT RATIOS

For upland species with high nutrient concentrations, mass-based N:P for plants with high nitrogen and high phosphorus concentrations is consistently about 10–12 (Wright et al. 2004; Han et al. 2005). Because high-resource plants should not be limited by nutrients, there would be no reason that N:P ratios would be skewed as a result of nutritional deficiency. As for low-nutrient species, there has been little investigation into the relative amounts of compounds that contain nitrogen and phosphorus to know whether plants that have an N:P of 10–12 have greater accumulation of secondary compounds or whether this is close to the optimal ratio of nitrogen and phosphorus for fast growth.

PHOTOSYNTHESIS AND RESPIRATION RATES

High-resource species have high maximum mass-based rates of photosynthesis and respiration. For example, some of the highest mass-based photosynthetic rates among wild plants belong to high-resource species such as the grassland dandelion (*Taraxacum officinale*), the alpine mountain sorrel (*Oxyria digyna*), the subtropical thorn apple (*Datura stramonium*), the desert fivespot (*Malvastrum rotundifolium*), and the temperate forest's cut-leaved toothwort (*Dentaria laciniata*), all of which can have maximum mass-based photosynthetic rates above 40 µmol g^{-1} s^{-1} (Wright et al. 2004). These rates are approximately 20 times greater than those of many low-nutrient species. When photosynthesizing, high-resource species have higher rates of stomatal conductance, which match the higher rates of photosynthesis. High-nutrient species can have stomatal conductance rates of over 1,000 mmol m^{-2} s^{-1}, more than 25 times that of low-nutrient species.

Respiration rates for these species are also high (ca. 3 µmol g^{-1} s^{-1}), but the increase in respiration rates (ca. 5- to 10-fold) are proportionally less than the increase in photosynthetic rates over low-nutrient species (Wright et al. 2004). As a consequence of their high dark respiration rates, high-resource species must have a high leaf-level light compensation point. For example, *Phragmites australis*, a high-resource grass, can have

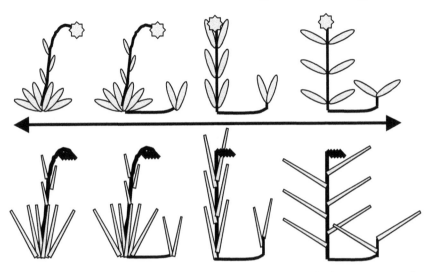

Figure 8.1. Growth forms of grassland plants from low to high nutrient supply (left to right). With increasing fertility, species are more likely to reproduce vegetatively, to hold their leaves more flatly, and to have leaves of equal size with increasing height on stems. Figure from Craine et al. 2001.

maximum photosynthesis and respiration rates of nearly 30 and 3 μmol CO_2 m^{-2} s^{-1}, respectively, and leaf-level light compensation points of nearly 60 μmol m^{-2} s^{-1} (Lessmann et al. 2001).

LIGHT INTERCEPTION

The leaves of high-nutrient species are generally held parallel to the ground (figure 8.1). For example, among Cedar Creek species growing in field, high-resource species such as the annual *Chenopodium album* and the perennial *Heliopsis helianthoides* held their leaves parallel to the ground, much flatter than the high leaf angles of low-nutrient species described in the previous chapter. Unlike low-nutrient species, the leaves of high-resource species do not diminish in size with height. Leaves of high-resource species also do not generally have structures that reflect away light, such as hairs or epidermal waxes.

NUTRIENT RESORPTION

The resorption efficiency of both nitrogen and phosphorus is lower for high-resource plants. As described for low-nutrient species, it is unknown whether the lower rates of resorption are constitutively low or are a consequence of growing in higher resource environments. As discussed in the previous chapter, patterns of resorption proficiency for high-resource species are currently poorly understood, in part because of experimental and statistical analysis limitations.

Roots

LONGEVITY

The fine roots of high-resource species do not live a long time. Whereas fine roots of low-nutrient species can live multiple years, the roots of fast-growing species often live just a few weeks. For example, in the long-term monocultures at Cedar Creek, the high-resource species *Lupinus perennis* and *Rudbeckia serotina* were estimated to have root longevities of only 30 and 45 days, respectively (Craine et al. 2002; Tjoelker et al. 2005).

STRUCTURAL INVESTMENT

Like their leaves, the roots of fast-growing plants have low structural investment. Whereas the roots of low-nutrient species might have a tissue density of 0.2 g cm^{-3}, the tissue density of high-resource species such as *Rudbeckia serotina* or *Baptisia leucantha* can be less than 0.1 g cm^{-3} (Craine et al. 2001). High-resource species have a greater ratio of the nutrient-acquiring cortex to stele and xylem elements with thinner walls (Wahl and Ryser 2000) (figure 8.2). The roots of fast-growing species are often thicker than those of low-nutrient species (Craine et al. 2001).

NUTRIENT CONCENTRATIONS

The roots of high-resource species have high nutrient concentrations. In contrast to low-nutrient species, high-resource species exhibit higher nutrient concentrations, in part by having greater nitrogen per unit volume, as well as through less dilution of nitrogen with cell wall material.

ACTIVITY RATES

With high protein concentrations, mass-based respiration rates of roots are also higher. For example, at Cedar Creek, low-nutrient species such as *Schizachyrium scoparium* could have root concentrations of approximately 5 mg N g^{-1} and a respiration rate of 0.5 μmol g^{-1} s^{-1}, while species associated with higher fertility conditions or disturbed areas, such as *Agropyron repens*, could have root nitrogen concentrations of 14 mg N g^{-1} and a respiration rate of 1.1 μmol CO_2 g^{-1} s^{-1} (Tjoelker et al. 2005). The roots of fast-growing species also have a high maximum specific rate of nutrient uptake, although the relationships between traits such as nitrogen concentrations and uptake parameters have not been quantified across species. Many high-resource species are nonmycorrhizal, and in general, high-resource species are less dependent on mycorrhizae, with almost no ectomycorrhizal or ericoid species considered high-resource species.

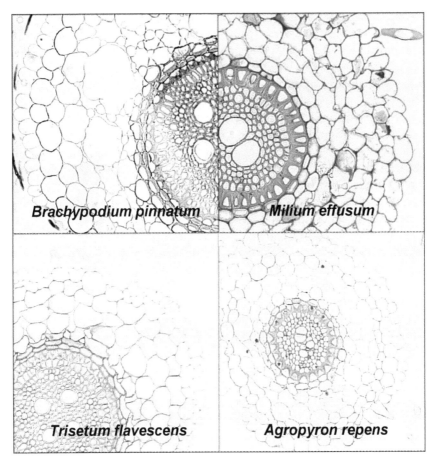

Figure 8.2. *Brachypodium pinnatum* is a slow-growing species from dry, nutrient-poor grasslands, *Milium effusum* is a low-light grass that grows in the understory of forests, *Trisetum flavescens* occurs on drier sites, and *Agropyron repens* is a high-resource grass that is often an arable weed. Photographs courtesy of Peter Ryser.

Defense

High-resource species frequently rely on inducible defenses rather than on constitutive defenses. For example, *Nicotiana attenuata* (Solanaceae), a wild relative of cultivated tobacco, inhabits post-fire, high-resource environments of the arid regions of western North America. Like cultivated tobacco, the wild relative produces nicotine, an alkaloid, in its leaves, as well as a host of other defenses. Mechanical damage by insects can increase a plant's content of nicotine by a factor of 10, resulting in up to 8% of a plant's nitrogen being contained in nicotine (e.g., Ohnmeiss and Baldwin 1994).

Van Zandt (2007) showed that inducible defenses were more common in high-resource herbaceous species and constitutive defenses were more common in low-resource species. For nine pairs of congeneric species, one was more common in low-nutrient, low-water sites (i.e., glade) and the other was more common in higher resource sites (i.e., prairie). A generalist caterpillar was used as a bioassay for defense levels. Caterpillars grew more poorly on undamaged glade species than on undamaged prairie species, an indication that the glade species had higher constitutive levels of defense. Yet, across a range of experimentally controlled damage, caterpillar growth declined more with increasing damage on the high-resource prairie species than on the low-resource glade species. From the functional response of the herbivore, the high-resource species were inducing more defensive chemicals than the low-resource species.

Fast-growing plants are more likely to contain nitrogen-containing chemical defenses than other species. Species such as the *Nicotiana* species discussed above have a high alkaloid content; others, like *Prunus* species, have high cyanogenic glycosides; wild *Brassica* species have glucosinolates; while others, like the tropical grass *Panicum maximum*, accumulate NO_3^- in their vacuoles.

High-resource species, primarily those that inhabit areas of high mammalian herbivore density, are likely to have structural defenses such as thorns. Trees with thorns, such as *Acacia* and *Cretaegus*, are more common in high-resource environments, often chronically disturbed by herbivores. Among herbaceous species, species such as *Cirsium* (thistle) also are common in high-resource areas that have been grazed heavily. The wire plants of New Zealand are also high-resource woody species with high defensive structural investment, occupying similar habitats as thorny plants in other regions of the world but in which herbivorous mammals have been rare or absent on evolutionary time scales.

Like leaves, the roots of high-resource species can also be defended by inducible, nitrogen-containing defenses. For example, *Nicotiana* species can allocate alkaloids to their roots on damage (Ohnmeiss and Baldwin 1994). Other nitrogen-containing defenses such as cyanogenic glycosides and glucosinolates can also be present in the roots of high-resource species.

Support

Like low-nutrient species, high-resource species can allocate significant resources to stem production. As discussed in the previous chapter, high-resource species do not necessarily allocate more to stem production than low-nutrient species do. Yet the stems that high-resource species do produce generally have less structural investment than the stems of other species. (Castro-Diez et al. 1998; Muller-Landau 2004; Falster and Wes-

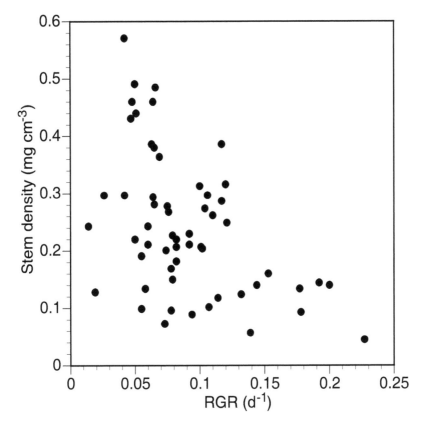

Figure 8.3. Relationship between relative growth rate (RGR) of 80 European woody and semiwoody species and stem tissue density. Plants were grown under controlled conditions and compared at similar ontogenetic phases. Plants with a high RGR also had wide xylem conduits. Data from Castro-Diez et al. 1998.

toby 2005; Wright et al. 2006). For example, among trees, high-resource *Cecropia* species may have a wood density less than 0.25 g cm⁻³ (Cordero 1999). This is less than one-third the wood density of other species, such as species in the genus *Quercus*, while other species have a wood density that exceeds 1.0 g cm⁻³. The lower wood density of high-resource species is also associated with higher conductance rates. For example, among a range of semiwoody species that varied little in maximum height, fast-growing species had greater xylem diameter, higher stem conductance rates, and lower tissue density (Castro-Diez et al. 1998) (figure 8.3).

Storage

For species that have undergone selection by frequent aboveground disturbance, large quantities of resources are often stored belowground.

When frequent soil disturbance kills plants regularly, there is no safe place to store resources, and perennation occurs with seeds. Hence, shifting from frequent aboveground disturbance to frequent soil disturbance shifts the storage of resources for postdisturbance growth from subterranean perennating organs to leaves. Although issues of reproduction are important in understanding the strategies of plants, questions regarding reproduction via vegetative organs and seeds are generally beyond the scope of this book.

High-resource species that have been selected to be successful in areas with frequent aboveground disturbance generally store resources for regrowth belowground. As Grime noted, many perennial fast-growing herbs maintain large belowground stores. Although plants can accumulate nutrients in response to increases in availability (Millard 1988, Kabeya and Sakai 2005, Monson et al. 2006), plants tend to store carbohydrates instead. The largest stores of carbon seem to occur when nutrient supplies are low and aboveground disturbance is relatively infrequent (Bellingham 2000).

WHOLE-PLANT TRAITS

Biomass Ratios

High-resource species have less of their biomass in roots than low-nutrient species do. As described in the previous chapter, the RWR of high-resource herbaceous species can be three times lower than that of low-nutrient species. Again, the lower RWR in part results from the more balanced longevities of leaves and roots.

Relative Growth Rate

The RGR_{max} of high-resource species is characteristically high. Comparing RGR_{max} among species requires standardizing for differences in size among species. With that, high-resource species have high RGR_{max}. For example, among the species of Sheffield, England, high-resource species had an RGR_{max} four times greater than that of low-resource species (Grime and Hunt 1975). Although RGR_{max} is high for high-resource species, natural selection has not selected for the greatest RGR_{max} possible. High-resource species still allocate significant resources to processes that utilize resources that could be allocated to further resource acquisition in the absence of competition. High-resource species likely allocate significantly more to stems and defense than they would if selected to grow in the absence of competition and herbivores. As described below, high-resource species also allocate to excessive resources to light acquisition, too. Consequently, most high-resource species have lower RGR_{max} than would be theoretically possible.

Effects on Nutrient Cycling

In contrast to plants decreasing nitrogen supplies through feedbacks from litter with low nutrient concentrations, high-resource species return litter with high-nutrient concentrations. It is sometimes suggested that plants can increase nitrogen supplies by returning litter to the soil that has a low C:N ratio. It is probably more correct to state that these species decrease nutrient supplies via immobilization less than other species rather than that they increase nitrogen supply.

For high-resource species to increase nutrient supplies, they would have to increase the rate of mineralization of nitrogen in extant organic matter. There is little evidence that high-resource species increase labile carbon fluxes to microbes more than other species do, and so this tactic would not be associated with greater nitrogen mining. High-resource species are also not generally associated with mycorrhizal fungi that increase nitrogen supply and are unlikely to increase nitrogen mining in this manner. Species that fix nitrogen at a high rate are included as high-resource species. As such, some high-resource species would be considered to increase nutrient availability.

Although the defensive chemicals of low-nutrient species can suppress nitrogen supplies, the effects of defensive chemicals that are more common with high-resource species on nutrient cycling are poorly understood. There is evidence that suggests that these chemicals might reduce microbial activity in the short term, but there have been no comprehensive studies of the consequences of chemicals such as alkaloids on decomposition.

Revising the High-Resource Strategy

Many of the same issues that featured prominently in revising the low-nutrient strategy are also pertinent for the high-resource strategy. As described in the previous chapter, interactions among physiological traits, growth rate, and nutrient supplies influence the expression of environmentally dependent traits such as tissue longevity and nutrient concentrations. Mirroring low-nutrient species, high-resource species can have low tissue nutrient concentrations and high leaf longevity as a consequence of short-term feedbacks to nutrient availability. For high-resource species, it is difficult to completely separate genetics and environment in understanding traits. Many of the traits that are considered part of the high-resource strategy are consequences of other traits that are less under the influence of environmental conditions.

The controls over RGR for high-resource species are better understood than for low-nutrient species, but the same issues that were raised for low-nutrient species are also relevant for high-resource species. High-resource species generally have high RGR_{max}, but there is variation in RGR_{max} for these species, and they still allocate resources to secondary purposes such as defense. Questions still remain as to whether high-resource species slow their growth rate through means other than competitive allocation of resources between primary and secondary growth (Roda and Baldwin 2003). For example, some plants when attacked release chemicals that directly slow growth in conjunction with upregulating allocation to inducible defenses.

Understanding the biomass ratios of high-resource species follows the same logic as was laid out for low-nutrient species. For high-resource species, variations in biomass ratios are not determined by differences in allocation rates to leaves, roots, and stems as much as by the relative longevity of the different organs. There is less variation in the longevity of leaves and roots in high-resource species than in low-nutrient species, which likely provides less variation in the ratios of fine roots to leaves.

Two issues remain outstanding in revising which traits constitute the high-resource strategy, as opposed to the significance of the traits. First, just as it was difficult to incorporate low-nutrient trees into the low-nutrient strategy, how to think of fast-growing trees in light of the high-resource strategy is an open question. In part, we lack an explicit understanding of how the frequency of disturbance has selected for differences among high-resource species. Second, it has been hypothesized that high-resource species rely more on their high RGR to cope with herbivory than on defenses. As such, they have been characterized as being less well defended than other species that have been selected to grow under low resource levels. As such, it is important to review whether high-resource species can be thought of as poorly defended or whether they are just defended differently than low-nutrient species.

Trees and the High-Resource Strategy

If the high-resource strategy involves maximizing the ability to attain leaf area dominance soon after a disturbance, can trees be considered to have this strategy? Certainly among trees, some species have traits that are congruent with the high-resource strategy. Species like the early-successional *Prunus pennsylvanica* of the northern temperate forests or

Cecropia insignis of tropical forests have high-activity, low-longevity leaves, just as other high-resource species do, but in having perennial stems and in growing more they 10 m in height, they also grow tall enough to be considered trees.

Although high-resource trees are likely to have lower RGRs than high-resource nonwoody plants, they still have many of the traits that should allow them to be considered high-resource species. Many of these species are clearly associated with postdisturbance environments but do not necessarily begin their lives beneath the canopies of others. Although it seems that the lower growth rates associated with greater allocation to stem production should disadvantage them relative to herbaceous species in the race for light, there are multiple reasons why these species might not have to compete against herbaceous species for the initial race. For example, having relatively large seeds that lie dormant in the soil allows some of these early-successional high-resource trees to preempt competition with herbaceous species with smaller seeds that must arrive from adjacent areas after a disturbance (Marks and Mohler 1985; Dalling and Hubbell 2002). Also, resprouting from storage organs belowground allows plants to attain leaf area dominance quickly after an aboveground disturbance. These high-resource trees also have greater canopy breadth than herbaceous species. Even if they initially are only a small percentage of the total number of seedlings after a stand-resetting disturbance, their larger canopies ensure they will grow over shorter herbaceous species relatively quickly.

Defenses

The most important question regarding defenses of plants using the high-resource strategy is whether high-resource species are well defended or not (Coley 1987). On the one hand, many high-resource plants can be consumed at high rates, which suggests that high-resource species might be poorly defended. Grime largely supported this hypothesis. His early work suggested that high-resource species were highly palatable. From first principles, he stated that "low expenditure of captured resources on anti-herbivore defences in productive vegetation is predictable from an evolutionary perspective. Species or genotypes which divert a high proportion of their resources into physical or chemical defence are likely to become vulnerable to competitive exclusion by neighbours that continue to allocate to new leaves and roots" (Grime 2001, p. 30). At the same time he recognized that many productive stands of vegetation are not eaten at a high rate. Grime suggested that the lack of herbivory might not be due to being well defended, as tritrophic interactions can limit herbivore numbers.

In contrast to the idea that high-resource species are poorly defended, some of the most toxic plants in the world are high-resource species. For example, *Datura stramonium* (Solanaceae), *Ricinus communis* (Euphorbiaceae), and *Conium maculata* (Apiaceae) are three of the most toxic species in the world and would all have to be considered well defended. They are also all high-resource species; for example, *Datura* is often found naturally on rhinoceros middens in South African savannas. Very few herbivores can consume even a small amount of their biomass without severe side effects or death.

Before attempting to answer whether high-resource species should be considered well defended in general or not, it is important to identify how the evaluation of defense is made. Different approaches to evaluating how well plants are defended can lead to different conclusions. Each approach has its particular limitations, which should be made explicit.

First, the amount of defense associated with a given unit of biomass can be compared among species. For example, a plant that has leaves with 100 mg g^{-1} of tannin would be considered to be better defended than one with just 5 mg g^{-1} of tannin. Although this seems straightforward, it is likely biased toward constitutive nitrogen-free defenses. Plants that have structural defenses can still allocate a high amount to defense, but it would not be included in leaf assays. Inducible defenses take time to develop. Nitrogen-containing defenses are often in lower amounts in leaves but contain nitrogen that is often expensive and would lead to a similar value of resources, although less in amount.

A second approach is to quantify the costs in growth for a particular level of defense. If plants with a defense allocation could be compared with plants in which such allocation has been "knocked out" genetically (Roda and Baldwin 2003), it would be possible to account for differences in values of different resources associated with the defense. A tannin-rich plant and a plant with alkaloids might have different amounts of defense but suffer the same reduction in growth as a consequence of allocating resources to defense. Even if specific defenses could be knocked out, however, this approach assumes there is no independent control on RGR. For example, if RGR is slowed by hormones that are independent physiologically from allocation to defense, there could be little increase in growth of plants that allocate a lot of resources to defense, even though the plants are well defended.

A third approach is to use bioassays to empirically assess the impact that defenses have on herbivores. For example, two plants that differ in their production of tannins and alkaloids might have similar effects on herbivores. Hence, both would be well defended. The difficulty with this approach lies in deciding which herbivore to use for the bioassay. Some herbivores have specialized abilities to consume plants with specific defenses. For example, to gypsy moths with a high gut pH that disassociates tannins and proteins, a tannin-rich leaf would seem to be poorly defended. A possible solution would be to use a number of herbivores and then look at average consumption, but again, the results would be biased by the choice of herbivores. How the plants are presented might also influence selection, and comparisons across regions with different herbivore guilds could be misleading.

In all, it is difficult to evaluate how well defended plant species are that use different types of defenses and grow in different environments. High-resource plants might have a smaller amount of resources allocated to defense but use a qualitative defense that provides just as much protection. In addition, rates of herbivory in the field might suggest that a plant is poorly defended, yet the plant might allocate a large number of resources to a defense but be attacked by a specialist herbivore, which would lead to a higher herbivory rate. As well, a plant might be eaten at a low rate in the field only because of its low protein concentrations, not because of any defense. If herbivores are supplemented with nitrogen via urea or by eating other plants with high nitrogen concentrations, the plants with low nitrogen concentrations can be consumed sustainably at a high rate. The reason why Grime observed that high-resource species were more palatable than low-nutrient species might have been that the defenses of high-resource species are often inducible. The bioassay approach that Grime used likely prevented defenses from being induced, since leaves are typically removed from a plant and then fed to herbivores under controlled conditions. Along these lines, the observation of numerous holes in the leaves of high-resource vegetation, which Grime noted, is also characteristic of inducible defenses, in which insects eat leaves until defenses are induced. It is not necessarily an indication of reliance on the third trophic level for protection.

With that, high-resource plants are not necessarily less well defended than low-nutrient plants. The basis for comparison is difficult to establish. It is sufficient to recognize all the ways that high-resource plants are defended and to understand that many high-resource plants are defended well enough that most generalist herbivores would not want to consume them.

SIGNIFICANCE OF TRAITS IN STRATEGY

It has long been recognized that disturbed, high-nutrient environments have unique plants. Early ecological theories assumed that the absence of some plants in high-resource habitats was largely due to the stress of high-nutrient availability. For example, Warming characterized the plants of disturbed, high-nutrient environments as "nitrophilous"; he also used the terms "nitrophytes" and "ruderals." Warming stated, "These thrive best in soil where compounds of ammonium and nitric acid are abundant . . . [T]hey belong to certain special families (Chenopodiaceae, Cruciferae, Solanaceae, and others), and nitrates occur in their cell sap. Other species develop feebly on such soil, because they take into their tissues more nitrate than they can endure" (Warming 1909, p. 68). For Warming, the high nitrate availability of disturbed, fertile ground was little different from the zinc of calamine soils or magnesium of serpentine soils. High nitrate availability stressed plants and led to the dominance of plants that could endure the nitrate levels that were toxic to other plants.

More recently, Grime presented a view similar to Warming's, holding that low-nutrient plants could be excluded from high-nutrient environments as a consequence of the detrimentally high availability of soil nutrients. He stated, "In a number of experiments . . . in which plants associated with nutrient-deficient habitats were supplied with high rates of mineral nutrients, elements appear to have been accumulated in quantities which were detrimental to the growth of plants" (Grime 2001, p. 59). Tilman's theories generally addressed nonselective disturbances that damaged all plants equally. He reasoned that disturbance reduced the intensity of competition and lessened the need to allocate resources to organs associated with competition for nutrients (roots) or light (stems). Hence, plants that dominated in disturbed areas grew quickly as a result of their higher allocation to leaves.

In this section the ecological significance of traits associated with high-resource species is addressed, along with the question of why they would have been consistently selected for among species that tend to dominate high-resource environments. The traits of high-resource annuals and perennials are quite similar with regard to vegetative growth (Grime 2001). For example, besides having similar organ-level traits and high RGR_{max}, many perennial species can reproduce in their first year of growth, just as annual species do. As such, annual and perennial species are considered together in what follows, the two distinguished only with regard to storage.

Shoots in the Race for Light

After a stand-resetting disturbance occurs on high-nutrient soils, light availability is high at the soil surface. Initially there might be little overlap of leaves among individuals. With high resource availability, there is little of the stress of low resource availability, and plants can grow quickly.

In most instances, however, the density of propagules or plants that can regrow from belowground parts should be high enough that the lack of resource stress is not likely to last long. Leaf area develops quickly, and the high RGR_{max} of these species becomes channeled into producing new leaves above old leaves, as the plants are now locked into a race for leaf area dominance. These high leaf and stem production rates requires high resource uptake rates to continue to produce new leaves above old leaves and to produce the support material to project the leaves higher. High photosynthetic rates allow carbon to be fixed at a high rate, and the low tissue density allows new leaf area to be produced at lower resource cost. With high nutrient availability, there is little cost to having high nutrient concentrations.

In concert with the high photosynthesis rate of leaves and their high production rates, the stems of high-resource species are often produced with a minimum of structural investment. Plants need high transport capacity from their stems to deliver water to high-activity leaves and just enough structural support to keep their canopies from falling over (see chapter 10). With the race for light at its greatest intensity, there is a premium on projecting leaves at height. Canopies must ascend quickly. Investing in stem structure that might resist physical stresses better also slows the height increment of plants. Plants that invest heavily in stem structure quickly find themselves beneath plants that invest less in stem tissue density.

The leaves of high-resource species tend not to live long, primarily as a consequence of high leaf production rates. High-resource species produce leaf area at a high rate, which causes leaves that were once in full sunlight to soon be in shade. Since they have high respiration rates, their leaf-level light compensation points (LCPs) are high, further hastening the speed at which they enter negative carbon balance. These leaves also have low tissue density, which might make them more susceptible to physical damage, but even if there is little cost to increasing structural investment in the leaves, there is little advantage to building them to live beyond the length of time at which they become shaded by new leaves.

If plants can grow for so little time at their RGR_{max}, why is RGR_{max} important? RGR_{max} allows plants to acquire resources at high rates when availability is high, and thus to have high potential reproductive output. A high RGR_{max} is also an index of plants' ability to compete well during the race for light. Plants with the highest RGR_{max} also tend to be the ones that can produce canopies that ascend the fastest.

Roots When Nutrient Supplies Are High

The roots of high-resource species should economically take up water and nutrients as fast as possible. When faced with producing a high-biomass, low-specific-uptake-rate root system or one that has less biomass and higher specific rates of nutrient acquisition, it is less expensive to build fewer roots with a high maximum rate of uptake. Because competition for nutrients is minimal when nutrient availability is high, there is little need for high root length density.

But why do high-resource species not have roots that live a long time? First, a long lifetime requires a high structural investment, which necessarily slows down the initial rate of root production. Hence a plant that invested heavily in root structure might be less able to acquire sufficient nutrients to produce leaves at as high a rate initially, as the lower root production rates might constrain initial nutrient uptake potential. Second, nutrient uptake capacity necessarily declines with root age. For plants to have high nutrient uptake rates, individual roots need to be young. Although the economics need to be worked out better, there is likely less benefit from investing in maintaining roots that have a low uptake rate for a long time than from producing new ones with a high uptake rate.

Although nutrient uptake by high-resource plants can lower nutrient availability, the typical high-resource plant has been selected to grow in environments where nutrient availability is sufficient to meet nutrient demand. Although short-term studies have shown reductions in nutrient availability as a consequence of uptake, there are many processes that replenish nutrient availability. For example, high-resource plants acquire a large amount of nutrients from the soil, but they also return a large amount of nutrients. High-resource plants generally return high-quality plant biomass to the soil, from which nutrients are released fairly quickly.

Defenses

There are three general theories concerning allocation to defense in fast-growing plants. The first is grounded on the fact that leaves and roots of fast-growing plants do not live a long time. As such, the theory holds, defenses that have a long payback time are less likely to be used. Instead, there is greater advantage for fast-growing plants to use defenses that can be induced when herbivores are present or that can be remobilized. The second theory is related to nitrogen availability. When nitrogen availability is high, the relative value of nitrogen is lower (Craine, Bond, et al. 2003). Hence, the theory proposes, when nitrogen availability is high, there is less cost to using nitrogen for secondary purposes, and nitrogen-containing defenses are relatively cheap. The third theory is mounted on trade-offs in growing in soils with high nutrient availability. When nutrient availability is high, plants are selected to grow quickly. Under conditions of high resource availability and pressure to grow quickly, the theory holds, there might be little plants can do to stop herbivory. In such situations there is little evolutionary recourse to sustaining high herbivory rates but to protect meristems so that the plant can regrow quickly after herbivory.

Along these lines, it has been hypothesized that there are trade-offs among species to either grow or defend. Within restricted sets of comparisons, such as comparisons among genotypes of a species or among closely related species, allocation to different defenses is often positively correlated (Agrawal and Fishbein 2006), and defense and RGR are negatively correlated. Moreover, there are often clear costs to the production of defenses (Gomez and Zamora 2002), such that allocation to defense reduces growth among individuals of the same species. These data support growth-defense trade-offs.

In broader comparisons, there are clearly trade-offs among defensive types, and it is evident that fast-growing plants can be well defended—perhaps not with the constitutive chemicals found in low-nutrient plants, but in other ways. The idea that the primary adaptation of high-resource plants is to outgrow their herbivores or rely on the third trophic level is misleading. Instead, it is more likely that high-resource plants have defenses that are compatible with high potential growth rates, such as inducible defenses that slow growth when herbivores are present, but allow high growth rates when they are not. Likewise, constitutive nitrogen-based defensive chemicals can be effective defenses but have little impact on growth when nitrogen is not limiting.

Whole-Plant Patterns

High-resource plants have a high RGR_{max}. There are two major hypotheses with which to interpret the high RGR_{max} of high-resource plants. On the one hand, the *growth maximization hypothesis* states that high-resource species can be thought of as maximizing their production and later reproduction when grown in high-resource environments. According to this hypothesis, high-resource plants have not been selected to compete well but to acquire resources as fast as possible before competition. Alternatively, the *light-race hypothesis* states that high-resource species can be thought of as having been selected to compete strongly for light soon after a general aboveground disturbance.

It is certainly true that high-resource species acquire resources at a high rate and have an RGR_{max} higher than that of most other types of species, which allows them to reproduce quickly and often prolifically. Although this evidence would support the growth maximization hypothesis, alternative evidence supports the light-race hypothesis. As described earlier, many high-resource species build their leaf canopies in ways that are best explained by competition for light and cause deviations from maximizing growth. Excess leaf area and flatly held leaves are good examples of why high-resource species should be considered good competitors for light and why the high RGR might have primary importance for the first stage of light competition.

Disturbance, Storage, and Regrowth

In understanding the allocation strategies of plants of high-resource environments, it is important to be explicit about the characteristics of the disturbance. The parameters include where biomass is removed (aboveground, belowground, or both), the severity of the disturbance (how much biomass is removed), the frequency of the disturbance, and its selectivity. Each aspect of the disturbance modifies the high-resource strategy in unique ways.

The location and the severity of the disturbance select for where a plant resprouts. When only aboveground biomass is removed, the severity of the disturbance influences the height from which biomass regrows. When the disturbance kills both aboveground and belowground biomass, increasing severity shifts allocation to seed production. When perennating organs are also killed, there is no option for regrowth but to regenerate from seed. Under these circumstances, seeds that are present in the seed bank or that arrive from adjacent areas create the next generation.

The frequency of the disturbance determines the height at which the race for light can progress. As the frequency of the aboveground disturbance increases, there is less benefit to having the potential to reach tall heights. As such, there is less and less allocation of resources to strengthening stems so that they can support and deliver resources to a tall canopy. With frequent aboveground disturbance, the race for light becomes a series of short races rather than fewer long races. In addition to setting the maximum potential height of plants, the more frequent aboveground disturbance of a given severity is, the more likely plants are to store resources for regrowth. If disturbance is too frequent, neither allocation to seed nor allocation to storage is enough to compensate for the high biomass removal rates.

In regard to storing resources for regrowth, there is little evidence that plants store nutrients for growth following a disturbance. High-resource species are more likely to store carbohydrates for regrowth. The pattern of storing carbohydrates and not nutrients is more obvious than the reasons why this pattern occurs. It is clear that both nutrients and energy are stored during seasons unfavorable for regrowth in the following growing season. What is unclear is the role stores that are not associated with seasonality play in regrowth following a disturbance. Regrowing plants need nutrients, but the remaining root system must have enough nutrient acquisition capacity to meet this demand. With severe defoliation in trees, there is often a lag between the defoliation event and production of new leaves, a lag that might be associated with acquiring nutrients from the soil. If this lag is associated with minimizing future herbivory, there might be no advantage to storing nutrients. It is also uncertain why many plants seem to have such large carbohydrate reserves. Leaves become self-sufficient for carbon relatively quickly and would depend little on carbohydrate reserves. It is possible that the large carbohydrate reserves are insurance against multiple disturbances, to maintain taller root systems until the carbon supply returns, or to hasten stem elongation rates. If disturbances are ground-based (large herbivores or fire) or of there is likely to be competition for light during the regrowth period, then having a tall canopy is just as important as having a large canopy.

One aspect of the disturbance regime that has rarely been discussed with regard to storage is the selectivity of the disturbance. When disturbance is selective, there may be less benefit to using stored resources to resprout. When tall trees are selectively knocked over, new shoots likely find themselves under plants that were once growing under the main canopy. In such cases there would be little benefit to resprouting. Alternatively, when disturbance affects all plants equally (or reduces their aboveground biomass to the same state), having large stores of carbohydrates to speed regrowth helps plants get out in front in the next race for light.

Why the Race Ends

It is not always obvious why, in the absence of disturbance, taller plants do not maintain their height advantage over shorter plants under their canopies (Fahey, Battles, and Wilson 1998; Reich 2000; Midgley 2003). There are many instances of shorter individuals growing up through the canopy of taller species without an obvious differential disturbance (Callaway 1992; Hunter and Barbour 2001). One possible explanation includes a shift in allocation from vegetative to reproductive biomass in the taller species that decreases their ability to grow in height. Alternatively, the fast growth and cheap stems that are characteristic of the dominants of high-resource environments could limit canopy height or constrain the efficient placement of leaves horizontally. More research is necessary to understand better what factors limit the height of canopies, and why subordinates can (or cannot) eventually produce taller canopies.

The race for light does not go on indefinitely, and the plants that are initially above other plants do not remain above other plants indefinitely. The first stage of competition for light ends when taller plants are killed or overtopped by previously shorter plants. The end of the first stage of light competition can come as a result of exogenous factors, such as selective disturbance of taller plants. For example, taller plants are often more susceptible to high winds than shorter plants, and the low stem tissue density of high-resource species only exacerbates their susceptibility to these disturbances.

Alternatively, the race for light can also end as a result of endogenous factors. Plants must begin to reproduce at some point. When a plant begins to allocate resources to reproduction, resources are drawn away from new leaf and stem production. Hence, high-resource plants that initially have leaf area dominance and begin to reproduce slow down their height increment and leaf area production. The redirection of resources away from maintaining an ascending canopy creates the opportunity for shorter plants to ascend to the canopy. Along these lines, high-resource species also might be less able to transport water to high leaves, reducing their ability to maintain leaf area at height. They also might suffer from declines in nutrient availability that inevitably accompany the negative feedbacks to nutrient availability when, for example, high C:N woody biomass begins to enter the decomposition cycle.

Once the initial race ends, the second stage of competition for light comes into prominence. Generally below the canopies of players in the initial race are species that have been selected to excel at the second stage of competition. These species have unique adaptations to the low light levels that exist beneath the canopies of others. As the next chapter discusses, these adaptations allow them to grow better at low light levels and become the dominant plants after the initial stage of light competition is over.

SYNTHESIS

As opposed to plants of low-nutrient habitats, plants of disturbed, high-nutrient environments are built to acquire resources at a high rate. Regardless of whether disturbance is just aboveground or also includes the soil, competition for light quickly ensues, and plants must continue to gain height to maintain leaf area dominance by producing new leaves above old leaves. Competition for light is diffuse, and plants are competing against adjacent plants, racing upward to maintain leaf area dominance and not be overtopped.

When growing in environments with high nutrient availability, high-resource species have leaves with high nutrient concentrations and consequently high rates of photosynthesis. A low structural investment in leaves reduces the resources required to produce a new leaf and increases the ability of plants to produce new leaves quickly with acquired resources. As a consequence of the continuing upward race for light, leaves quickly become shaded by new leaves, and there is little benefit to being built to live a long time. With high nitrogen concentrations associated with high protein concentrations and therefore high rates of respiration, high-resource species have high leaf-level LCPs and are poor at having positive net photosynthesis in shade. Hence, the leaves of high-resource species live a short time for two reasons: they experience negative carbon balance quickly, and they are more susceptible to damage, owing to their low structural investment.

The roots of high-resource species are built to maintain high specific uptake rates. With high nutrient availability in the soil, there is little importance to competition for nutrients and little decline in root surface nutrient concentrations as plants grow. Even if nutrient availability declines in the short term due to uptake, the return of high-quality litter and subsequently high rates of decomposition ensures consistently high nutrient availability. For high-resource species, new roots are continually produced to maintain high specific rates of uptake and to keep up with the high nutrient demands of a quickly growing canopy. There is little structural investment in roots, so that new root biomass can be produced quickly, and there is little advantage to maintaining roots a long time. Roots can be thicker owing to an increase in the need for transport for a given root and a decrease in the importance of maximizing root length when competition for nutrients has low importance.

High-resource plants are well defended and do not just rely on their high growth rate to cope with herbivores. The defense syndromes of high-resource plants are geared to be compatible with a high growth rate and low longevity of organs. Inducible defenses that can be turned on in the presence of herbivores are favored over constitutive defenses. Other inducible defenses are indirect and signal parasitoids and predators of insects. With high nitrogen availability, nitrogen-based defensive chemicals have a relatively low cost and are relatively common. With the presence of specialized herbivores that can thwart defenses and less of a premium on nutrient retention, structural defenses that do not completely protect leaves but do protect meristems well are common among high-resource species.

Associated with a premium for rapid ascension of canopies, high-resource species have a low structural investment in their stems, which increases height increment per unit of resource allocated to stem growth. The stems of high-resource species are built to have high transport rates at low cost.

As with the low-nutrient strategy, disturbance regimes intersect with high nutrient availability to produce different expressions of the high-resource strategy. With aboveground disturbance, plants are more likely to store carbohydrates to facilitate postdisturbance regrowth. With belowground disturbance that kills perennating organs, plants are more likely to allocate resources to seed production than to storage. As disturbance frequency decreases, high-resource species allocate more resources to stems to accommodate the greater height to which the race for light proceeds.

In all, the combination of high-activity leaves and roots with a flexible high-resource defense strategy allows plants to grow at a high rate. Although high-resource plants can grow at a high rate in the absence of competition, most plants in the evolutionary history of the species likely grew with neighbors, and the traits of the high-resource strategy can also be thought of as helping plants to succeed in the race for light and continuing to maintain leaf area dominance.

The race for light can continue with a disturbance that removes enough aboveground biomass such that light availability at the soil surface is high. The initial race for light—the first stage of light competition—can end for endogenous reasons, such as increased allocation to reproduction by canopy plants that slows their ability to produce leaf area at height. It also can end when canopy plants are selectively disturbed, leaving understory plants to dominate. For example, high winds selectively disturb taller trees but have little effect on the understory species.

When the initial race for light ends, the second stage of light competition comes into prominence. Generally beneath the primary race for light are species that grow in the shade of others. As the next chapter describes, plants in the understory are not necessarily best considered the losers of the race, for they often excel during the second stage. Many of these species have been selected to grow well in the shade of others in order to capitalize on the opportunity for their moment in the sun.

CHAPTER 9

The Low-Light Strategy

UNDERNEATH THE INITIAL RACE for light that follows an aboveground disturbance in an ecosystem with high nutrient availability, the second stage of competition for light ensues. The species that have been selected to succeed during the first stage of competition have traits that allow them to quickly attain and then maintain leaf area dominance when nutrient availability and light levels are high. Although the shade cast by the canopies of high-resource species prevents them from maintaining additional leaves beneath their canopies, sufficient light still passes through their canopies to allow other species to grow. Natural selection associated with the reduction of light levels beneath high-resource species has favored species that can grow at these lower light levels.

These low-light species have not necessarily been selected just to tolerate low light levels while waiting for pulses of high light availability. During the second stage of competition for light, low-light species actively grow better at low light levels than other species, which is an important part of the process of competition for light. Although light competition is size-asymmetric, these low-light species, which are shorter than the high-resource species above them, are nonetheless engaged in competition for light. Low-light species continue to grow and have the potential to attain leaf area dominance over the currently taller high-resource species. Low-light species further reduce light levels below their canopies and position themselves to reduce light levels to the next generation of high-resource species that would begin growing after a selective aboveground disturbance.

The process of natural selection for low-light species has selected for a suite of traits that share some similarities with those of low-nutrient species. Yet there are trade-offs for growing successfully when light levels are low as opposed to when nutrient availability is low. Although it could be argued that the low-light and low-nutrient strategies are similar enough to be considered part of the same general strategy, the reasons for the similarities are quite different, and the strategies deserve to be clearly separated.

This chapter describes the keys to success under low light availability and the second stage of competition. In describing the low-light strategy, the chapter draws on examples from the most extreme low-light species, including species that eventually dominate the canopy as well as those that are obligate understory species. The low-light strategy is most important for plants in the understory. Yet many low-light species eventually come to dominate the canopy, and so the characteristics of low-light species under high light levels are also covered.

Chief among the traits of low-light species when growing under low light are a low whole-plant light compensation point (LCP_{wp}) and efficient light-gathering strategies. A low LCP_{wp} is driven by a combination of low leaf-level LCP as well as by allocation strategies that reduce respiratory demand. Efficient light gathering encompasses leaf physiological traits, structural characteristics of the leaves, and strategies for arranging leaves.

Low-light species present many paradoxes regarding theories of natural selection and growth strategies that are important to explore. For example, the resource availability hypothesis would predict that since low-light species predominate in areas of high nitrogen availability relative to light, they would be defended with nitrogen-based chemicals. Yet low-light species generally are defended with constitutive nitrogen-free chemicals. As another example, the presence of low-light species can alter the light environment of a stand to favor the further recruitment of low-light species. These positive effects on recruitment, however, are unstable. Under most conditions, seedlings of low-light species cannot be maintained in the understory of a canopy dominated by low-light species. Low-light species also likely reduce nutrient availability, which likely reduces the relative importance of low light availability at some time scales. Finally, contrary to some theories of growth in low light, low-light species are not better adapted to utilize sunflecks than high-resource species for what can be a major source of light availability in the understory.

After explaining some of the intellectual tension regarding hypotheses about the low-light strategy, this chapter covers the end of the second stage of competition for light. Once the processes that lead to canopy dominance of low-light species are detailed, the dynamics that follow the death of overstory low-light species plants and the concomitant increase in the availability of light to the ground are important components of selection pressures on low-light species. Because there is generally little advance regeneration under the most extreme low-light species, any disturbance of the canopy of low-light species becomes a general one. As such, which species are favored depends less on the selectivity of the disturbance than on the spatial scale of the disturbance. Owing to the changing angle of the sun's rays over the course of a day, small disturbances favor the recruitment of low-light species. Large-scale disturbances are required for a general increase in understory light levels that is high enough and consistent enough to recruit high-resource species.

Physiological Traits

A number of key physiological traits of low-light species are associated with success in low-light environments. These traits include those of the leaves, roots, and stems. More is known about leaves than about other parts of the plants, and leaf traits are discussed in greater detail in this section than root and stem traits. Because most low-light species eventually find themselves growing at high irradiance, the performance of these traits at high light is discussed later.

Leaves

LONGEVITY

Low-light species have leaves that live a long time. Their leaves do not necessarily live longer than those of low-nutrient species, but leaf longevity is generally higher than for high-resource species. In temperate ecosystems, deciduous tree species that have the low-light strategy often have a maximum leaf longevity similar to that of high-resource species, although the low-light species may rarely exhibit indeterminant growth patterns that lead to the production of leaves with shorter longevity later in the growing season. In northern temperate forests, low-light herbaceous species often have leaves that live a full year, in contrast to the high-light ephemeral understory species that have leaves that live only a month or two (Rothstein and Zak 2001). There are also temperate evergreen tree species that grow well under low light, and these species also have high leaf longevity. For example, the needles of hemlock species growing in the understory can live longer than five years. In tropical forests, low-light tree species also have high leaf longevity. For example, the leaves of *Ouratea* species may live five years (Kursar and Coley 2003), in contrast to the leaves of high-resource *Cecropia* species, which might live only 40 days.

STRUCTURAL INVESTMENT

Associated with the greater leaf longevity, the leaves of low-light species have low specific leaf area (SLA). For example, Walters and Reich (1999) showed that on average, seedlings of low-light species had approximately half the SLA of more light-demanding species.

Again, SLA can be decomposed to thickness and tissue density, and it is important to examine the association of both with the low-light strategy. At the global scale, there is twofold variation in incident daily mean solar radiation. Niinemets (2001) found that sites with higher incident radiation had leaves that were on average both thicker and denser. In addition, both the lower and upper bounds of the relationship between radiation and thickness or density increased. As such, sites with lower solar inputs had leaves that were thinner and had lower tissue density.

Within a canopy, there is greater variation in light levels than on a global basis. Although light levels globally might vary on average by a factor of 2, light levels within a canopy might vary by 100-fold. Data that decompose SLA into thickness and tissue density for low-light species are rare, in contrast to the global patterns of leaf characteristics with radiation. However, it appears that species that specialize in the low-light portions of canopies have greater tissue density (Ryser and Eek 2000). That said, there are data to the contrary. For example, Ryser and Wahl (2001) found that of 24 grasses, those associated with shadier habitats had a *higher* SLA than other species. The higher SLA was the result of *thinner* leaves, not of lower tissue density. Separating the leaf characteristics of low-light and low-nutrient species is an important area for future research, but the pattern of other traits supports the generalization of greater tissue density causing the lower SLA.

Besides the generally lower SLA and greater tissue density, low-light species have leaf structural adaptations that enhance light acquisition. For example, leaf mesophyll tissue of low-light species has a high number of spongy cells, which scatter light within the leaf and increase the absorption of diffuse and far-red wavelengths of light (DeLucia et al. 1996). Without internal reflectance of light, photosynthesis by low-light species grown in low light (20 μmol m^{-2} s^{-1}) would be reduced by half. Other species have epidermal cells that act as lenses to focus light onto photosynthetic pigments, while some species have pigments in the abaxial cells that reflect light upward back to chloroplasts (Lee, Lowry, and Stone 1979).

NUTRIENT CONCENTRATIONS

In addition to the greater leaf longevity and greater structural investment, evidence suggests that low-light species also have low nutrient concentrations in their leaves. For example, Kaelke, Kruger, and Reich (2001) compared the growth of low-light sugar maple with high-light aspen and the intermediate red oak. The low-light sugar maple consistently had lower leaf nitrogen concentrations than more light-demanding species. Because there has been little research on this issue in general, there are few studies that explicitly examine nutrient ratios for shade-tolerant species. There also has been little research to help understand whether the low nutrient concentrations are a consequence solely of a greater structural investment that dilutes nutrient investment or whether low-light plants allocate less biomass per unit of leaf volume.

PHOTOSYNTHESIS AND RESPIRATION RATES

It has been known for more than a century that leaves of plants grown under low-light conditions have lower potential photosynthetic rates than those grown in high light. For example, in comparing sun- and shade-grown leaves, Warming (1909) stated that "Heliophylls respire and assimilate more rapidly than do sciophylls of the same species." With lower nutrient concentrations, low-light species have a lower respiration rate and a lower maximum photosynthetic rate (Walters and Reich 1999). For example, the maximum photosynthetic rate of a low-light species might be 2 $\mu mol\ m^{-2}\ s^{-1}$, while a high-resource species might attain 50 $\mu mol\ m^{-2}\ s^{-1}$.

In addition to having low respiration rates, low-light species also have a lower leaf-level LCP. Although in a recent review of photosynthetic traits of species that differed in their ability to grow in shade, low-light species had lower dark respiration rates, a lower LCP for shade-tolerant species were not detected (Walters and Reich 1999). Craine and Reich (2005) reanalyzed the data to strengthen the statistical power of the analyses (along with adding more recently published data). They found that low-light species had statistically significantly lower leaf-level LCP. For example, low-light species typically have positive photosynthetic rates to light levels as low as 5 $\mu mol\ m^{-2}\ s^{-1}$ (and as low as 1 $\mu mol\ m^{-2}\ s^{-1}$), while the average species considered intolerant of shade had a leaf-level LCP of 9 $\mu mol\ m^{-2}\ s^{-1}$, with the LCP for some species as high as 40 $\mu mol\ m^{-2}\ s^{-1}$. Lower LCP values were also associated with higher quantum yields, indicating greater use of absorbed radiation for photosynthesis (Craine and Reich 2005).

Associated with differences in maximum photosynthetic rates and LCP, low-light species often have less capacity to dissipate excess energy that is absorbed by photosynthetic pigments. In addition, their ratios of chlorophyll A to B were low, considered an adaptation to enhancing absorption of low levels of low-energy light that is left after passing through overstory canopies (Niinemets and Tenhunen 1997).

LIGHT INTERCEPTION

To maximize light acquisition, low-light species hold their leaves at a low angle and array their leaves to minimize overlap. Low-light species also have very little investment in structures that increase reflectance. It is rare to find low-light species with dense coverings of hair or wax on their leaves.

NUTRIENT RESORPTION

Reviews of nutrient resorption have generally considered only leaf nitrogen concentrations as a covariate and have not distinguished low-light from low-nutrient species. As such, it is assumed they also have higher nutrient resorption rates, but many of the same caveats associated with resorption for low-nutrient species hold for low-light species. For example, little work has been done to compare the resorption of nutrients between low-light and high-resource species at a common irradiance or nutrient supply.

STORAGE

Low-light species do not appear to have greater carbohydrate stores than high-resource species. Although carbohydrate reserves can be important for maintenance of function in shade and recovery of growth after low-intensity disturbances, there is little evidence that low-light species actually store more carbohydrates to deal with the potential of variation in light availability or disturbance.

Roots

There has been little work to understand the unique characteristics of the roots of low-light species. Beyond the lack of work in general, most of the work on characteristics of roots of low-light species has been done on northern temperate trees, where soil freezing is likely a strong constraint on root characteristics. Little investigation has been carried out on the root traits of low-light species in tropical habitats that could be used to compare to the patterns of temperate systems.

Among root traits, it is undetermined whether the roots of low-light species typically live longer than those of high-resource species. Comas and Eissenstat (2004) showed few consistent differences in the specific respiration rates of low-light tree species compared to others that are more demanding of light. Likewise, little is known about whether low-light species invest more in root structure than high-resource species do. Uptake kinetics and dependence on mycorrhizal fungi are also poorly characterized.

Stems

The stems of woody low-light species have a higher tissue density than those of high-resource species. Kitajima (1994) showed that tropical tree species with a low mortality when grown in shade (2% full sun) also had higher stem tissue density. For example, *Ochroma pyramidale*, which had a mortality rate of 15% per week in the understory of a tropical forest, had a wood tissue density of only 0.24 g cm^{-3}. In contrast, the low-light species *Tachigalia versicolor* had a mortality rate of only 0.05% per week and a wood tissue density of 0.58 g cm^{-3}.

Defenses

Although few quantitative comparisons across species have been done, in relation to the major defense types, there is little evidence that low-light species are generally defended with nitrogen-containing defenses or structural defenses such as thorns. Instead, most low-light species are defended with nitrogen-free secondary chemicals that are mostly constitutive as opposed to inducible. For example, hemlock species have tannins and terpenoids, while *Acer saccharum* has tannins. Among temperate low-light shrubs and small trees, *Rhamnus* species have the nitrogen-free anthraquinone emodin, while *Lonicera* species have iriodoid glycosides. Low-light tropical trees and understory plants seem to follow the same pattern, with only a small fraction of species in the understory showing evidence of nitrogen-containing chemicals, such as alkaloids and nonprotein amino acids (Kursar and Coley 2003; Coley et al. 2005). Likely the most low-light tree species in temperate forests that has nitrogen-containing defenses is *Prunus virginiana*, which has cyanogenic glycosides, but *Prunus* is still considered a shade-intolerant species. *Nothofagus* species can have cyanogenic glycosides, with different patterns in young and old leaves, but there is little indication that shade-tolerant *Nothofagus* species have nitrogen-based defenses.

WHOLE-PLANT TRAITS

Relative Growth Rates

Low-light species have a low potential RGR_{max}. When the growth of 15 tropical rainforest tree species was examined across a range of light environments, low-light species had RGR_{max} values just one-third those of more light-demanding species (Poorter 1999). There does not seem to be any study that compares the RGR_{max} of low-light and high-resource species while also controlling for plant biomass (Niinemets 2006). It can take a long time, sometimes six months to two years, for small-seeded species to attain the mass that a large-seeded species has initially (Walters and Reich 1999; Rose and Poorter 2003). Most studies of RGR do not run this long to allow these standardized comparisons to be made. Moreover, short-term measurements of LCP_{wp} can be more than three times lower than those observed in the field, with poor correlation among species between the two (Baltzer and Thomas 2007). That said, low-light species consistently have lower maximum rates of photosynthesis (A_{max}) and higher tissue construction costs, which should be associated with a lower RGR_{max}.

The greater RGR_{max} of light-demanding species compared with low-light species does not necessarily translate to a lower RGR at low light levels. Although some studies have observed greater actual RGR for low-light species than for more light-demanding species under low light, light-demanding species are often found to have a greater RGR than low-light species at low light levels. For example, in their review of previous research on growth at low light, Walters and Reich showed that even at low light, shade-intolerant species had a greater RGR than shade-tolerant species. Within an individual study, the same pattern is often observed. For example, Kitajima (1994) compared the RGR over two months of 13 tropical tree species in the seedling stage at high light (23% full sun) and low light (2% full sun, both with and without lowered red:far red ratios. Species that had the highest RGR in sun also had the highest RGR in shade.

Although there is some debate on the issue (Kitajima and Bolker 2003; Sack and Grubb 2003), the differences in RGR between low-light and high-resource species are a result of complex interactions among the length of observation, the light levels plants are grown at, the plant size at which species are compared, and differences in the degree to which plants have been selected to grow at low or high light levels. As the length of observation increases, plant size increases, or light levels decline, low-light species exhibit higher RGR at low light levels than at high light levels when compared with high-resource species. Sack and Grubb (2001) showed that only in the short term (<10 weeks) do high-resource species have a higher RGR than low-light species. In studies that exceed 40 weeks, low-light species have a higher RGR than high-resource species when light levels are less than 3% full sun. At 60 weeks, this crossover point approaches 5% full sun.

Biomass Ratios

Shade-tolerant species appear to allocate a lower fraction of their biomass aboveground than high-resource species. Kitajima (1994) found an inverse relationship between the shade tolerance of tropical seedlings and root weight ratio (RWR) in seedlings. In their review, Walters and Reich (1999) showed that shade-intolerant deciduous species had a lower RWR than shade-tolerant deciduous species, but there were no differences among shade-tolerant and shade-intolerant broadleaf evergreen species. Again, these analyses did not control for plant size and might have been allometrically influenced.

As described earlier, the biomass ratios of plants grown long enough for biomass to begin to turn over are often more reflective of relative longevity than of relative allocation. Walters and Reich (2000) showed that leaf weight ratio (LWR) declined with increasing plant size for deciduous and broadleaf evergreen species. Although LWR declined with increasing plant size for both species, RWR declined for broadleaf evergreen species but increased for deciduous species. Again, this pattern likely reflects the differential accumulation of biomass in leaves and roots associated with differences in longevity. The leaves of evergreen species live longer than the leaves of deciduous species, and it would be expected that for a given allocation rate, LWR should decline less for evergreen species as for deciduous species. Without better data on root longevity, it is hard to know whether these observations reflect changes in allocation or can be explained largely by the relative longevity of leaves and roots. Unlike low-nutrient species, there is no evidence that low-light species accumulate a large, dense root system.

Canopy Light Interception

Low-light species build canopies that are more efficient at intercepting light (Pearcy et al. 2004). In addition to their low leaf angle, the arrangement of leaves often minimizes overlap. With low leaf and branch-level LCP values, low-light species absorb a higher fraction of incident radiation, casting dense shade below their canopies. The deeper shade is not a result of higher light extinction coefficients of leaves but of deeper crowns, that is, of having a higher leaf area index (LAI) (Canham et al. 1999).

It is currently unknown whether low-light species allocate their nitrogen within the canopy in a manner to optimize canopy-level photosynthesis or whether they allocate nitrogen in a manner similar to the way high-resource species do (Anten 2005). Along these lines, it is unknown whether low-light species maintain a higher LAI than is optimal. The species for which the patterns of nitrogen allocation and LAI accumulation have been analyzed have all been high-resource species. These patterns are likely to be more important for plants with deeper canopies than just seedlings, but fundamental questions remain about the allocation strategies of low-light species.

Maximum Height

There is still some debate as to whether there is a general relationship between maximum tree height and the ability to grow at low light. Thomas and Bazzaz showed that among Malaysian rain forest species, trees that attained taller maximum heights had higher maximum photosynthetic rates. Although in general, maximum photosynthetic rates and LCP are inversely related, Thomas and Bazzaz (1999) found no relationship between maximum height and LCP. Similarly, Cai, Rijkers, and Bongers (2005) concluded that having a high maximum tree height did not indicate a poor ability to grow in shade.

Effects on Nutrient Cycling

There has been little empirical or theoretical research on the effects of low-light species on nutrient cycling. Whether low-light species increase or decrease nutrient availability on average is poorly understood. From first principles, low-light species, like low-nutrient species, produce tissues with low nutrient concentrations. As with low-nutrient species, at short to medium time scales the low litter quality of low-light species should reduce nutrient availability. It does not appear that the low-light strategy is associated with high rates of N_2 fixation, even though many tropical trees are of the legume family. Most examples of plants that increase phosphorus availability are from high-light environments in which phosphorus limitation is strong enough to prevent a closed canopy for forming. That said, there is little research on nitrogen mining in understory environments, and it is likely that many low-light species associate with mycorrhizal fungi that can increase nitrogen or phosphorus availability, or both.

Traits under High Light

Low-light species in the understory experience periods of higher light levels on three time scales. At the daily scale, there are always short periods of high light as the sun crosses the sky. With the movement of the sun, short-duration pulses of sunlight in the understory (sunflecks) arise through small gaps in the canopy. Seasonally, understory species experience greater light levels in some stands as leaf area in the overstory declines. For example, in the spring in temperate deciduous forests, light levels can average 300 μM m^{-2} s^{-1} in the understory, almost 100 times greater than after canopy development (Rothstein and Zak 2001). Third, with selective and general disturbance, understory plants experience high light levels as a consequence of the creation of relatively large gaps in the overstory. Both diffuse and direct beam radiation can increase, with the magnitude of the change depending on the size of the gap. With large general disturbances, light levels can increase to full sun for understory plants quickly and for a sustained period.

The induction of photosynthesis with a sunfleck is qualitatively similar among most species. Upregulating photosynthetic capacity involves opening stomata and activating photosynthetic enzymes (Pearcy 1990). In some studies, with a sunfleck, low-light species can recover to A_{max} faster. Cai, Rijkers, and Bongers (2005) found that the time required to achieve 90% of A_{max} was less than half that required by more light-demanding species. Even though Cai, Rijkers, and Bongers (2005) concluded that the most extreme low-light species "can use short periods of direct sunlight (sunflecks) more efficiently" than the more light-demanding species, there is little evidence that low-light species are better able to utilize the sunflecks. The true measure of how well a species utilizes a pulse of resource availability is not which species can increase its activity relative to its maximum activity rate but which species has the higher activity rate at a given point in time. The quicker time to recovery of A_{max} for low-light species is associated with a lower A_{max}. In Cai, Rijkers, and Bongers (2005), after 60 s of exposure to a sunfleck, obligate shade species had lower absolute photosynthetic rates than transient shade species. If anything, low-light and high-resource species utilize sunflecks similarly.

Sunflecks can increase net carbon gain for shade species, but shade species are not optimized to utilize sunflecks, and sunflecks are not essential to the growth and persistence of shade species below the canopy of other plants (Naumburg and Ellsworth 2000). Although sunflecks under species that are not adapted to low-light levels can provide a significant fraction of the daily light interception (Naumburg and Ellsworth 2000), in an *Acer saccharum* forest, light levels in the understory are below 20 µmol m^{-2} s^{-1} more than 90% of the time, and most of the light that reaches a given point is diffuse and low intensity in nature (Ellsworth and Reich 1992).

The seasonal changes in light in deciduous forests are accommodated in a manner that is similar to the differences between low-light and high-resource species. Many woody and herbaceous understory species in northern temperate forests accomplish most of their carbon gain during the high-light period and function more like high-resource species. For example, among 13 tree species, understory individuals of 10 species experienced bud break earlier than overstory individuals of the same species (8 days on average), while for 11 species, full leaf expansion occurred before those of overstory individuals (6 days on average) (Augspurger and Bartlett 2003). This phenological offset between overstory and understory individuals was responsible for a large fraction of the total light acquired by understory individuals. Augspurger, Cheeseman, and Salk (2005) showed that seedlings of five tree species in the understory acquired between 36% and 98% of their annual irradiance by producing leaves before overstory trees leaved out.

Understory species that produce leaves before overstory species do have a relatively high LCP and high A_{max} (Rothstein and Zak 2001). In contrast, other understory species that produce their leaves at the same time that overstory plants do function more like low-light species, not having foliage under high light until the following spring. Their leaves have a low LCP and low A_{max}. Across most species, whether through changes in existing leaves or the production of new leaves, the changes that occur with the closing of the canopy generally include acclimation of extant leaves and the production of new leaves that have greater ratios of chlorophyll to Rubisco, lower A_{max}, and lower LCP.

On the longest time scale, the increases in light levels can also be high and sustained as the canopy opens up. With increases in light levels of this magnitude, soil moisture often decreases and nutrient availability increases owing to declines in uptake. The process of adjustment to high light levels includes altering the physiology of current leaves while also producing new ones that are better suited for the high light levels. With a sustained increase in light levels, low-light species grown under low light initially show increased damage to light-harvesting structures. Fluorescence increases and quantum efficiency decreases as photosystems are damaged (Maxwell and Johnson 2000). Over time, fluorescence declines as leaves are held at a higher angle relative to incoming radiation (Ludlow and Bjorkman 1984; Lovelock, Jebb, and Osmond 1994) and light-harvesting complexes become protected with additional pigments.

Kursar and Coley (1999) showed that when two low-light species were transferred to a high-light environment, both were initially inhibited by high light. Within 17 days, however, the species that had greater leaf longevity (ca. 5 years) had increased the photosynthetic capacity of old leaves. The species with shorter leaf longevity (ca. 1 year) had produced new leaves with higher photosynthetic capacity but showed little acclimation of existing leaves. Other low-light species in other ecosystems depend strongly on the production of new foliage for the acclimation response (Mohammed and Parker 1999). For example, hemlock seedlings transferred from a low-light to a high-light environment showed a greater mortality than those grown continually under low or high light. For the species that were transferred to high light, there was some adjustment of photosynthetic characteristics of existing foliage, but only new foliage had characteristics similar to that of plants grown in the high-light environment.

The degree to which low-light species can adjust is regulated by resource availability. For example, less photoinhibition in plants is observed when nutrient supply is high enough to allow new leaves to be produced. In general, after having been acclimated to high light, low-light species still have a lower A_{max} and greater leaf longevity than high-resource species.

Why These Patterns

Past Statements

Since the time of Warming, shade has been considered a stress, and low-light species have been distinguished from other species that grow best under high-light conditions. For example, Warming stated, "Forest trees may be divided into— (a) Light-demanding trees, which demand much light and endure but little shade; (b) Shade-enduring trees, which are content with less light and can endure deeper shade." These early separations and the emphasis on "endurance" reflect the idea of low-light species tolerating low light as opposed to growing well at low light.

Warming understood many of the traits associated with the low-light strategy as well as ontogenetic changes in LCP_{wp}:

> The reasons for these distinctions must be sought for in the specific distinctions in the chlorophyll, rather than in any difference in the architecture (structure of the shoot, phyllotaxy, and form of the leaf) of the species. . . . It is worthy of note and biologically important that nearly all trees can endure deeper shade in early youth than they can later in life. It may be added that the power to endure shade also depends upon the fertility of the soil. (Warming 1909, p. 18)

The dichotomy of approaches in explaining the patterns generally revolved around low-light species having a greater ability to acquire light as opposed to low-light species having a greater ability to conserve the energy they acquire.

For example, Henry Horn (1971) hypothesized that shade-tolerant plants optimized growth in low light by constructing single-layer canopies as opposed to the multilayer canopies of early-successional, high-resource species. Whereas Horn assumed that all species had similar LCP, Olle Björkman had long noted that the low respiration rates allowed low-light species to have greater net photosynthesis at low light levels (Björkman 1981). David King had extended these arguments by arguing for low-light species having low LCP_{wp} in the absence of herbivory (King 1994).

Counter to the idea that shade-tolerant species are better at acquiring light, there has been the alternative hypothesis that low-light species are better at not losing acquired resources. Grime long advocated that low-light species were better at resisting stress and disturbance, not acquiring resources. This basic hypothesis is still elevated by some researchers. For example, Erik Veneklaas and Lourens Poorter (1998) state, "[W]hat has been reported for nutrient-limited plants (Van der Werf et al. 1993) may also hold for light-limited plants: adaptation of species to low-[productivity] environments is not necessarily associated with a high growth rate in that environment, but rather with persistence." Low-light species are not better at acquiring, photosynthesizing, or growing at low light levels but instead are better at resisting herbivory or mechanical damage.

It was only recently that the traits of low-light species were linked to nutrient stress. Although Grime had earlier associated low-light species with a more positive carbon balance under low-light conditions than other species, he later assumed that the low nutrient concentrations were best explained by nutrient stress as opposed to light stress.

Reconciling Growth and Mortality at Low Light

Growth is the balance between resource gain (e.g., photosynthesis) and resource loss (e.g., tissue turnover and disturbance). In the second stage of competition, low-light species have been selected to be able to (1) grow faster than high-resource species at low light levels and (2) grow at lower light levels than fast-growing species. Both a superior ability to acquire carbon under a uniformly low light supply and greater ability to resist disturbances such as mechanical damage, disease, and herbivory can cause the differential success of low-light species in low-light environments.

On the one hand, there is plenty of evidence that low-light species are built to maximize net carbon balance at a uniform low irradiance. Their leaves have low respiration rates, which generates a low leaf-level LCP (Craine and Reich 2005). Their leaves are also often structured to max-imize the capture of low-intensity, low-energy light with specialized struc-tures such as light-focusing epidermal cells, light-scattering mesophyll cells, and light-reflecting pigments on the undersides of leaves. At the whole-plant level, stems and root systems also have low respiration rates, which generates a low LCP_{wp}, and canopies are structured to maximize the efficiency of light absorption. Scaling from the organ level to the whole-plant level, at low light levels, individuals of low-light species should be able to acquire light and grow better than individuals of other species of comparable size as a consequence of maintaining a positive net carbon balance at very low light levels at which other species would experience negative carbon balance.

On the other hand, empirical growth rate data have often shown that high-resource species can experience a higher RGR than low-light species in the absence of selective disturbance agents. Although the greater real-ized RGR apparently disappears with longer observation periods and larger plants, it does not seem that light levels in the understory fall so low that it is impossible for high-resource species to grow at all.

Part of the ignorance about growth in shade is that seedlings might grow in such a manner that prevents a quasi-steady-state biomass from being reached at a given light level in the absence of disturbance agents (figure 9.1). Once plants of some species enter negative whole-plant carbon balance at a given light level, they might increasingly lose biomass as opposed to maintaining a given biomass. For example, as plants increase in size or age, the ratio of heterotrophic biomass to leaf biomass increases, setting plants on a trajectory that dictates a maximum biomass that occurs when light acquisition becomes balanced by heterotrophic requirements. If so, then focusing on RGR at a given light level is less important than understanding the maximum (or equilibrium) biomass that can be obtained by an individual at a given light level. Givnish (1988) argued that plants require a certain light level at a particular size. However, it might be more instructive to reverse the focus and ask what size a given species can attain at a given light level. Based on seed size and RGR at a given light level, this would set how long a plant could persist in the understory before entering a negative carbon balance trajectory.

If plants can reach a steady-state biomass in the absence of disturbance, then the second stage of light competition cannot be considered to be driven solely by differential carbon gain ability. High-resource species might begin to experience neutral carbon balance at a smaller size than low-light species, but they can grow at low light and from first principles should be able to maintain some biomass in low-light conditions. As such, other factors must be in part responsible for their absence in low-light environments. A secondary explanatory factor such as competition between low-light and high-resource seedlings or differential susceptibility to selective disturbance agents must be invoked to explain their poorer success or absence.

There seems to be some support for the idea that high-resource species are generally excluded from low-light environments as a consequence of their greater susceptibility to disturbance agents. Consistently, the leaves of low-light species experience lower rates of herbivory than leaves of high-resource species do in a low-light environment. For example, "pioneer" and "persistent" species in the understory of a Panamanian rain forest experience similar rates of herbivory for expanding leaves, but pioneer species experienced six times greater rates than persistent species for expanded leaves (Coley 1983). Similarly, Poorter et al. (2004) observed that low-light, late-successional species in a Bolivian rain forest experienced lower rates of herbivory than high-resource, early-successional species.

Although the lower rates of herbivory have been highlighted as a reason for the success of low-light species in low-light environments, the data can be interpreted as not supporting the hypothesis that low-light species are less susceptible to herbivory at low light. To understand the resource economics of leaves, the rates of herbivory need to be scaled to activity

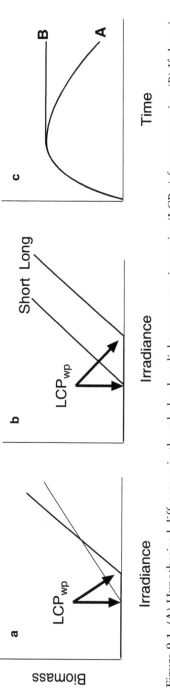

Figure 9.1. (A) Hypothesized differences in the whole-plant light compensation point (LCP$_{wp}$) for two species. (B) If there is size dependency to LCP$_{wp}$, then LCP$_{wp}$ should increase as the period of observation increases. (C) With size dependency, biomass should also decrease with increasing time of observation at low light (A) as opposed to the absence of size dependency (B).

levels and longevities. For example, a short-lived, high-activity leaf that experiences greater herbivory rates than a long-lived, low-activity leaf might still return a similar amount of carbon over its life span. Low-light species experience lower herbivory rates than high-resource species, but they also have higher initial costs and lower photosynthetic rates. Over the long life span of a leaf of a low-light species, similar percentages of material are often removed, and presumably carbon gain is reduced to a similar degree as for high-resource species. For example, although Poorter found lower herbivory rates for low-light species, there was no pattern in the fraction of biomass removed by herbivores over the life span of the leaf with successional status (Poorter et al. 2004).

Pathogens, such as the fungi that attack seeds and seedlings, are considered to cause as much mortality as herbivores in the understory. Evidence regarding any greater resistance of shade-tolerant species to pathogens is also mixed. Augspurger and Kelly (1984) showed that among 16 tree species of a Panamanian forest, species with higher wood density, that is, low-light species, had lower rates of pathogen-induced mortality in seedlings. In contrast, Pringle et al. (2007) quantified the susceptibility of seeds of 16 tree species of the Peruvian Amazon to pathogen attack. There, the seeds of shade-tolerant species were actually more susceptible to pathogens, even though they were on average larger than shade-intolerant species.

Physical damage is another factor that can cause significant mortality to seedlings. As tall plants grow, they periodically shed leaves and branches, which fall and can damage seedlings (Gillman et al. 2004; Peters et al. 2004). Over the years that understory plants must spend in shade, there is a high probability that seedlings are hit by falling material. It has been suggested that there are important differences in seedling traits in their interactions with falling material (Pauw et al. 2004). In comparing the susceptibility of seedlings of different species to physical damage, Clark and Clark (1991) found that high-resource species actually experienced lower rates of physical damage than low-light species, but this was a consequence of being preferentially found in canopy gaps, where there would be a lower rate of falling branches that cause physical damage, not of greater resistance. Presumably, under the same conditions, high-resource species would be more susceptible to physical damage. That said, there is no evidence that they suffered more, even with greater damage rates, since their greater potential growth rates could compensate for the greater susceptibility to damage.

Without better whole-plant growth models that incorporate the construction costs, damage rates, and carbon gains of leaves, it is premature to state that either a greater ability to acquire light or a greater resistance to disturbance agents is the predominant explanation for the differential success of low-light species over high-resource species in low-light environments. It is likely that both aspects of growth contribute to the success of low-light species in low-light environment. However, it is important to begin to partition the relative importance of the two factors in the success of these species through a series of modeling and empirical exercises. This endeavor will likely prove difficult, as there are likely interactions between carbon gain and resistance to disturbance agents that might make partitioning the relative importance of the factors complex. While awaiting further research on the issue, it is important to recognize that both a superior ability to gain carbon and a superior ability to resist disturbance are likely important for the low-light strategy.

The Tension between Nutrients and Light

Abundant evidence supports differentiating low-light and low-nutrient strategies. Low-nutrient species are unable to maintain positive growth or a high equilibrium biomass at low light. The development of large, dense root systems, erect leaves, and morphological characteristics that reduce incident light increases the LCP_{wp} of low-nutrient species above the irradiance to which overstory plants reduce it. In contrast, low-light species would be unsuccessful at competing for nutrients against low-nutrient species, and many species are unable to persist under the high radiation levels of an open area. Moreover, there are also relatively few examples of closely-related species in which one species succeeds under low light and the other succeeds when nutrient availability is low. As such, it seems unlikely that only a small number of genes would need to be altered to transform a low-nutrient species into a low-light species—another reason to think of the low-light and low-nutrient strategies as fundamentally different.

Although there are clear differences in plant traits and performance in different environments, low-light species exhibit many traits similar to those of low-nutrient species grown under low nutrient availability. In their respective habitats, both have leaves with low nutrient concentrations, low respiration rates, and high longevity. Their leaves are defended with constitutive, nitrogen-free chemicals. Their RGR_{max} values are low in both cases relative to those of high-resource plants.

The overlap of what are considered to be key traits for any strategy could lead one to support the commonality hypothesis and consider the low-light and low-nutrient strategies variations on the same general strategy. For example, Grime considered the species that dominated low-light environments and those that dominated environments with low nutrient supplies to both be examples of the same general "stress-tolerant" strategy. He went so far as to suggest that the reason why the similarities arose was because low-light strategies are actually limited by nutrients in the understory.

Even though there is good evidence that plants in low-light environments are not strongly limited by nutrients (see chapter 6), the similarity in traits among plants growing in low light and low nutrient availability raises questions about whether selection has been a result of low nutrient availability to plants growing in shade. For example, the traits of shade species should also reduce nutrient availability on some time scales. As such, it is possible that low-light plants would often face at some point in their life cycle strong nutrient limitation, too. Second, basic economic theory predicts that plants should be co-limited by light and a belowground resource, even in deep shade. Perhaps plants growing in low-light do tend to be nutrient limited, causing them to be selected to have many traits similar to those of low-nutrient species. Although these ideas cannot be ruled out, the more parsimonious explanation is that the similarities are caused by something other than nutrient limitation rather than that natural selection as a result of nutrient limitation has shaped low-light species.

As an alternative to the hypothesis that low-light species have been shaped by nutrient limitation, the convergence hypothesis proposes that light limitation and nutrient limitation have selected for similar traits, but for different reasons. The low nutrient concentrations and low respiration rates might be a consequence of selection for minimizing carbon loss as opposed to maximizing nutrient use efficiency. Low-light species might have long-lived leaves simply because of a low probability of being self-shaded or shaded by a similarly sized neighbor.

One of the most difficult parallels to reconcile is that low-light species do not rely on nitrogen-containing defenses but instead rely on many of the same nitrogen-free chemicals that predominate in low-nutrient habitats. The resource availability hypothesis would predict that when the availability of nitrogen is high relative to other resources, nitrogen should be preferentially used in defense. Indeed, when phosphorus is limiting, nitrogen-based chemicals are more common. Yet when light limitation is relatively important, nitrogen-based chemicals are not observed at a higher frequency. Although this could be considered evidence against the idea that nitrogen is not limiting in shade, there are probably complexities to using nitrogen-based chemicals for defense that might be easy to overlook. For example, nitrogen-based chemicals might be easy to circumvent with greater costs for growth in a low-light environment than in a high-resource environment. Also, using nitrogen-containing chemicals might incur high carbon costs over the long term, owing to the respiratory requirements of maintaining nitrogen-based chemicals. We know too little at this point to be certain one way or the other.

Even if it is accepted that a low availability of different resources drives the similarity in some of the traits between low-light and low-nutrient species, it could still be argued that the two strategies are similar enough to be considered essentially the same strategy. To pursue this idea, the relative contribution to a given strategy of traits that are similar between low-light and low-nutrient species would have to be weighted against the relative contribution of those traits that differ. In essence, the question would come down to asking which is more important in defining a strategy, leaf longevity or leaf reflectance?

In the end, debates over lumping and splitting can be philosophical endeavors as much as scientific ones, but it is important to state the criteria that are used in considering two strategies as essentially similar or different. Although much research on these topics is required, the balance of evidence supports designating the low-light strategy as fundamentally different from the low-nutrient strategy. Although plants of low-nutrient and low-light species can share traits, there are four primary reasons that support the low-light strategy as fundamentally different from the low-nutrient strategy.

First, low-nutrient species do not always have "low-nutrient" traits. As discussed in chapter 7, many of the traits associated with low-nutrient species (and maybe even with low-light species) are consequences of the environment they grow in, if not their effects on the environment. It is hard to argue that the strategies should be considered similar when the centrality of the traits in the strategy cannot even be certified. Second, there is little evidence of the same species succeeding in both habitats, or of closely related species occupying both low-light and low-nutrient habitats. Genetic relatedness is relative, but pines (*Pinus*) are almost exclusively intolerant of shade, and firs (*Abies*) are almost exclusively low-light species. Third, many traits unique to low-light species are likely crucial to their success at growing at low light. And fourth, many of the important keys to success come at the whole-plant level and are associated with competition for resources. Low-light species do not develop the dense root systems that low-nutrient species do. Future research is needed to examine the canopies of low-nutrient and low-light species to see if there are differences in how nitrogen is allocated and how leaf area develops.

The End of the Second Stage of Competition

As secondary succession progresses, there is sequential replacement of species that have increasingly greater ability to grow at low light. As described earlier, initially after a nonselective aboveground disturbance, the upper canopy is dominated by high-resource species. Yet below the canopy of high-resource species are plants of species that are better adapted to grow at low light. As these low-light species grow taller in the shade of the canopy of high-resource species, below the low-light species are ones that can grow at even lower light levels. Although the patterns have yet to be quantified (J. Battles, personal communication), light levels near the ground should decline with successional time in forests, all other things equal.

The sequential replacement of species during secondary succession with species that have the ability to grow at even lower light levels requires that species be able to grow below the canopies of others. From first principles, a plant of a given species should not be able to grow underneath the canopy of a plant of the same species. The same constraints that regulate the lowest leaves of the taller plant regulate the ability of shorter plants to acquire light. As such, it is rare for there to be advance regeneration of plants of one species under the canopy of the same species. Interpretation of this pattern depends strongly on the size dependence of LCP_{wp}. An apparent contradiction to this rule can be found in sugar maple forests, where a bank of sugar maple seedlings can be found growing below intact canopies of sugar maples. In this case, there does not appear to be evidence of carbon transfer from taller plants to the seedlings. Although the seedlings might have lower a LCP than the taller trees, understory sugar maple individuals have most of their net carbon gain before the taller trees leaf out in the spring and after the leaves of the taller plants fall in the autumn. In a manner similar to what is seen in spring ephemeral plants of temperate deciduous forests, as much as 98% of the annual net photosynthesis of the seedlings occurs during the time when the taller trees do not have leaves (Augspurger and Bartlett 2003). Taller trees do not restrict their photosynthetic season to aid understory individuals. Instead, seedlings, because they are closer to the ground, experience a modulated temperature environment that extends the potential growing season over that experienced by taller trees, which inhabit a harsher environment.

Although with increasing time after a general aboveground disturbance, the progressive replacement of species with species that can grow at lower light levels is not without limit, there are absolute limits to the light flux required for plants to have net positive carbon gain. Even though seedlings should have a lower LCP than taller trees (or the lowest branches of tall trees), often, beneath the most extreme low-light species, the understory is bare save the occasional obligate understory species or plants relying on seed reserves to maintain themselves. In temperate forests there is generally little in the understory of *Abies balsamea*, *Tsuga canadensis*, or *Nothofagus* stands.

As the replacement of species reaches its terminus with species that have the lowest LCP_{wp} values, even though plants of these species cannot be maintained under the canopies of the same species, selective disturbances can favor seedlings of the species. When an individual tree is removed from the canopy, the light levels on the forest floor are not a small patch of full sun that is analogous to a general disturbance. Instead, as a consequence of the sun constantly moving across the sky and light coming at an oblique angle, light levels in the gap are generally low throughout the day. A particular spot on the forest floor experiences high light levels only briefly. Although direct sunlight is only briefly elevated in the gap, there is still an increase in diffuse light entering through the gap, causing light levels to be high enough to support low-light species but not high-resource species. Consequently, the low-light species that become established in the gap can continue to grow and fill the gap in the canopy. With isolated gaps, the second stage of competition can be maintained, with different plants of the most low-light species competing against one another. Large-scale gaps are required to favor high-resource species and shift light competition back to the race for light.

Synthesis

In the absence of general aboveground disturbance in environments with high nutrient availability, low-light species eventually come to dominate. Low-light species do not simply tolerate low light levels while waiting for sunflecks or pulses of light associated with canopy gaps. Low leaf-level and whole-plant LCPs allow low-light species to grow well at low light levels as well as to successfully compete for light. Under the canopies of high-resource species, low-light species are able to continue putting on height and to overtop high-resource species in the absence of a selective disturbance of the taller plants. As light levels decline with species replacement in the absence of a general disturbance, understory species are less able to grow tall quickly in the deeper shade. Yet the height and leaf area they can attain are important components of competing well for light. Although their leaf area has no impact on the plants above them, a larger leaf area reduces light availability to seedlings that would establish beneath them and positions understory species to preempt light supplies from higher resource species after a selective disturbance of the taller trees occurs or the taller trees slow in height increment.

Low-light species are able to attain a low LCP_{wp} through a mixture of organ-level and whole-plant-level traits. Leaves have low respiration rates, which allows them the potential of low leaf-level LCP. Unlike low-nutrient species that also have low respiration rates, low-light species lack reflective structures on upper surfaces that reduce LCP, and they have biochemical and structural features that maximize light acquisition. In addition, in contrast to low-nutrient species, low-light species arrange their leaves to minimize overlap and maximize light interception.

Low-light species are not differentiated from other species by leaf traits alone. Roots have low respiration rates, and root systems do not become large and dense. The stems of low-light species that eventually enter the upper canopy of a forest also have high tissue density, most likely reflecting the lack of need to transport large amounts of water to the canopy and the eventually large canopy that these plants can support. In conjunction with greater carbon gain in low light over long periods, there is also evidence that low-light species are able to resist disturbance agents such as herbivores, pathogens, and mechanical damage from falling plant material.

In having a low LCP_{wp}, low-light species are better able to grow under the canopies of high-resource species. This drives the replacement of species from high-light to low-light species in the absence of major canopy disturbance. As a consequence of having lower leaf-level and likely branch-level LCPs, low-light species are able to maintain a deeper canopy that lets less light through than the canopies of high-resource species. High-resource species are unable to establish underneath the canopies of low-light species, but there are open questions regarding whether this is primarily due to light levels being too low or an inability to accommodate disturbance agents while growing at low light.

In the end, whether a given assemblage continues to be dominated by low-light species that have been selected to excel in the second stage of competition revolves around the patterns of disturbance. Small, isolated removal of canopy individuals continues to favor low-light species. As the sun moves across the sky, the light levels at a particular point on the ground adjacent to the canopy gap are elevated only for a brief period each day, and the elevated but still low light levels continue to favor low-light species. Large gaps, at least on the order of multiple trees, are required for light levels to be high enough to favor high-resource species over low-light species, especially when high-resource species are beginning from seed. Whether high-resource species attain leaf area dominance next depends on factors such as the density of low-light species and the height and leaf area they were able to attain before the disturbance.

There are still some important issues to work through for the low-light strategy. Chief among them is understanding the trajectory of growth for low-light and other species under low light levels, including canopy photosynthesis and the respiratory demand of support biomass. In addition, there are no estimates of the relative importance of a superior ability to acquire light versus resist disturbance in contributing to the greater success of low-light species in the understory relative to other species such as high-resource species. Finally, there are seemingly philosophical issues regarding whether the low-light and low-nutrient strategies are similar enough to be considered variations on the same "resource-conserving" strategy or whether the two strategies are fundamentally different. This uncertainty underscores a basic lack of knowledge of the centrality of different traits in the success of plants in different environments. In lieu of more research to the contrary, it is still important to recognize the unique aspects of the low-light strategy and differentiate it from the low-nutrient strategy, while continuing to work to understand the proximal and distal reasons for the apparent convergence of some traits, such as the reliance on constitutive nitrogen-free defensive chemicals.

CHAPTER 10

The Low-Water and Low-CO$_2$ Strategies

THE PREVIOUS THREE CHAPTERS examined the strategies associated with low nutrient availability, high resource availability, and low light availability. Like low nutrient and light availability, low water availability has had a profound effect on plants over evolutionary time scales, as have low atmospheric CO$_2$ concentrations. Understanding the strategies for low water and low CO$_2$ entails many similar analyses as for nutrients and light. It is important to understand how the resources are supplied to plants, how plants acquire them, and their eventual loss. Within this framework, plants can be reduced in abundance or excluded from a habitat as a result of the stress of the low resource availability in the absence of competition, in the presence of competition with other species for the resource, and in the presence of agents of disturbance.

This chapter briefly reviews the basic components of the strategies associated with low water availability and low availability of atmospheric CO$_2$. Adaptations to low water and low CO$_2$ in many ways are linked because of unavoidable exchanges between the two resources that occur during photosynthesis. For every molecule of CO$_2$ that a plant fixes, hundreds of molecules of water can be lost. Because of trade-offs during photosynthesis between water and CO$_2$, many of these adaptations, if not strategies, for low availability of the two resources may be similar. Yet there are unique adaptations that separate the strategies for growing under low-water and low-CO$_2$ regimes. More important, the two strategies differ fundamentally from strategies for growing under low-nutrient and low-light regimes. Any similarities would have to be considered a result of convergence, and there is little evidence for nutrients or light commonly limiting growth at low CO$_2$.

WATER

In many ways, water and nutrients are analogous resources. Both are primarily acquired by plants from the soil. The same unit of root length that is produced to acquire nutrients can also acquire water. Both resources are allocated from roots to leaves in order to acquire light energy and carbon. From these similarities, many have considered the natural selection pressure that results from low availability of the two resources as being generally similar. For example, phenotypic and genotypic responses to a low availability of either resource would generally be considered to be greater allocation to roots and higher root:shoot ratios.

Although water and nutrients are not more dissimilar than, for example, water and light, there are some fundamental differences between water and nutrients that differentiate the strategies that allow for success when each is limiting. First, for ecosystems in which water limits growth, the supply of water is fundamentally different from the supply of nutrients in low-nutrient habitats. By the very nature of precipitation, pulses of water availability can also be important and have resulted in a unique strategy for storing water that has no consistent analog in the storage of nutrients in low-nutrient environments. Second, unique physical stresses are generated under low water availability to move water from the soil to leaves. These pressures are not generated when nutrient availability is low. These stresses have had a profound impact on the evolution of plants from roots to stems to leaves, and the adaptations that result from them are uniquely adaptations to low water availability. Finally, water can only be used for photosynthesis as it is lost from the plant, whereas nutrients can be used productively without immediate lost. These differences in trade-offs dictate that light is less likely to co-limit production with water than nutrients.

Although it would be a great advance to develop an understanding of water limitation and low-water strategies equivalent to the understanding of nutrient supplies, some key unanswered questions prevent this advance. For example, little is known about the mechanisms of competition for water, and little research has been done on the relative importance of factors such as herbivory in determining assemblage composition and natural selection of species. Because there are still some major questions about the low-water strategy, this section lays out the basic patterns of water availability and then details the two major strategies associated with low-water environments that depend on water supply characteristics. Two important questions that are critical to understanding the low-water strategy are then explored: how water supplies are partitioned among individuals, and the interactions between water and nutrient limitation.

Supply and Availability of Water

In ecosystems where water is ultimately limiting to productivity, water supplies vary spatially and temporally. Water supplies to plants vary at a range of temporal scales from daily to annual, with differences occurring not only in the spacing between rainfall events but also in the magnitude of events. Climate further affects water availability by altering evaporation and transpiration rates, with hot ecosystems having high rates of evapotranspiration and plants experiencing greater water stress. Soil properties such as texture affect infiltration rates and the vertical distribution of water in the soil, as well as the availability of water at a given soil moisture content. Landscape characteristics, such as topography, redistribute water, concentrating it through runoff and groundwater flow.

The productivity of plants in arid lands responds to soil water availability. The availability of water at any one point in time is generally considered to be the force that is required for roots to extract water from the soil and move it to leaves. A number of forces factor into soil water availability, including the matric potential of water in the soil, which is the force required to pull water off soil particles. Most plants cannot extract water from soil at water potentials lower than −1.5 MPa, while some specially adapted plants can remove water when potentials are lower than −6 MPa (Lambers, Chapin, and Pons 1998). As soils dry, movement of the remaining water toward roots slows as the attraction between soil particles and water increases when water films become thinner. In addition to this greater resistance to water movement, contact between the root and soil water can diminish, further increasing the resistance to water uptake. Hence, more force is required to acquire a unit of water in a dry soil than in the same soil with a higher water content.

In short, to move water from soil to leaves, plants must generate enough force to exceed the matric potential of the soil, but also to exceed the capillary forces that attract water to xylem surfaces. Plants generate negative pressure at the leaf with transpiration, and this is conducted down the xylem to roots and into the soil. For a plant to acquire water from dry soils, it must be able to generate and withstand immense negative pressures in the xylem. As detailed below, if negative pressures become too great and plants cannot exclude air from the xylem, the stream of water can undergo cavitation, in which the water column in xylem abruptly suffers an embolism and snaps.

It is clear that soils must dry for water to be limiting to plants. At some level, it is axiomatic to state that precipitation must be insufficient for water to be limiting, yet the link between precipitation and water availability is not entirely obvious. Although precipitation reaches ecosystems in discrete events, Reynolds et al. (2004) have modified the "pulse-reserve" model of aridland productivity (Noy-Meir 1973) to demonstrate that water supplies are best understood when considered as a series of events rather than individual events. Soil water availability and the depth of infiltration are affected by the magnitude of an individual precipitation event, but they are better understood when individual events are aggregated at different temporal scales. For example, most individual precipitation events in a desert are small (<5 mm) and by themselves are insufficient to wet the soil layers that have roots (Reynolds et al. 2004). Yet aggregated small events can serially wet the soil and have large impacts on available moisture, as well as on infiltration of water to deeper depths.

With aggregated precipitation events as opposed to individual events needing to be assessed, the patterns of soil moisture availability are driven by heterogeneity of precipitation. If soil moisture is available for long periods of time in a dry ecosystem at shallow depths, high-resource species tend to dominate. For example, in the Chihuahuan desert, annuals proliferate with summer rains (Guo and Brown 1996). These species are often considered "drought avoiders," since they grow well when moisture is available and are able to complete their life cycle during the season when water is highly available, leaving behind seeds to germinate the next season. The traits of these species are quite similar to those of other high-resource species having high RGR_{max}, high tissue nutrient concentrations, and high specific rates of water use. There are specific adaptations to succeeding to life in a desert for these species, but they are largely just variants on the high-resource strategies.

For there to be selection for a low-water-strategy plant, the patterns of water availability must be such that high-resource plants would be under water stress, if not killed by the low availability. Among all the different functional groups that are often distinguished among the plants that inhabit low-water environments, there are only two main low-water strategies. The first strategy is a response to pulses of high water availability that are not large enough for plants to complete their life cycle. As a result of these pulses, plants can experience high water availability for a period, but then must persist in a vegetative state through times of low water availability if they are to survive in the environment. The second strategy arises when water is available relatively uniformly, but largely at low availability. The reasons why the two strategies have been selected for and the main traits that can be found in species of each strategy are described next.

Strategy for Small Pulses of Water

Long periods of high water availability generated by large or frequent precipitation events during the growing season (especially on fine-textured soils) favor high-resource species. Enough water is available for long enough for plants to realize a return on the investment in tissues that are lost when soils dry if not avoiding drought by completing their life cycle, that is, needing to acquire water at low water potential. Although there are unique adaptations in the life cycle of these "drought avoiders," their traits are largely congruent with those of high-resource species. For example, desert annuals are little distinguished from the annuals of disturbed ground. Other perennials flush leaves and roots with new rains and then drop them when the soil dries. The balance between the two types of species might depend on the size and duration of the pulses and intervening drought periods, but both follow the same basic strategy.

When moisture is made available in aggregated pulses that are large enough to be biologically significant but not large enough to provide sufficient water for plants to complete their life cycle or to realize a return on investment in leaves or roots that must be produced and then dropped, the *pulse-store* water strategy is selected for. High-resource plants acquire water at a high rate and simultaneously transpire water at a high rate. Plants with the pulse-store water strategy acquire water at a high rate but transpire the water slowly over longer periods. The key to extending transpiration is storage.

There is a gradient of strategies among plants to acquire and store water for use during times of greater water stress. Large trees often store water at night to reduce water stress mid-day. Some trees store water in the wet season to flush flowers or leaves during the dry season. Although both have aspects of the pulse-store water strategy, at the end of the spectrum are "succulent" species such as cacti, euphorbs, and mesems. These species are distinguished by acquiring water at a high rate but using it slowly and constantly during times when water availability is low.

To acquire water at a high rate, these species produce roots rapidly after an initial pulse of water. The roots conduct water at a high rate, which allows them to acquire water before it evaporates or is acquired by other plants (see below on questions of competition for water). These roots are short-lived and have little ability to acquire water at low potential, and are only functional at high water potential. The conductivity of cacti roots can be as high as that of many high-resource species (Dubrovsky, North, and Nobel 1998). Belowground, pulse-water species are not very different from high-resource species.

Pulse-water species not only store water during dry times but remain photosynthetically active long after water potentials have dropped below the level at which roots can take up water. To conserve water during dry times, the shoots of succulents can be leafless, which reduces the surface area through which water can be lost when stomata are closed, that is, cuticular transpiration. The stems are also often covered with thick waxes or hairs, which perform multiple functions, including further conservation of water. Photosynthesis occurs near the surface of the stems, generally with the crassulacean acid metabolism (CAM) photosynthetic pathway, which further increases photosynthetic water use efficiency. The water use efficiency (WUE) of CAM species can be three times higher than that of WUE-efficient C_4 species and five times higher than that of efficient

C_3 species (Nobel 1991). With CAM photosynthesis, stomata open only at night, when temperatures and transpiration rates are lower. Light energy that has been stored during the day is then used to fix CO_2 at night.

The key to the greater WUE and to maintaining function during dry times is the ability to store water. The difficulty of storing water lies not only in creating internal vessels to hold the large amounts of water but also in maintaining osmotic function in cells. Many succulents have cells in their stems that can expand when water is highly available and collapse when stores are depleted, ensuring that water is made available for metabolically-active cells (Mauseth 1993, 1995). Others have large belowground storage organs that also can store water, these organs exceeding the size of the shoot by an order of magnitude.

The benefit of increasing water use efficiency comes at a cost of lower light use efficiency and a poor ability to compete for light. These plants reflect a large proportion of the incident light away and develop little potential to shade other plants. Yet, since the relative value of light is low in dry ecosystems, there is little premium to using light efficiently or competing well for light. Plants with the pulse-store strategy also have a low RGR_{max}, as the high allocation to storage, structure, and protection, as well as the low potential to acquire CO_2, reduces the potential for high growth rates. Although RGR_{max} is low, this does not mean that the plants are slow to respond to events, as new roots are produced quickly.

Strategy for Uniformly Low Availability

As with nutrients, no water supply is ever exactly uniform over a given year. Yet the second strategy for success when water is low in availability parallels the low-nutrient strategy and is best considered the strategy for uniformly low water availability. The central trait of the low-water strategy is the ability to withstand high pressures, that is, a low Ψ_{min}. Plants with a low Ψ_{min} and the low-water strategy are generally unresponsive to pulses of high availability of water. Instead, they are best suited to grow at low water availability and, in fact, are the best competitors for low, uniform water supplies. Although pulses of water of varying magnitude are present in habitats occupied by low-water species and are certainly used by low-water species, these plants do not require the pulses to dominate.

For example, at depths greater than approximately 1 m, removal of water occurs largely by transpiration as opposed to evaporation. As such, deep soil water potentials are regulated by the Ψ_{min} of species with roots in deep soil, as the removal of vegetation leads to much greater soil water potential (Scanlon et al. 2005; Seyfried et al. 2005). These data reinforce the idea that for many plants, soil water potential is relatively constant throughout the growing season, and the potential is determined by the plants as well as by other state factors. As would be expected under approximate steady-state conditions, when limited by a single resource, the plant that can best lower availability is competitively superior, thereby driving natural selection to ever lower Ψ_{min}.

The low-water strategy is not limited to plants with deep roots but is best exemplified by deeply rooted plants. Some shallow-rooted, drought-deciduous plants also have low Ψ_{min}, and it would be appropriate to consider these species low-water species also. For example, Sperry and Hacke (2002) observed that the greatest resistance to cavitation among a suite of Great Basin shrubs was in the shallow-rooted, summer deciduous species such as *Grayia spinosa* and *Tetradymia glabrata*. Not all deeply rooted species in arid ecosystems have been selected for the low-water strategy, though. Phreatophytic plants also have deep roots but are able to tap into groundwater and rarely experience declines in water potential. As expected, they have a relatively high Ψ_{min} and are highly susceptible to cavitation (Sperry and Hacke 2002). Grime was likely correct in considering these species as nutrient limited. In tapping into stable high-water availability, they are likely to be strongly limited by nutrients.

To further develop the low-water strategy, it is important to examine the specific adaptations to low water availability. The remainder of this section reviews the most important adaptations to low water availability, focusing on the characteristics of roots, leaves, and xylem.

XYLEM

The largest number of advances in recent years regarding the low-water strategy have been in understanding the adaptations of xylem to low water potential and the mechanisms by which xylem fails at very low water potential (Sperry, Stiller, and Hacke 2003; Hacke et al. 2006). In general, there is considered to be a trade-off between the ability of xylem to move water efficiently and the resistance of xylem to cavitation (Zimmermann 1983; Tyree, Davis, and Cochard 1994). Because there are costs to cavitation resistance, natural selection should optimize the balance between the costs of resistance and the costs of failure in any given environment. In short, resisting cavitation requires producing xylem that can withstand the high negative pressures, as well as ensuring that air is not allowed to "seed into" the water stream (Sperry et al. 1996). It has been hypothesized that withstanding high negative pressures entails a small vessel diameter and reinforced xylem cell walls (Hacke et al. 2001). To keep xylem conduits from imploding, cell walls have to be thick, with thicker walls needed for wider diameter conduits. The ratio of cell wall thickness to conduit diameter scales nonlinearly but predictably with cavitation resistance.

Current knowledge of cavitation suggests that in addition to reinforced cell walls, selection for conductance at low water potential involves in large part minimizing pit area per xylem vessel. To keep air from being drawn into the xylem, interconduit pits that connect xylem vertically and laterally are constructed to act as safety valves and seal against air movement by capillary forces. The more pits there are that connect xylem elements, the more likely it is that one of those pits is a large one and hence subject to introducing air into the xylem at high pressure (Wheeler et al. 2005). Minimizing the area of pits that a vessel has involves low diameter and short vessel length. Although less susceptible to cavitation, shorter, narrower vessels have a greater resistance to water flow, in large part because the pits generate half of the resistance of water moving through the xylem (Sperry, Hacke, and Wheeler 2005). Although it seems that selection would have favored plants with fewer pits per unit of surface area, pits are important for water to flow vertically and laterally. Lateral flow among xylem vessels is important because it allows wounds to be circumvented, as well as diffusing the connections between individual roots and sections of the canopy (Orians et al. 2004).

ROOTS

When examined per unit area, root surfaces have the greatest resistance to water flow in the entire soil-plant-air continuum. The conductivity of water through the root cortex and endodermis is approximately eight orders of magnitude lower than that for the same cross-sectional area of xylem (Sperry 2002). Yet a given plant has much more root surface area than it does xylem cross-sectional area, equalizing the resistance to water flow between the root surface and xylem.

Part of being adapted to low water availability is that roots rarely experience saturated soils and the low oxygen conditions that can accompany high soil moisture content. Many low-water species have high oxygen demands and little ability to persist under conditions of anoxia (Lunt, Letey, and Clark 1973). In addition, low-water species need to maintain good contact with the soil, as tension in the water column can cause the water rope to snap in the rhizosphere. This requires plants to be able to maintain a high root surface area at low water potential (Sperry 2002).

LEAVES

Leaf nitrogen concentrations have often been considered to have been greater for xeric shrubs than for more woody species from mesic environments (West 1981). Killingbeck and Whitford (1996) compared leaf nitrogen concentrations for xeric shrubs and woody plants in other biomes and concluded that "the tenet that desert shrubs support extraordinarily nitrogen-rich foliage can no longer be supported." The lack of support for desert shrubs having higher nitrogen concentrations than woody plants in other biomes does not imply that they have low nitrogen concentrations. They found that the mean nitrogen concentrations of 78 shrubs growing in 11 deserts on five continents was 2.2%, similar to the leaf nitrogen concentrations of trees and shrubs growing in temperate deciduous forests (2.2%) and the overstory trees of tropical wet forests (2.0%).

With caveats for the lack of true common garden experiments to understand genotypic variation among species, although low-water species might not have higher nitrogen concentrations, they do have higher nitrogen concentrations per unit of leaf area than plants in other biomes. Cunningham, Summerhayes, and Westoby (1999) showed there are clear differences in how nitrogen is allocated between sites with low water and sites with low nutrient availability. Speces present in sites with low water availability have higher nitrogen per unit area than related species that grow in high-precipitation sites (figure 10.1). The leaves of low-water species are not necessarily more dense than in other habitats, but they are thick (Wright, Reich, and Westoby 2001). This overall thickness does not come solely as a consequence of increased thickness of the cuticle. Low-water species have high photosynthetic capacity per unit area, which allows them to generate low internal CO$_2$ concentrations (Wright, Reich, and Westoby 2001). With a greater driving force for CO$_2$ to enter the leaf, photosynthetic water use efficiency is higher (Reich, Buschena, et al. 2003).

In addition to having greater nitrogen per unit of leaf area to increase water use efficiency, the leaves of low-water species have other traits that increase water use efficiency and allow the plants to photosynthesize at low water potential. The leaves of low-water species tend to be small (Fonseca et al. 2000), which helps prevent overheating, especially if transpiration declines. The leaves of low-water species also often have thick, waxy cuticles, which reduces cuticular transpiration. To maintain physiological function at low water potential, the leaves of low-water species must be able to generate the osmotic potential to draw water into the leaves. This is accomplished in part by the accumulation of osmoticants, which are common among low-water species.

The leaves of low-water species are generally defended by nitrogen-free secondary compounds. For example, *Juniperus monosperma* has high concentrations of terpenes and phenolics (Adams et al. 1981; Dearing, Mangione, and Karasov 2000), *Larrea tridentata* (creosote bush) has high concentrations of resins, and *Ceanothus* species of the chaparral have high concentrations of phenolics (Mills 1986). Although many of the secondary compounds of low-water species would decrease the nutritive value of the plant biomass to herbivores, water can be more limiting to herbivores than protein in a low-water ecosystem. Not surprisingly, low-

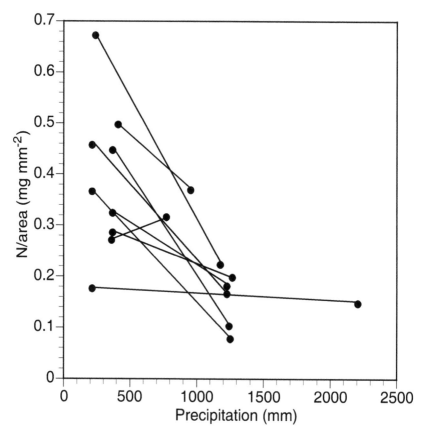

Figure 10.1. Relationship between mean annual precipitation and nitrogen per unit of leaf area for pairs of related species. Data from Cunningham et al. 1999.

water species uniquely have chemicals that exacerbate water stress in herbivores. These chemicals act as diuretics, increasing urine volume or decreasing the osmolarity of urine (Dearing et al. 1999; Dearing, Mangione, and Karasov 2002). Many of these chemicals are nitrogen-free, such as alpha-pinene of *Juniperus monosperma*, but others, such as caffeine, contain nitrogen (Dearing, Mangione, and Karasov 2002).

Competition for Water

Soil water is depleted by abiotic processes such as evaporation and leaching, and is also drawn down by plant uptake. When water is limiting and plants are reducing its availability, adjacent plants should be considered to be competing for water.

When water is supplied in pulses, competition likely takes the form of preemption, in which the plant that can take up water the fastest has the most biomass. Differences in uptake are not sufficient to exclude species, as uptake would likely have to be paired with size-dependent mortality to exclude species that take up water more slowly. When water is supplied more uniformly, R^* considerations likely apply. The plant that can acquire water at the lowest water potential should be able to reduce water potentials to levels lower than could be acquired by competitors. Here, competitors would be excluded by their inability to grow at low water potential.

Competition between the two functional groups seems pretty straight-forward when water is the sole limiting resources. For example, Sala et al. (1989) manipulated the abundance of shallowly rooted grasses (here, the analog is to pulsed-water species) and more deeply rooted shrubs (here, the analog is to low-water species) in Patagonia. Removal of shrubs had little effect on the grasses, while removal of the grasses allowed more water to penetrate to depth, promoting the growth of shrubs. Insofar as shrubs have little shallow root biomass, it would be interesting to know whether low-water species would have a negative effect on pulsed-water species if their root systems overlapped.

Although competition for water seems straightforward and the pro-cesses the dictate soil water movement to and into roots are well under-stood, competition for water is poorly understood (Tinker and Nye 2000). For example, transpiration can deplete soil water around a root on the order of multiple centimeters (Dunham and Nye 1973). Little is known, however, about what traits confer competitive superiority under a given soil water regime. Should roots take up water quickly, be able to acquire water at a low water potential, or have high root length density, like plants competing for nutrients? Pulse-store species such as cacti have high rates of inflow, which suggests that this is advantageous when plants are competing for pulses of water. Low-water species can acquire water at a low water potential. Is this advantageous when competing for low, uniform supplies of water? Unfortunately, there has been little theoretical investigation of these questions.

Other questions that come to mind concerning the consequences of competition for water for selection in low-water environments have to do with whether plants overallocate to roots or root function. Has natural selection that arises as a result of competition for water selected for plants that produce or maintain more roots than would be optimal in the ab-sence of competition, just as happened for nutrients? Although nutrient uptake when supplies are uniformly low is not benefited from increases in uptake capacity, it is possible that water uptake can be enhanced by having higher rates of water uptake or conductance than would be opti-mal in the absence of competition.

Although these questions and other related questions about the consequences of water competition for natural selection have not been addressed, there is evidence that competition for water has selected for root placement in soil profiles that is suboptimal in the absence of competition. Van Wijk and Bouten (2001) examined the distribution of roots in four forests in the Netherlands (figure 10.2). They then used a simulation to determine what should be the distribution of roots that maximized water uptake in the absence and presence of competition, given the precipitation regimes and soil properties at each site. For three of the four sites, actual root distributions most closely resembled those that optimized water uptake under competition, not in the absence of competition. Competition for water alters natural selection to favor shallower root distributions than are optimal in the absence of competition. The authors reasoned that in most soils, water that falls on the soil surface percolates down to lower roots eventually. By maintaining roots at depth, during dry years, the deeper roots would benefit from capillary rise of groundwater, while still being able to acquire rainwater. Maintaining shallow root systems preempts water from plants that hold their roots deep, even at the cost of reduced access to water during dry years. For these forests, which rarely experience water stress, the consequences of competition theoretically reduced 10-year transpiration by 10%–20% among three of the four forests.

In addition to altering the vertical distribution of roots in the soil profile, competition has likely altered the response of roots to soil drying. Again, evidence for this is at best suggestive (at worst, speculative), but there appear to be clear differences among species in the way that root production responds to drying soil. Liang and Harris (2005) examined the response among a number of species of lateral root formation when root systems were exposed to abscisic acid (ABA). ABA is a plant hormone that is released when plants are stressed for water and is critical in a plant's response to stress (Chapin 1991). Interestingly, some plants responded to exposure to ABA by increasing their lateral root production, while others decreased their production. The dichotomy of responses could be associated with whether low water availability has primarily occurred as a consequence of competition, in which case it might be beneficial to increase root production, or whether competition is unimportant in soil drying, in which case there might be little benefit to increasing root production, since increasing root biomass does not increase the fraction of the water supply that plants acquire.

The potential consequences of these studies warrant further investigation. For example, van Wijk and Bouten (2001) note that the need to acquire nutrients might have also led to the shallower root distributions that were seen in the Netherlands forests relative to the theoretically opti-

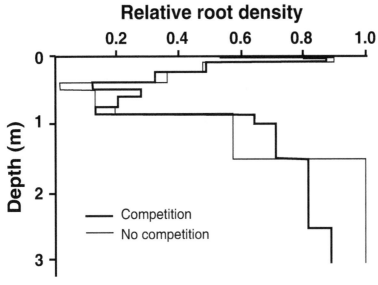

Figure 10.2. Distribution of root biomass for trees in northern Europe (Competition) versus the theoretical distribution that would optimize production in the absence of competition (No competition). With competition, more roots are placed shallow, potentially to intercept rainfall before reaching deeper depths, although the potential for nutrient acquisition to alter rooting depths was not investigated. In the absence of competition, plants would show 10%–20% greater productivity by being able to better access deeper soil water during dry times. Data from van Wijk and Bouten.

mal distributions. Nevertheless, natural selection for plants to compete for water has likely altered root distributions and root functioning in ways that are not quite currently understood. Hopefully, this will be an area of thoughtful research in the near future.

Separating Water and Nutrient Limitation

In an earlier section of his book, Grime recognized the same two strategies associated with low water availability and ascribed some of the same characteristics to the strategies as has been done here. With the convergence and commonality hypotheses erected (see chapter 2), he then asks whether the low-water strategies are a result of nutrient limitation in low-water environments, or whether they can be explained by water limitation alone.

The two pages that Grime devotes to favoring the commonality hypothesis over the convergence hypothesis are interesting. Grime states that "low rainfall and soil infertility coincide" and that many high-nutrient habitats in dry environments are dominated by high resource species. His two main arguments are that models of nutrient uptake show that "restricted nutrient uptake is unavoidable in perennials exploiting habitats in low rainfall conditions." He then states that most of the evidence (at the time) that might refute the commonality hypothesis (e.g., Cunningham, Summerhayes, and Westoby 1999) is an artifact of "restricting the comparison to perennial species; it can be argued that successful exploitation of habitats combining high soil fertility with low rainfall rests almost exclusively with ephemeral species" (Grime 2001, p. 69).

As Grime did, it is important to separate the convergence and commonality hypotheses. Nutrient limitation in low-water environments is poorly understood. A major unanswered question regarding low-water strategies is the interaction between nutrient and water stress. It is clear that low-water species have some plant traits that are congruent with those of low-nutrient species. For example, leaves can live a relatively long time, and plants can have a low RGR_{max}. Yet there are no models that can differentiate as to whether these traits can be explained strictly as a consequence of water limitation or whether plants in low-water environments are also limited by nutrients, which has selected for the low-nutrient traits.

One place to start in examining whether nutrients are strongly limiting in low-water habitats is with fertilization experiments. David Hooper and Loretta Johnson (1999) examined the relationship between precipitation and the response of aboveground net primary production (ANPP) to fertilization with nitrogen in a literature survey of fertilization experiments. From their data it is clear that dry ecosystems (<400 mm mean annual precipitation, MAP) could respond to increases in nitrogen availability, although the dominant pattern is that nitrogen limitation is greater at high precipitation, regardless of whether the greater precipitation comes as a result of interannual variation or regional patterns. As such, in a wet year at a dry site, productivity of the resident plants is nitrogen limited. Water seems to be a lot more limiting than nitrogen to stand-level productivity in an average year at a dry site. Yet, echoing Grime's earlier arguments, it is hard to know whether low-water plants were nitrogen-limited or had the potential to respond to additional precipitation, as much of the biomass response might have come from high-resource plants. Along those lines, it is hard to extend the results of Hooper and Johnson to any statement on whether low-water species have been selected to have what appear to be low-nutrient traits as a result of evolutionary-scale nutrient limitation or whether the apparently low-nutrient traits have not been influenced by nutrient limitation.

While on the traits of low-water species, can a conceptual argument be made for nutrient limitation having been important in the evolution of the species? Is it possible that it is primarily nutrient limitation that is driving low-water plants to be able to acquire water at low water potential? For example, if plant water availability is variable over time, there might be less cost to plants that are not limited by nutrients to drop their leaves than the costs of reinforced xylem and lower conductance when water is more available. This argument rests in part on the temporal variability of water availability. For example, if the periodicity of variability is high, there will be greater costs of replacing leaves each time water availability declines, since leaves would have to be replaced often. If water availability declines at a low frequency, then it is more likely that it is the nutrient costs of replacing leaves that favor plants that can withstand low water potential. As such, it might be less costly to develop the ability to withstand the occasional low soil water potential than to drop and replace leaves during these occasional times.

Other evidence raises further questions that need to be answered before the low-water strategy can be understood. For example, low-water species often tap into soil water in deeper layers. If water was limiting, these plants should be competing for the deep soil water. In this case there is no benefit to leaving water in the soil, nor is it an evolutionarily stable strategy, as genotypes that use remaining water would produce more biomass and be more successful. In some ecosystems, deep water (>5 m) is drawn down by transpiration to the low wilting points of low-water species (<−5 MPa) (Robinson, Harper, and Smettem 2006). Yet in many ecosystems with pronounced dry seasons, water is not drawn down to wilting points during the dry season (Williams et al. 1997), indicating that other factors such as nutrients are likely limiting.

By no means are the extent and nature of nutrient limitation on a global scale understood. For the pulse-store water strategy, however, it is hard to argue that this strategy arose as a response to low nutrient availability. The roots of plants using this strategy grow quickly, not slowly. Species with leaves that exhibit the pulse-store strategy have leaves with high activity, high nutrient concentrations, and short longevity. The progenitor of cactus, *Pereskia*, resembles a high-resource species in this regard, as do the leaves of other euphorbia and "leafy succulents" such as ocotillo (*Foquieria splendens*) of the deserts of the southwestern United States and northern Mexico. It is hard to argue that the final selection pressure that took what might be considered a high-resource plant and shaped it into a leafless succulent was nutrient stress. These plants lost leaves not because the leaves came at too high a nutrient cost but because they came at too high a water cost.

It is also plausible that any "low-nutrient" traits that low-water species have could be explained solely by low water availability. Low-water species are the species that converge most in traits with low-nutrient species. As Grime recognized, they have small scleromorphic leaves that can live a relatively long time, and the plants have low RGR_{max}. The argument for nutrient limitation that Grime made based on models of nutrient limitation is at best a half-truth. It is true that nutrient diffusion declines as soil water volume declines, but this does not in any way support the hypothesis that plants should be more limited by nutrients than by water in low-water environments. Likewise, it is possible that researchers have ignored annuals in low-water environments, and their consistent absence might be due to consistent low nutrient availability. To disprove this, one would have to show that with fertilization, high-resource species outcompete low-water species in a low-water environment or that the high-resource species cannot persist in the presence of low-water species.

Although an understanding of nutrients in low-water environments is poor, it could be argued that water availability alone could explain the low-water strategy. For example, if water availability is uniformly low over long periods for some species, the roots, stems, and leaves of those species must be able to withstand the high negative pressures that develop as water availability declines. This adaptation would require additional allocation to cell walls, increasing tissue density, possibly decreasing leaf nitrogen concentrations, and slowing maximum growth rates. A more thorough theoretical treatment of this idea is warranted, but nutrients do not have to be limiting for plants to be selected to have the "low-nutrient" suite of leaf or root traits.

In addition to this conceptual evidence of convergence, Cunningham et al. (1999) showed there are clear differences in how nitrogen is allocated between sites with low water and sites with low nutrient availability. Leaf nitrogen concentrations in plants that occupy dry sites are often low in nitrogen concentrations, but low-water species have higher nitrogen per unit area than relatives that grow in high-precipitation sites (figure 10.1). Wright et al. (2005) reasoned that the high leaf nitrogen concentrations on an areal basis allow plants to draw down intercellular CO_2 concentrations, which generates a higher photosynthetic WUE. If low water availability created selection pressures primarily through low nutrient availability, there would be no reason for leaves of dry sites to have different relationships between nitrogen concentrations and other functional traits than leaves of in wetter, low-nutrient sites.

Nutrient limitation has likely affected the adaptations of low-water species. At this point, just as with light and nutrients, the convergence hypothesis is a more parsimonious explanation than the commonality hypothesis for the similarity in some traits of low-water and low-nutrient species. Yet nutrients, like other resources, have the potential to co-limit production with water in low-water environments. Co-limitation between water and other resources is a critical aspect of the low-water strategy and is the topic of the next section.

Co-limitation and Water

In the absence of aboveground disturbance, low nutrient supplies are often associated with co-limitation between light and nutrients for plants. As described in chapter 7, removing constraints on leaf longevity increases the ability of species to maintain high leaf area. With greater leaf longevity generating greater leaf area, light can co-limit plants along with nutrients, even in ecosystems that, had they been dominated by other species shaped by frequent aboveground disturbance, would have been considered strongly nutrient limited.

But what about water? What resources co-limit production with water in dry ecosystems? Are there basic properties of low-water environments that are better understood by identifying any co-limitation, or are there reasons why resources might not co-limit production with water?

Shallowly rooted plants are unlikely to exhibit strong trade-offs in allocation for acquisition of water and nutrients. The same shallow roots that acquire water also likely acquire nutrients. For plants with shallow and deep roots, there might be trade-offs between the two parts of the root systems, with deep roots acquiring water and shallow roots acquiring nutrients. However, recent work has begun to identify deep roots as a source of nutrient acquisition too. In all, if co-limitation exists between water and nutrients in low-water environments, it is likely to be a result of supplies matching demand, independent of plant traits, and not a result of trade-offs in allocation. For example, denitrification rates can be high in dry ecosystems (Austin and Sala 1999), which would lower the availability of nitrogen when supplied in excess to plant demand. Any observed limitation of production by nitrogen in low-water environments is likely more associated with serial limitation than with true co-limitation.

Light is unlikely to co-limit production with water. Many low-water plants have a host of adaptations to reduce light absorption, and there is little reason to believe that increasing light availability would increase growth in arid ecosystems. But why would light co-limit production with nutrients but not with water? Low-water ecosystems do not necessarily suffer frequent aboveground disturbance that would limit leaf longevity and leaf area accumulation. The fundamental difference between water and nutrients is that for water to be used for photosynthesis, it must be lost immediately from the plant. Nutrients can be used while still being retained, at least until leaves are shed, at which time only half the amount of most nutrients is lost. By increasing leaf longevity, plants can increase the mean residence time of nutrients and allow leaf area to accumulate as nitrogen content of the canopy accumulates.

This cannot be done for water. Plants can increase the mean residence time of water, but only by storing it nonproductively. If plants do increase their leaf area in a dry environment by increasing leaf longevity, water-limited plants do not have greater canopy-level photosynthesis. Water stress develops more quickly as leaf area increases, and water-limited plants with greater leaf area have to close their stomata earlier. Low-nutrient plants can use resources to increase supplies of water, but plants competing for water have little ability to do this. Water supplies are strictly regulated by state factors. In all, although natural selection can produce plants that can be co-limited by nutrients and light in ecosystems with low nutrient supplies, the analog for water cannot be generated. Low-water environments must have open canopies.

Over historical times, water-limited plants have been co-limited by an aboveground resource, but that resource is not light. The exchanges that dominate photosynthesis are those between water and CO_2. Although the responses of low-water plants to elevated CO_2 levels are complex and depend on what CO_2 concentrations are being compared, increasing CO_2 can increase the WUE of photosynthesis for low-water plants (Huxman et al. 1998, Smith et al. 2000; Anderson et al. 2001). The adaptations to low CO_2, which in part reflect the consequences for water availability, are described in the next section.

Carbon Dioxide

CO_2 is the major building block of plants, serving both to provide structure and as the primary initial repository for metabolic energy. Although CO_2 concentrations in the air surrounding plants vary seasonally, diurnally, and spatially, most of the selective pressure associated with variation in CO_2 concentrations has been on geological time scales. The first land plants evolved during a period when CO_2 concentrations were high, and therefore periods of low CO_2 concentrations are considered to have had the strongest selective pressure. With the ancestral condition being high atmospheric CO_2, it was low, not high, CO_2 concentrations that would have caused plants to diverge from their ancestral state.

This section briefly reviews the geological scale patterns of atmospheric CO_2 concentrations and the major radiations that occurred during times of extremely low CO_2 concentrations. The relative importance of factors under low CO_2 concentrations is reviewed next, for a better understanding of the nature of natural selection during these times. Finally, with an understanding of how the importance of some factors might have changed owing to recent anthropogenic increases in atmospheric CO_2 concentrations, the adaptations that arose as a consequence of low atmospheric CO_2 concentrations are addressed. Low CO_2 concentrations exacerbate water limitation as a consequence of inherent trade-offs between acquisition of CO_2 and loss of water during photosynthesis. As such, water stress and selection for low-water strategies likely were more extreme during periods of low atmospheric CO_2.

Concentrations of CO_2 and Radiations

Before the rise of vascular land plants, CO_2 concentrations in the atmosphere were estimated to be on the order of 4,000 ppm, more than ten times higher than the anthropogenically enriched concentrations of today. Since then, there have been two major periods of relatively low CO_2 concentrations. With vascular plants spreading over the terrestrial surface, CO_2 concentrations were reduced strongly after land plants spread across the globe. CO_2 concentrations declined to approximately 500 ppm between the Devonian and Carboniferous periods, more than 300 MYA (Willis and McElwain 2002). Land plants weather rocks, which react with atmospheric CO_2 to produce carbonates, but also to produce recalcitrant organic matter, which can be stored for long periods. CO_2 concentrations rose during the Mesozoic, began to fall during the latter half of the Mesozoic, and reached low values again during the Tertiary. During the mid- to late Miocene (<15 MYA), CO_2 concentrations fell again to low concentrations, often declining below 200 ppm at different times in the last few million years.

Although many of the initial radiations of land plants occurred during times of low CO_2 300 MYA, assessing the importance of factors and adaptations to low CO_2 is restricted to the past 15 million years. During the Miocene there were a large number of radiations, such as in grasses and members of the Aizoaceae family (Klak, Reeves, and Hedderson 2004). These radiations were coupled with the development of many novel ecosystems, such as grasslands and the Karoo in South Africa. During this period, C_4 and CAM plants evolved for the first time. While these plant lines were undergoing radiations, more than just CO_2 concentrations were declining. Aridity and fire also increased as rain shadows developed with the uplift of mountain ranges. Although many factors were changing during this period, from experimental work and analyses of radiations it is possible to reconstruct some of the direct effects of low CO_2 and the strategies that arose to deal with the decline in resource levels.

Importance of Factors for C_3 Plants at Low CO_2

As for other resource limitations, three hypotheses could explain how low CO_2 concentrations allowed some species to dominate and how low concentrations directed natural selection. First, applying the stress resistance hypothesis produces the hypothesis that some species are unable to grow at the low CO_2 concentrations that were experienced during the Miocene and the Pleistocene. Because there were no virtually no refuges of high CO_2 when CO_2 concentrations dropped below 200 ppm, any species that could not grow at these low concentrations would have been extirpated. Although it is possible that some species perished solely because of low CO_2 concentrations, it is almost virtually impossible that any C_3 species that is around today would not be able to reproduce in the absence of other stresses or disturbances at low CO_2, as there would have been virtually no refuge from low atmospheric CO_2 concentrations.

Second, competition for CO_2 cannot explain the relative abundance of plants in a low-CO_2 world, no less selection during this time. In contrast to competition for water, nutrients, and light, individual plants are not considered to compete for atmospheric CO_2. The air around plants is coupled well to the general atmosphere, and replenishment of CO_2 to the local environment around adjacent plants occurs relatively quickly. As such, the effects of one plant drawing down CO_2 concentrations are incredibly diffuse, with little local interaction that could be considered competition.

Because all modern species should have been able to grow and persist at low CO_2 concentrations in the absence of competition for resources and disturbance, the question turns to the third hypothesis, which is that low CO_2 concentrations altered the relative importance of other stresses, such as low water or low nutrient availability, compared to that of disturbances in determining the relative abundance of species at low CO_2, no less selection during these times. Understanding the effects of low CO_2 on plant performance requires understanding the effects of low CO_2 on the impact of the stresses of other resources, competition for those resources, and susceptibility to other stresses and disturbances such as herbivory. The next section covers the basic responses of plants to low CO_2, followed by the likely main adaptations to low CO_2.

Plant Growth at Low CO_2

Experimental reduction in CO_2 concentrations directly affects photosynthesis and has a cascade of effects that alters the relative availability of other resources, as well as the interaction between plants and herbivores. A decrease in CO_2 concentrations decreases the driving gradient in CO_2 from outside the leaf to inside the leaf. As such, for a given degree of stomatal opening, the short-term consequences of declining CO_2 are to reduce photosynthesis.

The best summary of the effects of low CO_2 on plants comes from an experiment carried out in the grasslands of Texas in which vegetation was exposed to a range of CO_2 concentrations from subambient (ca. 200 ppm) to superambient (ca. 550 ppm) for more than three years (Gill et al. 2002). Although many of the grasses were C$_4$ grasses, C$_4$ grasses are not entirely unresponsive to CO$_2$ concentrations. As such, the qualitative response of the plants and the changes in the ecosystem characteristics form a good analog for the selection pressures that exist in a low-CO$_2$ world.

When plants grown at the concentrations of CO$_2$ that plants would have experienced during full glacial times (~200 ppm) were compared with plants grown at modern ambient CO$_2$ concentrations, the former were found to have lower photosynthetic rates. There are some compensatory mechanisms that plants can use to adjust to lower CO$_2$ concentrations—reducing CO$_2$ concentrations by half does not necessarily halve photosynthetic rates. Yet the basic condition of greater carbon stress at low CO$_2$ is clear (figure 10.3).

The consequences of lower photosynthetic rates cascade throughout the plant and the ecosystem. First, lower photosynthetic rates lower biomass production rates, a natural if not necessary consequence of plants being limited by carbon. Second, with less carbon being fixed, nitrogen concentrations in the leaves and roots are higher. With higher tissue nitrogen concentrations, biomass entering the decomposition cycle also has higher nitrogen concentrations, and there is less immobilization of nitrogen by microbes. Consequently, soil nitrogen availability increases.

Third, with less carbon being fixed, carbon-demanding secondary processes suffer disproportionally from carbon stress. In accordance with the carbon-nutrient balance hypothesis (Bryant, Chapin, and Klein 1983), carbon-based secondary chemicals are reduced in abundance. In the Texas grassland, *Bothriochloa ischaemum*, commonly known as stinkgrass, showed declining levels of phenolics in its roots with declining CO$_2$ concentrations (figure 10.3). Other experiments have shown that allocation of carbon to thorns also declines at low CO$_2$ (Bond and Kgope, unpublished). Even though thorns are associated with high nutrient supply, their construction is carbon intensive and suffers at low CO$_2$. There has been no experimental test to investigate the consequences of low CO$_2$ on concentrations of nitrogen-containing defensive chemicals. Nevertheless, the increased tissue nitrogen concentrations and decreased carbon-based defenses suggest that many species were much better to eat when CO$_2$ concentrations were lower than they are today. In addition to a reduction in the production of secondary chemicals, allocation of carbon to stem production also declined (Bond, Midgley, and Woodward 2003; Bond personal communication), as plants put on height at a lower rate with declining atmospheric CO$_2$ concentrations.

The consequences of carbon stress for coupled carbon-nitrogen cycling are clear. Plants that are under greater carbon stress have lower photosynthetic rates, produce less biomass, have higher tissue nitrogen concentra-

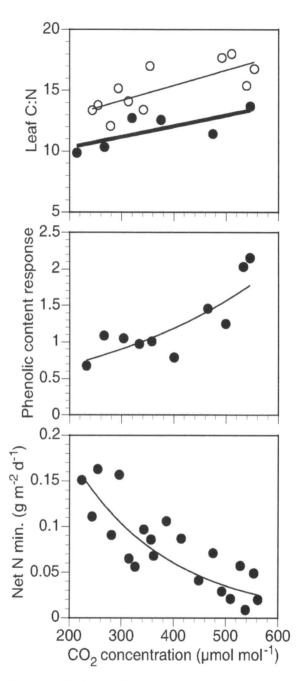

Figure 10.3. Changes in leaf and soil characteristics across a range of CO_2 concentrations from a grassland in Texas. As CO_2 concentrations decline, leaf C:N declines, leaf phenolic concentrations decline, and net nitrogen mineralization increases. Data from Gill et al. 2002.

tions, and have lower amounts of C-based structural and chemical defenses. These plants are less proficient at competing for nutrients and water and would be more susceptible to herbivory and ground-based disturbances such as fire. While there is a strong trade-off between carbon and nitrogen in plants, there are also strong trade-offs between CO$_2$ and water, as highlighted in the section on low-water strategies. If so, what are the consequences for a plant's water relations in a low-CO$_2$ world?

As mentioned earlier, the decline in photosynthesis that accompanies low CO$_2$ concentrations does not scale with the decline in CO$_2$ concentrations themselves. Plants can partially compensate for low CO$_2$ concentrations at physiological, tissue, organ, and whole-plant levels. One of the major ways in which plants adjust to low CO$_2$ concentrations is to open their stomata more or to produce leaves with greater stomatal density (Polley, Johnson, Marino, et al. 1993; Beerling 2005). The consequence of having a greater stomatal opening to allow more CO$_2$ to enter the leaves is that more water escapes the leaves. As such, low CO$_2$ concentrations increase transpiration rates in plants and decrease short-term water availability. All other things equal, plants in a low-CO$_2$ world are more likely to be stressed for water.

Before we proceed to the adaptations of plants to low CO$_2$ availability, there are sets of feedbacks that extend beyond the ability of most experiments to incorporate but that provide an important context for interpreting experimental results. For coupled carbon-nitrogen cycles, it is important to consider long-term feedbacks among plant productivity, litter quality, SOM dynamics, and nitrogen cycling. Just as short-term responses of microbial immobilization to the input of high C:N litter might not match long-term responses (see chapter 7), so too the short-term responses of nitrogen cycling to low CO$_2$ might not match long-term responses. Nitrogen mineralization might be elevated for a period but not long term, as soil nitrogen content and possibly N$_2$ fixation decline. For water, plants might transpire more in experiments, but at regional scales this might be associated with greater precipitation. Moreover, times of low CO$_2$ concentrations were cooler on average, which might have resulted in decreased evapotranspiration as well. Certainly glacial times were considered more arid in many ways than today, but there are some negative feedbacks on lower water availability that might ameliorate plant water stress.

For example, *Juniperus* wood recovered from the Rancho La Brea tar pit recorded internal CO$_2$ concentrations for the plants from 7 to 55 kyr ago (Ward et al. 2005). The trees growing during times of low CO$_2$ concentrations had much lower internal CO$_2$ concentrations than modern *Juniperus* trees, indicating that the plants would have been highly stressed for carbon. Internal CO$_2$ concentrations were calculated to be 113 ppm, as opposed to 150 ppm for pre-industrial plants and 187 for modern plants. Although internal CO_2 concentrations were lower, trees growing at low CO_2 concentrations maintained similar ratios of internal to external CO_2 concentrations, which can only be accomplished by having more stomata open. With more open stomata, transpiration should have been greater, but the isotopic composition of the wood suggested that plants did not suffer more from water stress during this time. Humidity in the air was calculated to be higher as well as temperatures lower, which alone might have reduced transpiration, but might have also been associated with greater precipitation.

The full ramifications of growing in an atmosphere with low CO_2 concentrations still remain to be worked through. Nevertheless, empirical evidence and first principles can be used to preliminarily identify some of the major adaptations to low atmospheric CO_2.

Adaptations to Low CO_2

In a low-CO_2 world, plant carbon stress affects almost every plant process and cascades throughout the soil and the food web. Plants have lower photosynthetic rates, less carbon available for biomass production, and less carbon available for C-demanding secondary allocation such as the production of defensive chemicals and stems. Many plants are less well defended, have higher protein concentrations, and cannot grow in height as quickly, rendering them more susceptible to ground-based disturbances. To compensate for low CO_2 concentrations, plants increase stomatal conductance, which increases transpiration and the importance of water stress. Many of the adaptations to low water availability have been selected for or strengthened as a result of low atmospheric CO_2.

Within that backdrop, what traits have led some species to prosper in a low-CO_2 world? What has been the shape of natural selection as a consequence of low CO_2? With little experimentation on the issue and even less surveying of plants, the full range of adaptations is unclear. There are two major components of the low-CO_2 strategy, the first of which, modifications to photosynthesis, has been well developed elsewhere, while the second, modifications to structure and defense, has been largely ignored but is likely just as important.

PHOTOSYNTHESIS

The best-known adaptations to low CO_2 are changes in morphology and biochemistry of leaves that alter the photosynthetic pathways. The C_4 and CAM photosynthetic pathways are both adaptations to low atmospheric CO_2 concentrations. Approximately 10% of the world's flora photosynthesize by one of the two pathways. Approximately 60% of the

10,000 species of monocots undergo C_4 photosynthesis, while only approximately 1,200 dicots have evolved the pathway (Sage 2004). There are estimated to be approximately 16,000 CAM species in the world (Winter and Smith 1996). Although C_4 photosynthesis arose at different times in different lineages (Sage 2004), in general, CO_2 concentrations were low when C_4 plants evolved. Because C_4 plants are distributed across wet and dry habitats (as opposed to CAM plants, which occur only in dry habitats), the C_4 pathway is more an adaptation to low CO_2 than to low water.

More comprehensive reviews of C_4 and CAM photosynthesis are presented elsewhere (Ting 1985; Sage 2004), but a few key characteristics of C_4 photosynthesis are highlighted here (CAM photosynthesis was described in an earlier section in this chapter). When CO_2 concentrations are low and temperature or light availability is high, the ratio of O_2 to CO_2 within the leaf can rise to the point at which Rubisco, the main photosynthetic enzyme, catalyzes the respiration of sugars with oxygen, rather than the synthesis of new sugars with CO_2. Under these conditions, this *photorespiration* can reduce net photosynthesis dramatically. To reduce photorespiration, C_4 photosynthesis involves structures within the leaf that concentrate and isolate chloroplasts. Paired with the structural modifications, C_4 photosynthesis involves the synthesis of enzymes that produce products that shuttle and concentrate CO_2 at the point of photosynthesis. With C_4 photosynthesis, the concentration of CO_2 at the chloroplasts can range between 1,000 and 2,000 ppm, virtually eliminating photorespiration.

Like other adaptations to low resource availability, the C_4 and CAM photosynthetic pathways come at a cost when resource availability is high. At high CO_2 concentrations, the additional allocation to cell walls and enzymes reduces maximum photosynthetic rates by about 30% (Chapin, Matson, and Mooney 2002). It is only when CO_2 concentrations are low that net photosynthesis and RGR can be higher for C_4 species than for C_3 species. The benefit of C_4 photosynthesis in having high net rates of photosynthesis at low CO_2 concentrations comes at the cost of having lower net photosynthesis and lower growth rates at high CO_2.

For other resources besides CO_2, it was possible that resource levels could be low enough naturally in some environments for plants to be able to successfully grow and reproduce. Light levels, water availability, and nutrient availability can each be too low for a plant to grow and reproduce. Like these resources, CO_2 concentrations can be too low for a plant to grow and reproduce in the absence of other stresses. For example, although sensitive to light, temperature, and oxygen levels, at modern CO_2 concentrations, C_3 species cannot have net photosynthesis below approximately 40–70 ppm, while C_4 plants can photosynthesize down to 3 ppm

(Nobel 1999). Assuming that these minimum concentrations correspond to differences in whole-plant CO_2 requirements, it is unlikely that stress from low CO_2 concentrations alone were sufficient to exclude C_3 species from a given habitat. Even though whole-plant CO_2 compensation points are higher than the compensation points of photosynthesis (Sage 2004), Miocene concentrations never declined below 180 ppm. Hence, any remaining C_3 plants should have been able to tolerate atmospheric concentrations at this level, else they likely would have gone extinct.

If all remaining plants can grow in the absence of stress from other resources at the lowest atmospheric CO_2 concentrations that occurred during the Miocene, then low CO_2 must have had an effect on the differential ability of plants to compete for other resources besides CO_2. Low CO_2 reduces the ability of some species to produce and maintain root length, potentially altering the relative ability of species to compete well for nutrients. For example, some C_4 grass species today are good competitors for nutrients, implying that nutrient competition was likely important at glacial CO_2 concentrations. Low CO_2 also increases the LCP of photosynthesis (Polley, Johnson, Mayeux, et al. 1993), presumably raising whole-plant LCPs. Although the C_4 pathway is not found in woody plants, low CO_2 still likely affected the competitive ability for light during the second stage of light competition, too. At the very least, trees would have been less able to reduce light levels and therefore less able to shade out C_4 grasses.

As water conductance and water stress increase at low CO_2, soils dry out faster, likely altering the ability of some species to reduce water levels quickly or to reduce water to a lower level in soil. C_4 and CAM photosynthesis also provide greater water use efficiency, but the greater WUE in and of itself is unlikely to provide an advantage if plants are competing for water. At low CO_2 concentrations, lower photosynthetic rates can be compensated for in part with greater stomatal conductance. Yet reducing uptake of water does not confer a competitive advantage. A plant that leaves water in the environment leaves it to be used by another plant. Hence, efficiency of use is of little benefit when competitors can compensate with increased uptake. The greater photosynthetic WUE of C_4 and CAM species does not necessarily imply greater dominance in a low CO_2 world. The greater efficiency becomes useful only when paired with similar or greater acquisition rates. In dry areas, CAM plants both rapidly acquire pulses of water and store the water. Later, the water is used more efficiently.

The last general hypothesis regarding low resource availability is differential disturbance resistance. Plants resist herbivores by producing defenses. Plants resist physical disturbances by producing structures, such as thick cell walls. The next section addresses the unique adaptations for defense and structure plants have developed in response to low atmospheric CO_2 that allow them to perform well in the face of agents of disturbance.

DEFENSE AND STRUCTURE

Photosynthetic adaptations increase the ability of plants to acquire carbon at low atmospheric CO_2 concentrations. Yet increasing the ability to acquire carbon at low atmospheric CO_2 comes at a cost of slower maximum growth rates, as well as greater costs of other resources such as water. Natural selection can alter photosynthetic pathways to reduce the effects of low CO_2 concentrations, but even C_4 plants grown at low CO_2 are still under carbon stress.

In general, to cope with stress caused by low availability of other resources, selection favored plants that had lower requirements for the limiting resource. For example, plants selected to perform well under stress from low nitrogen supplies had lower nitrogen demands as a result of producing tissues with lower nitrogen concentrations, using secondary compounds that did not require nitrogen, and increasing resorption efficiencies. To cope with carbon stress, it is difficult to decrease the carbon requirements of plants. Respiration rates are determined by metabolically active nitrogen, and the ratio between nitrogen and respiration is relatively inflexible. Carbon resorption from leaves cannot be increased much as most carbon in leaves is not easy to break down. Also, the carbon content of most structures is fixed—there is no way to build a unit of cellulose or lignin with less carbon. It seems that coping with carbon stress can only be accomplished by reducing the allocation of carbon to secondary processes, not by altering the carbon requirement of the processes.

Although there might seem to be little opportunity to substitute other resources for carbon, there are some functions for which there are substitutes for carbon. Silica (SiO_2) is found in the most ancient of land plants, such as horsetails and ferns. Among recent radiations, silica is well-known to occur in high concentrations in the leaves of grasses (Hodson et al. 2005). For example, wheat (*Avena sativa*) can have more than 10% silicon by mass, *Panicum texanum* has been reported to have more than 7% silicon, and *Lolium perenne* to have more than 6% silicon by mass. Silica is also found in other angiosperms besides grasses. For example, *Fagus sylvatica* leaves have been observed to have 11% silicon dry mass, which is more than 23% silica. Other species observed to have high silicon concentrations include *Abies pectinata* (noble fir, 6.25%), *Celtis occidentalis* (common hackberry, 4.1%), and *Urtica dioica* (stinging nettle, 1.75%).

Not all species have silica in their leaves. For example, *Typha angustifolium* (narrow-leaved cattail) can have less than 0.1% silicon, grasses such as *Cynodon dactylon* can have 0.15% silicon, and *Chenopodium album* has been noted to have no detectable silica in its leaves. Some of the variation is likely environmental or genotypic within species. For example, other studies of wheat have found foliar silicon concentrations below 0.3%. Some soils are low in minerals containing silica, while silica is poorly available to plants at high pH, which might explain some of the variation observed within species. It should also be recognized that there have been no large-scale common garden studies to examine silica accumulation among species, and so there is little understanding of genotypic variation among species in silica use.

If silica is present in some species at apparently high concentrations, is its presence potentially adaptive under low CO_2 concentrations? Silicon, one of the two elements comprising silica, is not considered an essential element for plant growth. Plants can grow and reproduce in its absence. Silica can be taken up passively in the transpiration stream, but it can also be actively acquired by roots (Liang, Si, and Romheld 2005), which might indicate that its presence is adaptive.

There are two main ways that silica is used in tissues. First, silica can be used as a defense. With the high carbon costs of many defensive chemicals, substituting an inorganic element for carbon would greatly benefit some species under low atmospheric CO_2. The rise in silica-rich grasses during the Miocene was associated with an increase in the height of the crowns of the teeth of herbivores. Silica is the main mineral in phytoliths, small shards of the mineral that sit between cell walls of many plant species (Epstein 1999). Phytoliths wear down teeth and increase the force that is required to chew or cut foliage, and also increase herbivore handling time of material (Lucas et al. 2000). Silica also cuts the soft tissues of animals and can elicit allergic reactions. Selection experiments have shown that rodents select against foliage with silica, choosing silica-free forage when given a choice (Gali-Muhtasib, Smith, and Higgins 1992). High silica concentrations in forage in concert with low water availability can also cause silica urolithiasis, in which the urethra of some mammals becomes blocked with silica deposits, preventing the mammal from urinating and causing what is colloquially known as "water-belly" in cattle (Parker 1957).

The second main use of silica in plants is as a cell-wall stiffener. In horticulture, hydroponically grown plants of species such as cucumber benefit from silica in solution. In field agriculture, sugar cane is also often fertilized with silica to enhance growth. In non-crop plants, McNaughton (1985) found that the presence of silica in a hydroponic solution of a C_4 grass led to greater growth, stiffer and taller stems, and greater flowering. The mechanisms by which silica enhances growth include stiffening cell walls, much as lignin does, but at a fraction of the carbon cost of lignin (Raven 2003). The presence of silica also confers greater resistance to disease, likely through its effects on cell walls or by allowing plants to shunt carbon to defense as opposed to structure.

The use of inorganic structures for structure and growth in low-CO$_2$ species is not limited to silica. For example, *Cactus* species can have high concentrations of calcium oxalate crystals (up to 85% dry mass) (Cheavin 1938). An open question is whether low CO$_2$ would have favored species with nitrogen-free secondary chemicals. If less carbon is available for quantitative chemicals, such as tannins, as well as for organic structural defenses, such as thorns, would low CO$_2$ favor nitrogen-based chemicals? Without targeted phylogenetic analyses of nitrogen-based defenses and experiments in which plants with different defenses are grown in low CO$_2$ in the presence of herbivores, one of the most intriguing questions about ecosystems and natural selection when atmospheric CO$_2$ concentrations were low cannot be answered.

SUMMARY

Although water and CO$_2$ are directly exchanged for one another during photosynthesis, there are fundamental differences in the strategies to succeed when each is limiting. Like nutrients, water is supplied to plants generally in the soil and transported to leaves for use in photosynthesis. Yet the strategies for low water availability are in many ways fundamentally different from the low-nutrient strategy. First, there are two strategies for low-water environments that depend on the nature of the water supply. Water can be supplied to plants in pulses as well as uniformly, but at low availability. Each generates its own strategy for success in low-water environments, including a strategy for acquiring water quickly, storing it, and using it slowly during periods of low water availability that has little analog for nutrients. Second, water stress generates unique physical stresses on plants that do not arise as a consequence of nutrient limitation. Third, water can only be used for photosynthesis as it is lost from the plant, while nutrients can be used productively while being retained. These differences in use dictate that light is less likely to co-limit production with water than nutrients and shapes the structure of low-water environments.

Water supplies to plants vary in many aspects, including the temporal heterogeneity of precipitation. When water supplies are pulsed in time but water availability is high enough for long enough, high-resource plants generally dominate. In such cases, drought functions like an annual disturbance. Plants can also tap into stable groundwater, but the presence of high water availability dictates that the plants are not water limited, even in an environment where other plants are.

Although these two plant functional groups are common in low-water environments, there are two general strategies for success when water is limiting. First, when pulses of high water availability are long enough for plants to acquire water quickly but not long enough for a plant to complete its life cycle or to justify the production of leaves, plants have evolved a strategy for rapid uptake of water, storage of the water, and increased WUE. This pulsed-water strategy is associated with plants that have roots similar to those of high-resource plants but shoots that transpire slowly, stretching water supplies between pulses of availability. These plants often use CAM photosynthesis, which greatly increases WUE by opening stomata only at night, when temperatures are lower.

With constitutively low water supplies, plants compete by reducing the availability of water, which requires being able to take up water at low potential. To maintain photosynthesis at low water potential, xylem walls must be reinforced and xylem conduits made smaller to reduce the probability of embolism. Leaves of low-water species often have high nutrient concentrations, which confers high WUE. These leaves are often defended with diuretic chemicals that exacerbate water stress in herbivores rather than reduced nutrition.

Competition for water is poorly understood, but, as far as can be conjectured from on the traits observed in the two strategies, likely involves rapidly acquiring water with pulsed supplies and the ability to reduce water availability to low levels when water is supplied uniformly. There is little evidence that water-limited plants are nutrient limited, or that they have been selected to perform well under nutrient limitation. With water limiting, light is unlikely to co-limit production. Leaf area cannot accumulate by increasing the mean residence time of water as it can for nutrients, making canopy closure, and the light limitation that comes with it, unlikely when water is limiting.

The last resource, atmospheric CO_2, is closely coupled to water, as water is lost through stomata as CO_2 is taken in. Atmospheric CO_2 concentrations have always been above the compensation points of plants, yet low atmospheric CO_2 does more than induce water stress. From experiments, plants that grow under low CO_2 concentrations experience carbon stress. Photosynthesis declines, along with the availability of carbon for secondary processes such as defense and structure. As carbon inputs to plants and soils decline, nitrogen availability increases, reducing nitrogen limitation. Low CO_2 also increases transpiration, but there might be some compensation at the ecosystem scale, as temperatures should be lower in a low-CO_2 world and precipitation might be higher.

The first set of adaptations to carbon starvation appears to involve alteration of photosynthetic pathways. C_4 and CAM photosynthetic pathways are advantageous under low CO_2, reducing photorespiration by increasing CO$_2$ concentrations at the site of photosynthesis. Like other adaptations to low resource availability, the additional allocation of resources to structure and biochemistry reduces photosynthesis and growth when the resource is not limiting.

The second set of adaptations to low atmospheric CO$_2$ affects the use of carbon in defense and structure. Many plants have evolved the ability to substitute inorganic compounds for carbon in defensive and structural application. Many plants that underwent radiations during the Miocene, including a wide range of grasses, herbaceous dicotyledonous angiosperms, and trees, are able to use silica for both defense and structure. Silica can be used in phytoliths, which cause abrasions and increase the handling time of food for herbivores, potentially reducing its digestibility. Silica can also be impregnated into the cell wall to stiffen it, much as lignin is used. In both cases, organic compounds are replaced with inorganic compounds, which can be produced at a fraction of the carbon cost. Other inorganic compounds are used for similar purposes as silica but are less common.

The survival strategies of plants under low water and low CO$_2$ availability are not simply variants of a low-resource strategy. Each is associated with a unique set of adaptations, and any similarities in traits either among these strategies or to other strategies such as the low-nutrient strategy represent convergence rather than having common limiting resources across environments.

CHAPTER 11

A Synthesis of Plant Strategies

MORE THAN A HUNDRED YEARS AGO, Eugenius Warming began to gather together the major components that drive the performance of species, sort them into communities, and act as agents of natural selection in shaping the evolution of species. Theories of plant strategies began to coalesce around Darwin's theories of natural selection and evolution, Liebig's and Sprengel's theories of limitation, the state factors that phytogeographers had recognized as determining the distributions of plants, traits associated with the ecophysiology of plants, and observations of interactions among organisms by early ecologists. Since then, our understanding of plant strategies has continued to grow, and so also has our understanding of the major patterns of plant evolution, as well as of the modern ecology of plants. For example, more than 25 years ago, with the research of Grime, Chapin, and Tilman, the importance of the stress of low nutrient availability began to be better understood, and competition for nutrients became a more prominent component of recognized plant strategies. Over the past quarter century, the framework on which plant strategies rests has been refined, and our understanding of plant strategies has continued to mature. Some of the key developments over the past quarter century include the following:

- The importance of a given factor in the performance of species is not solely a function of the environment and differs for dominant, rare, and absent species. Whether environments are considered "high stress" or "highly competitive" depends on the species of interest. Often, multiple factors determine the relative abundance of species in ways that cannot be separated experimentally.
- Selective and general agents of stress and disturbance can differentially affect the performance of species in a given environment. Selective agents preferentially affect some species more than others. Even general disturbances can be localized aboveground or belowground. Describing the importance of disturbance in a given environment requires defining the type of disturbance that is being discussed.
- Plant strategies are tightly linked to the nature of resource supplies. Natural selection and the abundance of species with different plant strategies depend on whether nutrients are made available in pulses or in slow bleeds, whether light is provided as sunflecks or as low

constitutive irradiance, and whether soil water comes from infrequent rain events or from chronically low but available soil moisture. In addition, plants can both increase and decrease nutrient supplies on different time scales, and supplies cannot be considered independent of plant activity.

- Co-limitation among resources is prevalent, and plants have been selected to grow in the face of multiple limiting resources. Progress in understanding co-limitation reflects a developing understanding of how resources are made available to plants and how plants acquire them. Those resources that are most likely to co-limit one another are ones for which there are trade-offs in allocation for their acquisition, but compensating loss rates can also promote co-limitation.

- Plant adaptations to low resource availability depend on whether the low resource availability is determined by low supplies or by uptake by other plants—the nature of resource competition is an explicit component of plant strategies. Although we still need to learn more about how plants compete for water, the basics of how plants compete for light and nutrients have become integrated into plant strategies. It is also clear that competition can lead to selection for traits that come at the expense of resource use efficiency.

- Scientists' understanding of the specific traits associated with performance in different environments has grown immensely. Only recently have we come to understand the importance of root length when nutrients are limiting, the role of small xylem conduits in withstanding the negative pressures associated with low water availability, and the importance of low respiration rates in determining growth in low light.

- There are four major strategies for growth when limiting resources are supplied uniformly over time (figure 11.1). There is less support for the theory of a general low-resource strategy with variations associated with limitation by different resources than there is for the theory of separate strategies for succeeding when water, nutrients, light, or CO_2 are strongly limiting. The availabilities of resources are somewhat independent from one another, and there are physiological and evolutionary trade-offs in producing traits for success for each resource availability. Consequently, there is no one general strategy that covers low availability of all resources. Being built to perform well under low light precludes being competitive for nutrients, which precludes acquiring water when soil water potential is low. All of these strategies might share a low RGR_{max}, but this appears to be a consequence of convergence. A fifth strategy is associated with success when the availabilities of all resources are high. Again, because

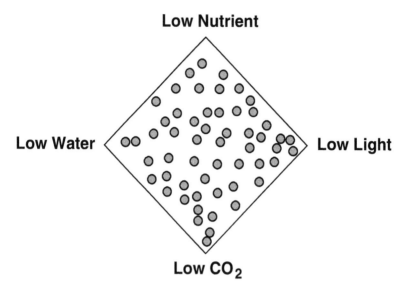

Figure 11.1. Theoretical distribution of a range of species across four plant strategy axes.

of trade-offs, species that perform well when a given resource is limiting are unable to outcompete high-resource species in the first stage of light competition (figure 11.2).

The five strategies outlined here are the most fundamental and widespread with regard to resources, but it is important to recognize that no one set of traits works best across all environments that have low availability of a given resource. For example, although both grasslands are limited by nutrients, phosphorus limitation in the fynbos of South Africa has selected for plants that are fundamentally different from those that dominate nitrogen-limited grasslands in Minnesota. Although both cacti and shrubs such as the creosote bush have long evolutionary histories in environments with low water availability, cacti have been selected to perform well when water is made available in short pulses, while the creosote bush reflects selection under chronic low water availability. African *Acacia* and New Zealand *Pennantia* both reflect a long evolutionary history with browsers in high-resource environments, but giraffe and moa feed fundamentally differently and show selection for uniquely different structural defenses. Both boreal forest and humid grassland species are regularly exposed to general agents of disturbance in nutrient-limited environments, yet the belowground disturbance of freezing soils has evolutionarily constrained root longevity in black spruce, while frequent burning has constrained leaf longevity in big bluestem. Heat, soil pH, salinity, and a long list of other non-resource factors have also modulated the

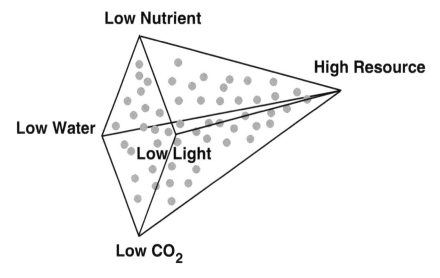

Figure 11.2. Distribution of species across five plant strategy axes. There are strong trade-offs among performance when different resources are limiting. High-resource species perform poorly at low resource availability.

expression of the basic resource strategies and have contributed to the diversity of plant life on Earth. And as Warming and Grime saw long ago, reproductive strategies are myriad and represent axes or categories of variation that can be largely independent of resource strategies.

APPLICATION AND THE WAY FORWARD

The univariate and multivariate approaches to arraying species and their traits, whether on axes or in triangles, diamonds, or pyramids, are not just geometries on which to hang species. The distribution of species along trait axes describes some of the basic patterns of evolution and ecological patterns. Knowledge of plant strategies already aids in understanding the evolution of species and the functioning of ecosystems. Nevertheless, further development of our understanding of plant strategies is required to answer longstanding ecological and evolutionary questions while aiding in the prediction of ecosystem function in the future.

The most important research need is straightforward: more traits need to be measured on more species. Within the past decade, large global data sets of select plant traits from plants studied under natural conditions have been synthesized, but if plant strategies are ever to have general explanatory or predictive power, important functional traits need to be assessed under controlled conditions on more than a handful of species.

Although the utility of measuring traits across a broad number of species can be denigrated as mere "screening" or "natural history" that fails to test hypotheses, a large amount of research in other disciplines consists of analogous work. Geneticists catalog tens of thousands of genes in genomes of multiple species, phylogeneticists compare sequences on thousands of species, and remote sensing scientists routinely collect data on the entire world pixellated to the square meter. These basic efforts form the scientific foundation of entire disciplines and are necessary for investigating massive questions.

The questions that surround plant strategies and their potential utility are no more or less massive than similar efforts in genetics, phylogenetics, or remote sensing. To date, most research on plant strategies has been limited in scope and balkanized among researchers. When larger syntheses that have emerged regarding plant traits are used as a guide, it is clear that questions about plant strategies will benefit from large-scale efforts. To better understand plant strategies and answer critical questions surrounding the functioning of vegetation in the past, present, and future, scores of traits for thousands, if not tens of thousands of species have to be measured in a coordinated fashion. These efforts, though immense, can be done in an efficient manner that will maximize our ability to later test key hypotheses by intelligently selecting the species to be measured and choosing which traits should be measured first.

Independent of expanding the scale and coordination of current efforts, there are critical, more focused areas that need to be developed for our understanding of plant strategies to develop. This chapter presents eight major areas where applying plant strategies helps to answer important ecological questions and to which future research should be targeted.

GENETICS, PLEIOTROPY, AND PLASTICITY

The nature of the control over some traits and the degree of potential plasticity in them make it difficult to know how to reliably compare traits among species. For example, nitrogen concentrations of tissues are considered a central trait to the ecology of plants. Yet not only does a given species exhibit a large degree of plasticity in its tissue nitrogen concentrations, tissue nitrogen concentrations at any one time are determined in part by the effects that plants have on nitrogen availability. Relative growth rates are another trait for which there is strong genetic control, but the nature of the control and the number of genes that determine most of the variation in RGR is unknown. Are there direct controls on RGR that explain variation among species in RGR_{max}, such as when Chapin posited that slow growth rates could be driven by constitutively high ABA expression? Or is low RGR$_{max}$ the consequence of any number of resource demands that drag down the ability to acquire and assimilate new resources quickly?

The ability to compare the genetic code of species has the potential to transform our understanding of plant strategies, but a road map is necessary if new techniques are to be harnessed effectively (Ackerly et al. 2000). For example, screening the code or activity of thousands of genes and then treating each gene as a trait could easily inundate research on plant strategies. When a single trait is controlled by multiple genes or when multiple genes are epistatic, there are also important questions to ask about the direct utility of examining the genetic code for many of the uses of plant strategies. If RGR was ultimately controlled by one of a number of genes in a given species, with each gene acting through a different mechanism, the ability to compare these genes for a number of species may provide little benefit for the utility of plant strategies. On the other hand, with pleiotropy, in which a single gene controls a number of traits, understanding the genetic code of species and signaling pathways might simplify our understanding of plant strategies.

Because understanding the genetic code of species presents great potential for understanding plant strategies but is also extremely broad-based, ecologists and geneticists should work closely together to unravel complicated targeted questions, such as the proximal and distal controls over traits that are central to the ecology of species, as among them tissue nutrient concentrations, plant defenses, and growth rates. Baldwin's research on understanding the interactions between herbivores and nicotine in plants is a good model for how investigating gene regulation can help answer ecological questions (Baldwin 2001; Halitschke and Baldwin 2003; Roda and Baldwin 2003). It is clear that the reductionism that genetics affords is not a panacea for the unanswered questions and that the nature of gene expression is sufficient justification to undertake research on traits separately from research on the genetics that might be controlling the traits. That said, in some areas, coupling ecology and genetics should yield a more robust understanding of plant strategies.

LIMITATION

As old and as fundamental to biology as the concept of resource limitation is, no other topic can seem more mysterious. There is an incredible number of open questions about why limitation occurs, where and when it is important, and the evolutionary consequences of growth in limiting environments. Ad hoc research on limitations is unlikely to progress rapidly enough to meet the demands that are being placed on ecologists to answer societal questions, no less to further understanding of plant strategies. At the very least, the unanswered questions that define the science of limitation are clear, such that if scientific resources were mobilized, the avenues for progress are apparent.

- The patterns of resource limitation are underdescribed. Although there are dozens of resource addition studies that have provided a foundation of knowledge concerning resource limitation, long-term resource augmentation experiments are relatively few and not well dispersed geographically. Rarely have multiple nutrients been added, water manipulation experiments in natural systems are even rarer, and studies that shed light on any ecosystem or part of an ecosystem are few. There are still too few—by an order of magnitude— CO_2 enrichment experiments in the world to allow accurate generalizations to be made about the effects of increasing atmospheric CO_2 concentrations at the global scale. Finally, in experiments, nutrients, water, and CO_2 are usually added to vegetation, while light is reduced. To further our understanding of limitation, however, it is just as important to reduce supplies of nutrients, water, and CO_2 and increase the supplies of light to vegetation.
- Why is co-limitation so common? What are the mechanisms that underlie co-limitation: compensating loss rates or trade-offs in allocation? Also, resource manipulation experiments generally augment only one resource. Future research on limitation needs to recognize that co-limitation is likely and to seek to understand which resources are co-limiting.
- How can limitation be assessed without fertilization experiments? Fertilization experiments are intensive undertakings, and methods that quickly screen plants for limitation are required if changes in limitation are to be assessed in conjunction with other ecological patterns. If internal ratios of elements are not a good predictor of relative limitation by different resources, can the identification of plant strategies and the quantification of abundances of plants with different strategies provide an alternative approach to predicting limitation?
- The statistics in quantifying co-limitation need further development. Simple errors are still made by researchers in how to test for co-limitation with ANOVA, and more sophisticated analyses are necessary to the different patterns of co-limitation in experiments, such as classic co-limitation from co-limitation by trade-off.
- Understanding the science of resource limitation can be improved only with a better understanding of how plants grow under resource stress. For light, water, and nutrients, experiments are required to

separate the relative importance of tolerance of low resource availability from the ability to resist stresses and disturbances under low
resource availability. The minimum supplies required for growth
need to be better quantified, as well as the determinants of self-thinning patterns, which modulate the relationship between supplies and
availability to plants.

The science of limitation is an important component to plant strategies,
and a better understanding of plant strategies will only aid in understanding limitation. Limitation is not a function of the environment alone; it is
also a function of the species that grow in that environment. Understanding the traits that species have evolved to cope with low resource availability is crucial to determining the resources that limit growth, as well as
to predicting how ecosystems will respond to future changes in resource
availability.

COMPETITION

Before Tilman's seminal research on competition, ecologists' treatment
of competition was largely phenomenological. Quantification of competition was synonymous with the interaction coefficients among species
in Lotka-Volterra equations. After Tilman's work on the mechanisms of
competition between phytoplankton, there was the potential to predict
those competition coefficients for terrestrial species by understanding
how plants reduced the availability of resources. This approach was
the beginning of important advances in understanding the nature of
competition, yet fundamental questions about competition still remain
unanswered.

When nutrient availability is chronically low and the supply is independent of plant activity, root length density is the key to reducing the availability of limiting nutrients to neighboring plants. Yet supplies are not
independent of plant activity. We currently have a poor understanding of
the interactions among plant activities that alter nutrient supplies and
the partitioning of limiting nutrient supplies. For example, if plants can
increase nutrient availability, is nutrient limitation another consequence
of evolutionary games associated with competition? Does the presence of
competition between individuals make nutrient limitation of assemblages
more likely?

Our understanding of competition for water lags far behind that for
nutrients. For example, the plant traits that allow one plant to displace
another when water is limiting are not well characterized. Much of what
worked in developing concepts of nutrient competition needs to be
adapted for water. This includes the following:

- Experiments that allow plants to compete for water, where availability varies in magnitude, temporally and spatially, are needed.
- More thorough examination of plant traits associated with competitive dominance when water is limiting should provide greater insights.
- Fine-scale spatial models of nutrients in soils need to be adapted to water to test hypotheses on the mechanisms and patterns of water limitation.

The dynamics of plants competing for light seem simple, yet the relative importance of the production of leaves at height, the breadth of canopies, and reduction of light availability in determining competitive dominance in the first stage of competition needs to be better understood under different environmental conditions. For example, under what conditions would a plant benefit from producing fewer leaves on taller stems as opposed to more leaves on shorter stems? During the second stage of competition, we still do not understand the proximal and distal controls that cause high-resource species to perish and the trajectory of growth for low-light species in shade.

Finally, the determinants of competitive interactions need to be tested broadly. For example, Tilman's R^* theory, despite being one of the most cited concepts ever in ecology, was never tested with terrestrial plants outside of Minnesota. Ecology is not physics or chemistry, domains in which dynamics can be considered universally applicable. Fundamental postulates about competition theory need to be tested by multiple researchers with different species in different environments. In some ways, a little more competition among researchers in competition research might be beneficial, although competition researchers should not forget that even if they believe most plants are in competition with one another, it still is beneficial for researchers to cooperate.

Defense and Herbivory

Herbivores and pathogens are some of the main agents of stress and disturbance to plants. Compared with 25 years ago, today we understand much better the specific actions of a large number of defenses and their role in plant strategies. Defenses have been subject to intense selection and are key components of plant strategies. The wrong type or amount of defense in a given environment can be fatal.

For all the advances, recent reviews of plant defenses have been more catabolic than anabolic. Hamilton and others (2001) deconstructed the carbon-nutrient balance hypothesis without acknowledging its explanatory power, and confusing short-term and long-term effects of differences in resource availability on the ecophysiology and evolution of species. Stamp (2003) assembled a detailed, disciplined review of defense strategies that reviewed the major defense theories. Yet, not unlike the Hamilton et al. review, most of the evaluation of the different theories seemed to be concerned with fine-scale physiological mechanisms rather than with the ability of the theories to explain broad patterns across species. In evaluating hypotheses, it is important to keep in mind that evolutionary patterns do not necessarily coincide with the physiological responses of individual plants. For example, phenotypic and genotypic responses to decreases in nutrient or light availability are generally opposite, not parallel. That does not imply that hypotheses to explain evolutionary patterns should be invalidated by the lack of concordance with physiological patterns.

The best hope for an improved synthesis of plant defenses as part of plant strategies rests on examining the broad patterns of defenses across species and environments. Many questions about defenses exist, such as the costs of having inducible defenses in different environments, how synthesis pathways constrain the evolution of defenses in different lineages, or how different defense strategies are paired among species. The following questions have the potential to provide the most rapid advances for our understanding of plant defenses against herbivores:

- Why do nitrogen-based defenses appear to be rare in low-light environments? Can this be explained by physiological resource balance arguments or by the specifics of herbivory in the understory? Put another way, what are the consequences for resource balance in the absence and presence of herbivores of allocating nitrogen to defenses in low-light environments?
- What are structural defenses protecting, and how do they operate? Do structural defenses like thorns primarily slow the rate of consumption of individual herbivores, or do they shift herbivory away from critical tissues such as meristems? Structural defenses are complex (Grubb 1992), but there are no studies that quantify the abundance of structural defenses across environmental gradients, which would begin to ally these traits with plant strategies and explain the selection pressures that favored them.
- What are the relationships between nutrient availability and the abundance of chemical defenses? Although nutrient supplies should be important determinants of the quantity and type of plant defenses, there are no studies that examine, for example, the relationship between nitrogen supplies and foliar tannin concentrations. Calculations show that nitrogen-free defenses should still be inexpensive to use when nutrient supplies are high, yet what restricts their abundance?

MECHANISMS OF COEXISTENCE

Understanding the diversity of assemblages is one of the grandest questions in ecology. When resource limitation, environmental stress, and disturbances are not enough to extirpate co-occurring species, coexistence results. Yet the mechanisms by which plants coexist have yet to be delineated. Predicting which species will coexist under a given set of conditions is just as difficult.

Plant strategies are key to understanding some of the basic patterns of coexistence. In nonequilibrium ecosystems, coexisting species can have major resource strategies that are different. As Grime noted in his discussions of succession (Grime 2001), soon after a disturbance, high-resource species form the upper layers of the canopy, while low-light species grow underneath. Many desert systems have high-resource annuals coexisting with pulse-store species and low-water perennials. In such systems, coexistence seems to be driven by partitioning rainfall spatially or temporally, or by an interannual variation that precludes competitive coexistence. Although these examples are prominent, it seems that in most low-resource environments, coexisting species have major resource strategies that are more similar than different. Low-light and low-water species are often absent from low-nutrient environments. Low-light environments do not have low-nutrient or low-water species. In these situations, coexisting species are more likely to differ within a given strategy than to use different strategies altogether.

The way forward in understanding plant strategies and coexistence among species includes analyses of assemblages across environmental contrasts, theoretical development, and experiments set up to test key hypotheses:

- Understanding coexistence begins with quantifying the patterns of strategies of coexisting species. The strategies of coexisting and non-coexisting species should be quantified to determine the types of species that are most likely to coexist, and what traits are associated with coexistence.
- There should be a small set of environmental factors that promote coexistence among species. These factors should be identified and their relative importance in different habitats tested. This approach would likely explain differences among environments in the types of species that coexist. For example, periodic aboveground disturbance might be more likely to promote species with different strategies, while the presence of selective herbivores might promote species with similar resource strategies but different defenses.

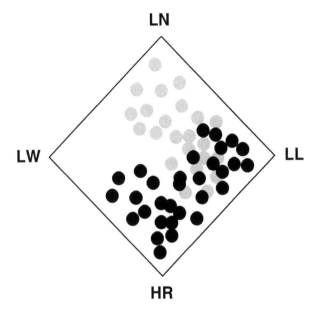

Figure 11.3. Comparison of species in two assemblages across four plant strategies (low-water, low-nutrient, low-light, and high-resource). Species from one assemblage had been filtered or irradiated in an environment that had a mixture of high resource availability and low-light environments (black), while the other assemblage primarily consisted of low-nutrient and low-light environments (gray). Differences in overlap of the assemblages for strategies would also drive the pattern of invasions. For example, the gray flora would be susceptible to invasion from the black flora if the gray region had high-resource environments.

- Experiments that directly manipulate factors that are hypothesized to be promoting coexistence need to be set up. These would include experiments that pair species that differ in traits that could lead to coexistence for a given environment. Other experiments should manipulate other factors to see how coexistence is affected.

BIOGEOGRAPHIC PATTERNS AND INVASIONS

As data on plant strategies accumulate for locations and regions, it will be possible to begin to compare the traits in different floras. Comparing functional traits and strategies of species (figure 11.3) will allow a quantitative comparison of the long-term importance of different environmental factors, the prediction of ecosystem responses to environmental changes, and the determination of patterns of invasion into assemblages.

For example, severe soil disturbance with high nutrient supplies favors annual species, yet the fraction of species in a flora that are annual in different parts of the world is not the same. New Zealand occupies an area of 27 Mha and has a flora of 2,000 native species. Although half the native diversity is found in herbaceous turf species; only four native species are annual. In comparison, the United Kingdom has an area of approximately 24 Mha and 1,400 native species, but at least 69 native annuals (Peat and Fitter 2008). The differences in annual species between the two regions could be ascribed to differences in the abundance of different types or to the frequency of agents of disturbance. Was it the presence of humans or herbivorous mammals in the British Isles that favored the presence of annual plants? In another case, although temperate grasslands are present on every continent, most of the world's major temperate pasture grasses originated in northern Europe, such as *Phleum pratense*, *Dactylis glomerata*, *Lolium perenne*, and *Poa pratensis*. This is not just a case of European colonization of different parts of the world. These types of species are unique to northern Europe and are not found in other parts of the world. Something is unique about the history of the environments of northern Europe relative to the rest of the world for these species to have arisen there and nowhere else.

Immigration, extirpation, and radiation are the three general factors that determine the functional diversity of a particular habitat. Collectively, they generate diversity in functional traits that reflects the relative importance of different factors over different time scales. Craine, Lee, and Walker (2006) applied biogeographic theory to plant strategies and hypothesized that as the spatiotemporal extent and continuity of a set of environmental conditions increased, a native assemblage would be more likely to have species well adapted to the general set of conditions that define the environment. If "niche" is taken to mean a set of environmental factors that consistently coincide, core niches are those that have a large spatiotemporal extent. Core niches are common, expansive, and continuous in space and time, leading to a high diversity or good matching between plant traits and environment. Novel niches are those that are rare or discontinuous in space and time, resulting in lower trait diversity in species that occupy that niche or a relatively poor match between traits and species. Along these lines, Funk and Vitousek (2007) argued that native species are not necessarily better adapted to the general environment of a habitat than non-native species and that invasions can be driven in the absence of recent increases in the availability of limiting resources. Moles, Gruber, and Bonser (2008) extended the limiting similarity hypothesis (Emery 2007) and argued a similar point as the novel niche hypothesis of invasion in postulating that some invasions represented species colonizing "vacant" niches, whether due to very recent or older changes in conditions.

Novel niches are more susceptible to invasion than core niches. In 2001, Grime asked, "Is there any consistent difference between the characteristics of colonizing and invading plant species and the circumstances encouraging their expansion?" In New Zealand as an example, it appears that there quite often are consistent differences in the traits and strategies of invaders and native species, and these differences reflect differences in the distribution of core and native habitats in the two regions. For example, for most of the past 70 million years, New Zealand habitats were warm and wet, had a low nutrient supply, lacked fire, and were subjected to avian herbivores. The novel habitats of New Zealand stand in contrast to the core habitats in being cold and dry, having a high nutrient supply, having experienced fire, or having been subjected to mammalian herbivores. In New Zealand there are very few invaders into the mesic, wet, undisturbed forests, which represent a set of conditions that has a long history in New Zealand. The short, discontinuous history in New Zealand of fire, aridity, high nutrient availability, and high-elevation, cold habitats generated a flora more depauperate of traits that led to success in these environments than in other regions of the world with longer histories of these conditions. These environments in New Zealand are the sites where invasions are most common and recalcitrant: high-elevation pines have invaded into alpine areas, annuals and browse-resistant shrubs have invaded into grazed arid regions, and high-nutrient species have invaded into fertilized pastures.

The observations of the traits of native and non-native species for areas like New Zealand are important first components of a broader synthesis of the importance of environmental factors in the development of assemblages. As traits and strategies are quantified for entire floras, the macroscopic patterns of evolution should start coming into focus. When traits among regions are compared, these data sets should not only shed light on the importance of environmental factors on evolutionary time scales but also help put in context the patterns of invasion.

GLOBAL CHANGE

The most important responsibility of ecologists today lies in predicting the future functioning of ecosystems. Humanity relies on ecosystems to provide a number of services. Ecosystems store carbon, maintain clean drinking water, modulate local temperatures, provide fuel, fiber, and food, are sources of recreation, and serve as repositories for biodiversity that is important economically as well as aesthetically. With CO_2 concentrations

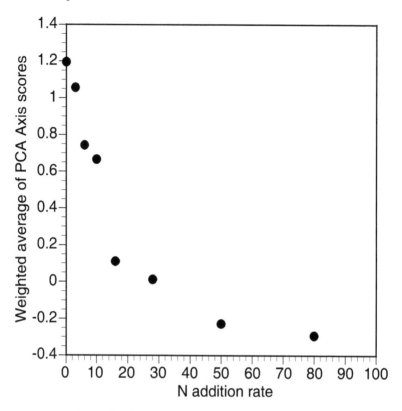

Figure 11.4. Relationship between nitrogen addition rate in a grassland experiment at Cedar Creek Natural History Area and the average scores on a multivariate trait axis of assemblages. High axis scores are associated with the traits of low-nutrient species. As nitrogen addition increased, low-nutrient species were replaced with high-resource species. Data from Craine et al. 2001.

and temperatures rising, precipitation patterns changing, continued anthropogenic nitrogen deposition, biotic assemblages shifting, and disturbance regimes being altered, there is great uncertainty in how ecosystems will function in providing these services in the future. The predictions of ecologists are an important tool in adjusting societal policies and managing ecosystems to maximize future benefits from ecosystems.

At the center of many of the predictions of future ecosystem function is knowledge of how vegetation will change in response to changes in multiple environmental factors. Some of these changes are likely to occur independent of the major resource strategies laid out here, but many will coincide with differences among the major plant resource strategies.

For example, it is clear that nutrient enrichment and disturbance favor high-resource species (Craine et al. 2001) (figure 11.4). As CO_2 concentrations continue to increase in the near future, however, will there be a shift

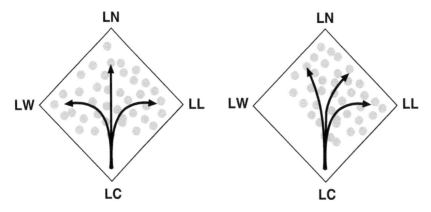

Figure 11.5. Will increasing CO_2 shift the relative abundance of species away from low-CO_2 species equally to all other strategies, or will it also lower the relative abundance of low-water species?

away from low-CO_2 species to more high-CO_2 species, and will this shift exert a stabilizing force on atmospheric CO_2 concentrations (figure 11.5)? If silica is really an integral part of the low-CO_2 strategy, then species that rely on silica for structure are more likely to diminish in abundance, while species that utilize more carbon-intensive secondary pathways for defense or structure can be expected to increase. Does this mean that both C_3 and C_4 grasses should diminish in the future? Although there are multiple determinants of abundances, and although increases in elevated CO_2 are complicated in understanding the indirect consequences for limitation by water or nutrients, broad patterns of shifts to woody species from grass species in many parts of the world could be explained in part by elevated CO_2 concentrations.

If there is to be a scientific basis for predicting how vegetation will respond to changes in environmental conditions, a major component of the science will need to incorporate the interactions between plant strategies and resource availability, as well as geographic maps of the strategies of species. To understand how increases in CO_2 concentrations or nutrient availability will affect vegetation, ecologists will have to know what the general strategies are for succeeding at different CO_2 and nutrient levels, and also the strategies held by species at a given location. Increases in the spread of species are rapidly minimizing differences in potential strategies on a global basis, which will increasingly threaten local species that are less well adapted to new environmental conditions. Even with a rapidly homogenizing global flora, fundamental holes in the envelope of resource strategies of many floras will constrain the ability of vegetation to respond to environmental changes.

A thorough understanding of the major plant resource strategies will not solve every question regarding future ecosystem function. Many of the future changes, such as increases in temperature, are likely to be more or less independent of changes in resource availability. Other goals in prediction might coincide with strategies, but they would not be tied together as a consequence of natural selection. For example, although species might differ in their ability to generate soil organic matter, it is unlikely that species were selected per se to store carbon in soil. That said, many of the plant strategies are closely aligned with both environmental conditions and ecosystem functions. As data on plant strategies on a global basis develop, spatially explicit predictions of future ecosystem function will improve, especially those relating to changes in resource availability.

TREE OF LIFE

In the end, there is no endeavor more central to biology than understanding the radiations of life on Earth. Major recent efforts have largely been to reconstruct the phylogenetic relationships among species and the timing of divergences. Yet the tree of life will soon be largely reconstructed. The next set of questions to tackle will have to do with the environmental forces that drove these radiations.

In the past, analyses that examined the relationships between functional traits and phylogeny with phylogenetic independent contrasts used a relatively narrow range of species. Certainly, these studies examined evolutionary patterns and directions, but directions within species or genera do not necessarily align with those at broader phylogenetic levels. Analyses of broader phylogenetic relationships have been limited to single traits (Moles et al. 2005) and have yet to be performed with traits important for the resource economy of species that have been quantified under controlled conditions, no less broader strategies.

As more traits and strategies are quantified for more species, some of the influences behind the branching in the tree of life will become clearer. For example, the timing of the evolution of C_4 and CAM plants in multiple lineages has been hypothesized to coincide with declines in atmospheric CO_2 or increases in aridity during the Miocene, or both. Yet what lies behind other radiations? Did lower CO_2 concentrations drive the expansion and radiations of species that use silica for structure? How recently evolved are the high-resource grasses of northern Europe? Are they products of the Holocene and human disturbance? Or are they more ancient, and driven by other factors?

The history of plant evolution involves tens of thousands of genes across a quarter million modern species. Every species represents a unique evolutionary history, as it is the product of a singular interplay between environment and genes. Yet there are likely broad, identifiable patterns to the radiations that will help us understand the evolutionary tree for all its branches. But first, there is a lot of work to do.

Bibliography

Ackerly, D. D., S. A. Dudley, S. E. Sultan, J. Schmitt, J. S. Coleman, C. R. Linder, D. R. Sandquist, M. A. Geber, A. S. Evans, T. E. Dawson, and M. J. Lachowicz. 2000. The evolution of plant ecophysiological traits: Recent advances and future directions. *Bioscience* 50:979–95.

Adams, R. P., T. A. Zanoni, E. Vonrudloff, and L. Hogge. 1981. The southwestern USA and northern Mexico one-seeded junipers: Their volatile oils and evolution. *Biochemical Systematics and Ecology* 9:93–96.

Aerts, R. 1995. The advantages of being evergreen. *Trends in Ecology & Evolution* 10:402–7.

———. 1996. Nutrient resorption from senescing leaves of perennials: Are there general patterns? *Journal of Ecology* 84:597–608.

Aerts, R., and F. S. Chapin III. 2000. The mineral nutrition of wild plants revisited: Re-evaluation of processes and patterns. *Advances in Ecological Research* 30:1–67.

Agrawal, A. A., and M. Fishbein. 2006. Plant defense syndromes. *Ecology* 87:S132–49.

Anderson, L. J., H. Maherali, H. B. Johnson, H. W. Polley, and R. B. Jackson. 2001. Gas exchange and photosynthetic acclimation over subambient to elevated CO_2 in a C-3-C-4 grassland. *Global Change Biology* 7:693–707.

Andresen, L. C., and A. Michelsen. 2005. Off-season uptake of nitrogen in temperate heath vegetation. *Oecologia* 144:585–97.

Anten, N. P. R. 2005. Optimal photosynthetic characteristics of individual plants in vegetation stands and implications for species coexistence. *Annals of Botany* 95:495–506.

Armas, C., R. Ordiales, and F. I. Pugnaire. 2004. Measuring plant interactions: A new comparative index. *Ecology* 85:2682–86.

Ashton, D. H. 1975. Seasonal growth of *Eucalyptus regnans* F. Muell. *Australian Journal of Botany* 23:239–52.

Augspurger, C. K., and E. A. Bartlett. 2003. Differences in leaf phenology between juvenile and adult trees in a temperate deciduous forest. *Tree Physiology* 23:517–25.

Augspurger, C. K., J. M. Cheeseman, and C. F. Salk. 2005. Light gains and physiological capacity of understorey woody plants during phenological avoidance of canopy shade. *Functional Ecology* 19:537–46.

Augspurger, C. K., and C. K. Kelly. 1984. Pathogen mortality of tropical tree seedlings: Experimental studies of the effects of dispersal distance, seedling density, and light conditions. *Oecologia* 61:211–17.

Austin, A. T., and O. E. Sala. 1999. Foliar delta15N is negatively correlated with rainfall along the IGBP transect in Australia. *Australian Journal of Plant Physiology* 26:293–95.

Baldwin, I. T. 2001. An ecologically motivated analysis of plant-herbivore interactions in native tobacco. *Plant Physiology* 127:1449–58.

Baltzer, J. L., and S. C. Thomas. 2007. Physiological and morphological correlates of whole-plant light compensation point in temperate deciduous tree seedlings. *Oecologia* 153:209–23.

Barbehenn, R. V., and E. A. Bernays. 1992. Relative nutritional quality of C-3 and C-4 grasses for a graminivorous lepidopteran, Paratrytone-Melane (Hesperiidae). *Oecologia* 92:97–103.

Barkmann, J., and C. R. Schwintzer. 1998. Rapid N-2 fixation in pines? Results of a Maine field. *Ecology* 79:1453–57.

Bausenwein, U., P. Millard, B. Thornton, and J. A. Raven. 2001. Seasonal nitrogen storage and remobilization in the forb *Rumex acetosa*. *Functional Ecology* 15:370–77.

Bazzaz, F. A., N. R. Chiariello, P. D. Coley, and L. F. Pitelka. 1987. Allocating resources to reproduction and defense. *Bioscience* 37:58–67.

Becerra, J. X., D. L. Venable, P. H. Evans, and W. S. Bowers. 2001. Interactions between chemical and mechanical defenses in the plant genus *Bursera* and their implications for herbivores. *American Zoologist* 41:865–76.

Beerling, D. J. 2005. Evolutionary responses of land plants to atmospheric CO_2. In *A History of Atmospheric CO_2 and Its Effects on Plants, Animals, and Ecosystems*, ed. J. R. Ehrlinger, T. E. Cerling, and M. D. Dearing, 114–32. New York: Springer-Verlag.

Belanger, G., F. Gastal, and F. R. Warembourg. 1994. Carbon balance of tall fescue (*Festuca arundinacea* Schreb): Effects of nitrogen fertilization and the growing season. *Annals of Botany* 74:653–59.

Bellingham, P. J. 2000. Resprouting as a life history strategy in woody plant communities. *Oikos* 89:409–16.

Bennett, R. N., and R. M. Wallsgrove. 1994. Tansley review no. 72: Secondary metabolites in plant defence mechanisms. *New Phytologist* 127:617–33.

Berenbaum, M. R. 2001. Chemical mediation of coevolution: Phylogenetic evidence for Apiaceae and associates. *Annals of the Missouri Botanical Garden* 88:45–59.

Berenbaum, M. R., J. K. Nitao, and A. R. Zangerl. 1991. Adaptive significance of Furanocoumarin diversity in Pastinaca-Sativa (Apiaceae). *Journal of Chemical Ecology* 17:207–15.

Berendse, F. 1994. Litter decomposability: A neglected component of plant fitness. *Journal of Ecology* 82:187–90.

Berendse, F., W. T. Elberse, and R. H. M. E. Geerts. 1992. Competition and nitrogen loss from plants in grassland ecosystems. *Ecology* 73:46–53.

Björkman, O. 1981. Responses to different quantum flux densities. In *Encyclopedia of Plant Physiology*, ed. P.S.N.O.L. Lange, C. B. Osmond, and H. Ziegler, 57–107. New York: Springer-Verlag.

Bloom, A. J., F. S. Chapin, III, and H. A. Mooney. 1985. Resource limitation in plants: An economic analogy. *Annual Review of Ecology and Systematics* 16:363–92.

Blumenthal, D. M., N. R. Jordan, and M. P. Russelle. 2003. Soil carbon addition controls weeds and facilitates prairie restoration. *Ecological Applications* 13:605–15.

Bond, W. J., K. J. M. Dickinson, and A. F. Mark. 2004. What limits the spread of fire-dependent vegetation? Evidence from geographic variation of serotiny in a New Zealand shrub. *Global Ecology and Biogeography* 13:115–27.

Bond, W. J., W. G. Lee, and J. M. Craine. 2004. Gondwana's evolutionary legacy: Plants defended against large avian browsers. *Oikos* 104:500–508.

Bond, W. J., G. F. Midgley, and F. I. Woodward. 2003. The importance of low atmospheric CO_2 and fire in promoting the spread of grasslands and savannas. *Global Change Biology* 9:973–82.

Bormann, B. T., F. H. Bormann, W. B. Bowden, R. S. Pierce, S. P. Hamburg, D. Wang, M. C. Snyder, C. Y. Li, and R. C. Ingersoll. 1993. Rapid nitrogen-2 fixation in pines, alder and locust: Evidence from the Sandbox Ecosystem Study. *Ecology* 74:583–98.

Breman, H., and C. T. de Wit. 1983. Rangeland productivity and exploitation in the Sahel. *Science* 221:1341–47.

Briggs, J. M., A. K. Knapp, J. M. Blair, J. L. Heisler, G. A. Hoch, M. S. Lett, and J. K. McCarron. 2005. An ecosystem in transition: Causes and consequences of the conversion of mesic grassland to shrubland. *Bioscience* 55:243–54.

Brooks, R., and N. Owen-Smith. 1994. Plant defences against mammalian herbivores: Are juvenile Acacia more heavily defended than mature trees? *Bothalia* 24:211–15.

Brune, A., and M. Friedrich. 2000. Microecology of the termite gut: Structure and function on a microscale. *Current Opinion in Microbiology* 3:263–69.

Bryant, J. P., F. S. Chapin III, and D. R. Klein. 1983. Carbon/nutrient balance of boreal plants in relation to vertebrate herbivory. *Oikos* 40:357–68.

Burt-Smith, G. S., J. P. Grime, and D. Tilman. 2003. Seedling resistance to herbivory as a predictor of relative abundance in a synthesised prairie community. *Oikos* 101:345–53.

Cai, Z. Q., T. Rijkers, and F. Bongers. 2005. Photosynthetic acclimation to light changes in tropical monsoon forest woody species differing in adult stature. *Tree Physiology* 25:1023–31.

Callaway, R. M. 1992. Effects of shrubs on recruitment of *Quercus douglasii* and *Quercus lobata* in California. *Ecology* 73:2118–28.

Callaway, R. M., R. W. Brooker, P. Choler, Z. Kikvldze, C. J. Lortie, R. Michalet, L. Paolini, et al. 2002. Positive interactions among alpine plants increase with stress. *Nature* 417:844–48.

Canham, C. D., A. R. Berkowitz, V. R. Kelly, G. M. Lovett, S. V. Ollinger, and J. Schnurr. 1996. Biomass allocation and multiple resource limitation in tree seedlings. *Canadian Journal of Forest Research-Revue Canadienne De Recherche Forestiere* 26:1521–30.

Canham, C. D., K. D. Coates, P. Bartemucci, and S. Quaglia. 1999. Measurement and modeling of spatially explicit variation in light transmission through interior cedar-hemlock forests of British Columbia. *Canadian Journal of Forest Research* 29:1775–83.

Cannell, M. G. R. 1989. Physiological basis of wood production. *Scandinavian Journal of Forest Research* 4:459–90.

Cargill, S. M., and R. L. Jefferies. 1984. The effects of grazing by lesser snow geese on the vegetation of a sub-Arctic salt-marsh. *Journal of Applied Ecology* 21:669–86.

Carson, W. P., and R. B. Root. 2000. Herbivory and plant species coexistence: Community regulation by an outbreaking phytophagous insect. *Ecological Monographs* 70:73–99.

Case, T. J., and M. E. Gilpin. 1974. Interference competition and niche theory. *Proceedings of the National Academy of Sciences of the United States of America* 71:3073–77.

Castro-Diez, P., J. P. Puyravaud, J. H. C. Cornelissen, and P. Villar-Salvador. 1998. Stem anatomy and relative growth rate in seedlings of a wide range of woody plant species and types. *Oecologia* 116:57–66.

Chapin, F. 1988. Ecological aspects of plant mineral nutrition. *Advances in Plant Nutrition* 3:161–91.

Chapin, F. S. 1974. Phosphate absorption capacity and acclimation potential in plants along a latitudinal gradient. *Science* 183:521–23.

———. 1979. Soil temperature and nutrient cycling in the tussock growth form of *Eriophorum vaginatum*. *Journal of Ecology* 67:169–89.

Chapin, F. S., R. J. Barsdate, and D. Barel. 1978. Phosphorus cycling in Alaskan coastal tundra: Hypothesis for the regulation of nutrient cycling. *Oikos* 31:189–99.

Chapin, F. S., P. A. Matson, and H. A. Mooney. 2002. *Principles of Terrestrial Ecosystem Ecology*. New York: Springer-Verlag.

Chapin, F. S., III. 1980. The mineral nutrition of wild plants. *Annual Review of Ecology and Systematics* 11:233–60.

———. 1989. The cost of tundra plant structures: Evaluation of concepts and currencies. *American Naturalist* 133:1–19.

———. 1991. Integrated responses of plants to stress. *Bioscience* 41:29–36.

Chapin, F. S., III, K. Autumn, and F. Pugnaire. 1993. Evolution of suites of traits in response to environmental stress. *American Naturalist* 142:S78–92.

Chapin, F. S., III, J. Follett, and K. F. O'Connor. 1982. Growth, phosphate absorption, and phosphorus chemical fractions in two *Chionochloa* species. *Journal of Ecology* 70:305–21.

Chapin, F. S. III, and S. J. McNaughton. 1989. Lack of compensatory growth under phosphorus deficiency in grazing adapted grasses from the Serengeti plains. *Oecologia* 79:551–57.

Chapin, F. S., III, and L. Moilanen. 1991. Nutritional controls over nitrogen and phosphorus resorption from Alaskan birch leaves. *Ecology* 72:709–15.

Chapin, F. S., III, L. Moilanen, and K. Kielland. 1993. Preferential use of organic nitrogen for growth by a non-mycorrhizal arctic sedge. *Nature* 361:150–53.

Chapin, F. S., III, E.-D. Schulze, and H. A. Mooney. 1990. The ecology and economics of storage in plants. *Annual Review of Ecology and Systematics* 21:423–48.

Chapin, F. S., III, G. R. Shaver, A. E. Giblin, K. J. Nadelhoffer, and J. A. Laundre. 1995. Response of arctic tundra to experimental and observed changes in climate. *Ecology* 76:694–711.

Chapin, F. S., III, G. R. Shaver, and R. A. Kedrowski. 1986. Environmental controls over carbon, nitrogen, and phosphorus chemical fractions in *Eriophorum vaginatum* L. in Alaskan tussock tundra. *Journal of Ecology* 74:167–95.

Chapin, F. S., III, P. M. Vitousek, and K. Van Cleve. 1986. The nature of nutrient limitation in plant communities. *American Naturalist* 127:48–58.

Chazdon, R. L., and R. W. Pearcy. 1991. The importance of sunflecks for forest understory plants: Photosynthetic machinery appears adapted to brief, unpredictable periods of radiation. *Bioscience* 41:760–66.

Choler, P., R. Michalet, and R. M. Callaway. 2001. Facilitation and competition on gradients in alpine plant communities. *Ecology* 82:3295–308.

Clarholm, M. 1981. Protozoan grazing of bacteria in soil: Impact and importance. *Microbial Ecology* 7:343–50.

Clark, D. B., and D. A. Clark. 1991. The impact of physical damage on canopy tree regeneration in tropical rain-forest. *Journal of Ecology* 79:447–57.

Clarkson, D. T. 1965. Calcium-uptake by calcicole and calcifuge species in the genus *Agrostis*-L. *Journal of Ecology* 53:427–35.

Clissold, F. J., G. D. Sanson, and J. Read. 2006. The paradoxical effects of nutrient ratios and supply rates on an outbreaking insect herbivore, the Australian plague locust. *Journal of Animal Ecology* 75:1000–1013.

Coley, P. D. 1983. Herbivory and defensive characteristics of tree species in a lowland tropical forest. *Ecological Monographs* 53:209–33.

———. 1986. Costs and benefits of defense by tannins in a neotropical tree. *Oecologia* 70:238–41.

———. 1987. Interspecific variation in plant anti-herbivore properties: The role of habitat quality and rate of disturbance. *New Phytologist* 106:251–63.

Coley, P. D., and J. A. Barone. 1996. Herbivory and plant defenses in tropical forests. *Annual Review in Ecology and Systematics* 27: 305–35.

Coley, P. D., J. Lokvam, K. Rudolph, K. Bromberg, T. E. Sackett, L. Wright, T. Brenes-Arguedas, et al. 2005. Divergent defensive strategies of young leaves in two species of Inga. *Ecology* 86:2633–43.

Comas, L. H., and D. M. Eissenstat. 2004. Linking fine root traits to maximum potential growth rate among 11 mature temperate tree species. *Functional Ecology* 18:388–97.

Connell, J. H. 1980. Diversity and the coevolution of competitors, or the ghost of competition past. *Oikos* 35:131–38.

Cook, G. D. 1994. The fate of nutrients during fires in a tropical savanna. *Australian Journal of Ecology* 19:359–65.

Coomes, D. A., and P. J. Grubb. 2000. Impacts of root competition in forests and woodlands: A theoretical framework and review of experiments. *Ecological Monographs* 70:171–207.

Cordero, R. A. 1999. Ecophysiology of *Cecropia schreberiana* saplings in two wind regimes in an elfin cloud forest: Growth, gas exchange, architecture and stem biomechanics. *Tree Physiology* 19:153–63.

Cowles, H. C. 1898. The ecological relations of the vegetation on the sand dunes of Lake Michigan. *Botanical Gazette* 27:361–91.

Craine, J. M. 2005. Reconciling plant strategy theories of Grime and Tilman. *Journal of Ecology* 93:1041–52.

———. 2006. Competition for nutrients and optimal root allocation. *Plant and Soil* 285:171–85.

Craine, J. M., D. M. Berin, P. B. Reich, D. G. Tilman, and J. M. H. Knops. 1999. Measurement of leaf longevity of 14 species of grasses and forbs using a novel approach. *New Phytologist* 142:475–81.

Craine, J., W. Bond, W. Lee, P. Reich, and S. Ollinger. 2003. The resource economics of chemical and structural defenses across nitrogen supply gradients. *Oecologia* 137:547–56.

Craine, J. M., J. Fargione, and S. Sugita. 2005. Supply pre-emption, not concentration reduction, is the mechanism of competition for nutrients. *New Phytologist* 166:933–40.

Craine, J. M., J. Froehle, D. G. Tilman, D. A. Wedin, and F. S. Chapin III. 2001. The relationships among root and leaf traits of 76 grassland species and relative abundance along fertility and disturbance gradients. *Oikos* 93:274–85.

Craine, J. M., W. G. Lee, W. J. Bond, R. J. Williams, and L. C. Johnson. 2005. Environmental constraints on a global relationship among leaf and root traits. *Ecology* 86:12–19.

Craine, J. M., W. G. Lee, and S. Walker. 2006. The context of plant invasions in New Zealand: Evolutionary history and novel niches. In *Biological Invasions in New Zealand,* ed. R. B. Allen and W. G. Lee. Heidelberg: Springer-Verlag.

Craine, J. M., and M. C. Mack. 1998. Nutrients in senesced leaves: Comment (and reply). *Ecology* 79:1818–20.

Craine, J. M., C. Morrow, and N. Fierer. 2007. Microbial nitrogen limitation increases decomposition. *Ecology* 88:2105–13.

Craine, J. M., C. Morrow, and W. D. Stock 2008. Nutrient concentration ratios and co-limitation of aboveground production by nitrogen and phosphorus in Kruger National Park, South Africa. *New Phytologist* 179:829–36.

Craine, J. M., and P. B. Reich. 2001. Elevated CO_2 and nitrogen supply alter leaf longevity of grassland species. *New Phytologist* 150:397–493.

———. 2005. Leaf-level light compensation points are lower in shade-tolerant woody seedlings: Evidence from a synthesis of 115 species. *New Phytologist* 166:710–13.

Craine, J. M., D. G. Tilman, D. A. Wedin, P. B. Reich, M. J. Tjoelker, and J. M. H. Knops. 2002. Functional traits, productivity and effects on nitrogen cycling of 33 grassland species. *Functional Ecology* 16:563–74.

Craine, J. M., D. A. Wedin, F. S. Chapin III, and P. B. Reich. 2003. Development of grassland root systems and their effects on ecosystem properties. *Plant and Soil* 250:39–47.

Cresswell, J. E., S. Z. Merritt, and M. M. Martin. 1992. The effect of dietary nicotine on the allocation of assimilated food to energy-metabolism and growth in 4th-instar larvae of the southern armyworm, Spodoptera-Eridania (Lepidoptera, Noctuidae). *Oecologia* 89:449–53.

Cruz, P. 1997. Growth and nitrogen nutrition of a *Dichanthium aristatum* pasture under shading. *Tropical Grasslands* 30:407–13.

Cunningham, S. A., B. Summerhayes, and M. Westoby. 1999. Evolutionary divergences in leaf structure and chemistry, comparing rainfall and soil nutrient gradients. *Ecological Monographs* 69:569–88.

Dalling, J. W., and S. P. Hubbell. 2002. Seed size, growth rate and gap microsite conditions as determinants of recruitment success for pioneer species. *Journal of Ecology* 90:557–68.

Dearing, M. D., W. J. Foley, and S. McLean. 2005. The influence of plant secondary metabolites on the nutritional ecology of herbivorous terrestrial vertebrates. *Annual Review of Ecology, Evolution and Systematics* 36:169–89.

Dearing, M. D., A. M. Mangione, and W. H. Karasov. 2000. Diet breadth of mammalian herbivores: Nutrient versus detoxification constraints. *Oecologia* 123:397–405.

———. 2002. Ingestion of plant secondary compounds causes diuresis in desert herbivores. *Oecologia* 130:576–84.

Dearing, M. D., J. Sorensen, A. M. Mangione, and W. H. Karasov. 1999. Detoxification differences of specialist and generalist herbivores. *American Zoologist* 39:31A–32A.

del-Val, E., and M. J. Crawley. 2005. What limits herb biomass in grasslands: Competition or herbivory? *Oecologia* 142:202–11.

Deluca, T. H., D. R. Keeney, and G. W. McCarty. 1992. Effect of freeze-thaw events on mineralization of soil-nitrogen. *Biology and Fertility of Soils* 14:116–20.

DeLucia, E. H., K. Nelson, T. C. Vogelmann, and W. K. Smith. 1996. Contribution of intercellular reflectance to photosynthesis in shade leaves. *Plant Cell and Environment* 19:159–70.

Demment, M. L., and P. J. Van Soest. 1985. A nutritional explanation for body-size patterns of ruminant and non-ruminant herbivores. *American Naturalist* 125:641–75.

Diaz, S., A. J. Symstad, F. S. Chapin III, D. A. Wardle, and L. F. Huenneke. 2003. Functional diversity revealed by removal experiments. *Trends in Ecology & Evolution* 18:140–46.

Dominguezbello, M. G., M. Lovera, P. Saurez, and F. Michelangeli. 1993. Microbial digestive symbionts of the crop of the hoatzin (*Opisthocomus-hoazin*): An avian foregut fermenter. *Physiological Zoology* 66:374–83.

Dubrovsky, J. G., G. B. North, and P. S. Nobel. 1998. Root growth, developmental changes in the apex, and hydraulic conductivity for *Opuntia ficus-indica* during drought. *New Phytologist* 138:75–82.

Dunham, R. J., and P. H. Nye. 1973. Influence of soil-water content on uptake of ions by roots. 1. Soil-water content gradients near a plane of onion roots. *Journal of Applied Ecology* 10:585–98.

Dybzinski, R., and D. Tilman. 2007. Resource use patterns predict long-term outcomes of plant competition for nutrients and light. *American Naturalist* 170:305–18.

Ehleringer, J., O. Bjorkman, and H. A. Mooney. 1976. Leaf pubescence: Effects on absorptance and photosynthesis in a desert shrub. *Science* 192:376–77.

Ellsworth, D. S., and P. B. Reich. 1992. Leaf mass per area, nitrogen-content and photosynthetic carbon gain in acer-saccharum seedlings in contrasting forest light environments. *Functional Ecology* 6:423–35.

Elser, J. J., M. E. S. Bracken, E. E. Cleland, D. S. Gruner, W. S. Harpole, H. Hillebrand, J. T. Ngai, E. W. Seabloom, J. B. Shurin, and J. E. Smith. 2007. Global analysis of nitrogen and phosphorus limitation of primary producers in freshwater, marine and terrestrial ecosystems. *Ecology Letters* 10:1135–42.

Emery, S. M. 2007. Limiting similarity between invaders and dominant species in herbaceous plant communities? *Journal of Ecology* 95:1027–35.

Epstein, E. 1999. Silicon. *Annual Review Plant Physiology and Plant Molecular Biology* 50:641–64.

Evans, J. R. 1989. Photosynthesis and nitrogen relationships in leaves of C3 plants.

Ewers, F. W. 1982. Secondary growth in needle leaves of *Pinus-longaeva* (bristlecone pine) and other conifers: Quantitative data. *American Journal of Botany* 69:1552–59.

Fahey, T. J., J. J. Battles, and G. F. Wilson. 1998. Responses of early successional northern hardwood forests to changes in nutrient availability. *Ecological Monographs* 68:183–212.

Falster, D. S., and M. Westoby. 2005. Tradeoffs between height growth rate, stem persistence and maximum height among plant species in a post-fire succession. *Oikos* 111:57–66.

Fargione, J., and D. Tilman. 2006. Plant species traits and capacity for resource reduction predict yield and abundance under competition in nitrogen-limited grassland. *Functional Ecology* 20:533–40.

Farley, R. A., and A. H. Fitter. 1999. Temporal and spatial variation in soil resources in a deciduous woodland. *Journal of Ecology* 87:688–96.

Fine, P. V. A., I. Mesones, and P. D. Coley. 2004. Herbivores promote habitat specialization by trees in Amazonian forests. *Science* 305:663–65.

Fonseca, C. R., J. M. Overton, B. Collins, and M. Westoby. 2000. Shifts in trait-combinations along rainfall and phosphorus gradients. *Journal of Ecology* 88:964–77.

Fraser, L. H., and J. P. Grime. 1999. Interacting effects of herbivory and fertility on a synthesized plant community. *Journal of Ecology* 87:514–25.

Fritz, H., and P. Duncan. 1994. On the carrying capacity for large ungulates of African savanna ecosystems. *Proceedings of the Royal Society of London, Series B, Biological Sciences* 256:77–82.

Gali-Muhtasib, H. U., C. C. Smith, and J. J. Higgins. 1992. The effect of silica in grasses on the feeding behavior of the prairie vole, *Microtus ochrogaster*. *Ecology* 73:1724–29.Garten, C. 1976. Correlations between concentrations of elements in plants. *Nature* 261:686–88.

Gholz, H. L., D. A. Wedin, S. M. Smitherman, M. E. Harmon, and W. J. Parton. 2000. Long-term dynamics of pine and hardwood litter in contrasting environments: Toward a global model of decomposition. *Global Change Biology* 6:751–65.

Gilbert, G. S. 2002. Evolutionary ecology of plant diseases in natural ecosystems. *Annual Review of Phytopathology* 40:13–43.

Gill, R. A., H. W. Polley, H. B. Johnson, L. J. Anderson, H. Maherali, and R. B. Jackson. 2002. Nonlinear grassland responses to past and future atmospheric CO_2. *Nature* 417:279–82.

Gillman, L. N., J. Ogden, S. D. Wright, K. L. Stewart, and D. P. Walsh. 2004. The influence of macro-litterfall and forest structure on litterfall damage to seedlings. *Austral Ecology* 29:305–12.

Givnish, T. J. 1988. Adaptation to sun and shade: A whole plant perspective. Australian *Journal of Plant Physiology* 15:63–92.

Gleadow, R. M., and I. E. Woodrow. 2000. Temporal and spatial variation in cyanogenic glycosides in *Eucalyptus cladocalyx*. *Tree Physiology* 20:591–98.

———. 2002. Constraints on effectiveness of cyanogenic glycosides in herbivore defense. *Journal of Chemical Ecology* 28:1301–13.

Gleeson, S. K., and D. Tilman. 1990. Allocation and the transient dynamics of succession on poor soils. *Ecology* 71:1144–55.

———. 1992. Plant allocation and the multiple limitation hypothesis. *American Naturalist* 139:1322–43.

———. 1994. Plant allocation, growth rate and successional status. *Functional Ecology* 8:543–50.

Goldberg, D. E., R. Turkington, L. Olsvig-Whittaker, and A. R. Dyer. 2001. Density dependence in an annual plant community: Variation among life history stages. *Ecological Monographs* 71:423–46.

Gomez, J. M., and R. Zamora. 2002. Thorns as induced mechanical defense in a long-lived shrub (*Hormathophylla spinosa*, Cruciferae). *Ecology* 83:885–90.

Grant, C. C., and M. C. Scholes. 2006. The importance of nutrient hot-spots in the conservation and management of large wild mammalian herbivores in semi-arid savannas. *Biological Conservation* 130:426–37.

Grant, P., and J. Weiner. 1999. *Ecology and Evolution of Darwin's Finches*. Princeton, NJ: Princeton University Press.

Green, E. S., A. R. Zangerl, and M. R. Berenbaum. 2001. Effects of phytic acid and xanthotoxin on growth and detoxification in caterpillars. *Journal of Chemical Ecology* 27:1763–73.

Grime, J. P. 1963. Factors determining the occurrence of calcifuge species on shallow soils over calcareous substrata. *Journal of Ecology* 51:375–90.

———. 1965. Shade tolerance in flowering plants. *Nature* 208:161–63.

———. 1973. Competitive exclusion in herbaceous vegetation. *Nature* 242:344–47.

———. 1977. Evidence for the existence of three primary strategies in plants and its relevance to ecological and evolutionary theory. *American Naturalist* 111:1169–94.

———. 1979. *Plant Strategies and Vegetation Processes*. Chichester, UK: John Wiley and Sons.

———. 1993. Ecology sans frontières. *Oikos* 68:385–92.

———. 2001. *Plant Strategies, Vegetation Processes, and Ecosystem Properties*, 2nd ed. Chichester, UK: John Wiley and Sons.

———. 2007. Plant strategy theories: A comment on Craine (2005). *Journal of Ecology* 95:227–30.

Grime, J. P., and A. V. Curtis. 1976. Interaction of drought and mineral nutrient stress in calcareous grassland. *Journal of Ecology* 64:975–88.

Grime, J. P., and R. Hunt. 1975. Relative growth-rate: Its range and adaptive significance in a local flora. *Journal of Ecology* 63:393–422.

Grime, J. P., S. F. MacPherson-Stewart, and R. S. Dearman. 1968. An investigation of leaf palatability using snail *Cepaea nemoralis* L. *Journal of Ecology* 56:405–20.

Grime, J. P., K. Thompson, R. Hunt, J. G. Hodgson, J. H. C. Cornelissen, I. H. Rorison, G. A. F. Hendry, et al. 1997. Integrated screening validates primary axes of specialisation in plants. *Oikos* 79:259–81.

Grubb, P. J. 1992. A positive distrust in simplicity: lessons from plant defences and from competition among plants and among animals. *Journal of Ecology* 80:585–610.

———. 1994. Root competition in soils of different fertility: A paradox resolved. *Phytocoenologia* 24:495–505.

———. 1998. A reassessment of the strategies of plants which cope with shortages of resources. *Perspectives in Plant Ecology Evolution and Systematics* 1:3–31.

Guo, Q. F., and J. H. Brown. 1996. Temporal fluctuations and experimental effects in desert plant communities. *Oecologia* 107:568–77.

Güsewell, S. 2004. N : P ratios in terrestrial plants: Variation and functional significance. *New Phytologist* 164:243–66.

Güsewell, S., U. Bollens, P. Ryser, and F. Klotzli. 2003. Contrasting effects of nitrogen, phosphorus and water regime on first- and second-year growth of 16 wetland plant species. *Functional Ecology* 17:754–65.

Hacke, U. G., J. S. Sperry, W. T. Pockman, S. D. Davis, and K. A. McCulloch. 2001. Trends in wood density and structure are linked to prevention of xylem implosion by negative pressure. *Oecologia* 126:457–61.

Hacke, U. G., J. S. Sperry, J. K. Wheeler, and L. Castro. 2006. Scaling of angiosperm xylem structure with safety and efficiency. *Tree Physiology* 26:689–701.

Hagerman, A. E., C. T. Robbins, Y. Weerasuriva, T. C. Wilson, and C. McArthur. 1992. Tannin chemistry in relation to digestion. *Journal of Range Management* 45:57–62.

Halitschke, R., and I. T. Baldwin. 2003. Antisense LOX expression increases herbivore performance by decreasing defense responses and inhibiting growth-related transcriptional reorganization in *Nicotiana attenuata*. *Plant Journal* 36:794–807.

Halkier, B. A., and J. Gershenzon. 2006. Biology and biochemistry of glucosinolates. *Annual Review of Plant Biology* 57:303–33.

Hamilton, J. G., A. R. Zangerl, E. H. DeLucia, and M. R. Berenbaum. 2001. The carbon-nutrient balance hypothesis: Its rise and fall. *Ecology Letters* 4:86–95.

Han, W. X., J. Y. Fang, D. L. Guo, and Y. Zhang. 2005. Leaf nitrogen and phosphorus stoichiometry across 753 terrestrial plant species in China. *New Phytologist* 168:377–85.

Harborne, J. B. 2001. Twenty-five years of chemical ecology. *Natural Product Reports* 18:361–79.

Harrington, R. A., J. H. Fownes, and P. M. Vitousek. 2001. Production and re-source use efficiencies in N- and P-limited tropical forests: A comparison of responses to long-term fertilization. *Ecosystems* 4:646–57.

Hilborn, R., T. A. Branch, B. Ernst, A. Magnusson, C. V. Minte-Vera, M. D. Scheuerell, and J. L. Valero. 2003. State of the world's fisheries. *Annual Review of Environment and Resources* 28:359–99.

Hilborn, R., and M. Mangel. 1997. *The Ecological Detective: Confronting Models with Data.* Princeton, NJ: Princeton University Press.

Hobbie, S. E. 1992. Effects of plant species on nutrient cycling. *Trends in Ecology & Evolution* 7:336–39.

———. 1996. Temperature and plant species control over litter decomposition in Alaskan tundra. *Ecological Monographs* 66:503–22.

Hobbs, N. T., D. S. Schimel, C. E. Owensby, and D. S. Ojima. 1991. Fire and grazing in the tallgrass prairie: Contingent effects on nitrogen budgets. *Ecology* 72:1374–82.

Hodge, A. 2003. Plant nitrogen capture from organic matter as affected by spatial dispersion, interspecific competition and mycorrhizal colonization. *New Phytologist* 157:303–14.

Hodge, A., C. D. Campbell, and A. H. Fitter. 2001. An arbuscular mycorrhizal fungus accelerates decomposition and acquires nitrogen directly from organic material. *Nature* 413:297–99.

Hodge, A., D. Robinson, B. S. Griffiths, and A. H. Fitter. 1999a. Nitrogen capture by plants grown in N-rich organic patches of contrasting size and strength. *Journal of Experimental Botany* 50:1243–52.

———. 1999b. Why plants bother: Root proliferation results in increased nitrogen capture from an organic patch when two grasses compete. *Plant, Cell and Environment* 22:811–20.

Hodson, M. J., P. J. White, A. Mead, and M. R. Broadley. 2005. Phylogenetic variation in the silicon composition of plants. *Annals of Botany* 96:1027–46.

Hooper, D. U., and L. Johnson. 1999. Nitrogen limitation in dryland ecosystems: Responses to geographical and temporal variation in precipitation. *Biogeochemistry* 46:247–93.

Horn, H. S. 1971. *The Adaptive Geometry of Trees.* Princeton, NJ: Princeton University Press.

Howe, H. F., J. S. Brown, and B. Zorn-Arnold. 2002. A rodent plague on prairie diversity. *Ecology Letters* 5:30–36.

Hunter, J. C., and M. G. Barbour. 2001. Through-growth of Douglas-fir: A model of rapid forest change without canopy gaps. *Journal of Vegetation Science* 12:445–52.

Huston, M. A., and D. L. Deangelis. 1994. Competition and coexistence: The effects of resource transport and supply rates. *American Naturalist* 144: 954–77.

Huxman, T. E., E. P. Hamerlynck, B. D. Moore, S. D. Smith, D. N. Jordan, S. F. Zitzer, R. S. Nowak, J. S. Coleman, and J. R. Seemann. 1998. Photosynthetic down-regulation in *Larrea tridentata* exposed to elevated atmospheric CO_2: Interaction with drought under glasshouse and field (FACE) exposure. *Plant Cell and Environment* 21:1153–61.

Iwasa, Y., and T. Kubo. 1997. Optimal size of storage for recovery after unpredictable disturbances. *Evolutionary Ecology* 11:41–65.

Joern, A., and S. T. Behmer. 1997. Importance of dietary nitrogen and carbohydrates to survival, growth, and reproduction in adults of the grasshopper *Ageneotettix deorum* (Orthoptera: Acrididae). *Oecologia* 112:201–8.

Johnston, A. E. 1994. The Rothamsted classical experiments. In *Long-Term Experiments in Agricultural and Ecological Sciences*, ed. R. A. Leigh and A. E. Johnston, 9–37. Wallingford: CAB International.

Johnston, T. J., J. W. Pendleton, D. B. Peters, and D. R. Hicks. 1969. Influence of supplemental light on apparent photosynthesis, yield, and yield components of soybeans. *Crop Science* 9:577–81.

Kabeya, D., and S. Sakai. 2005. The relative importance of carbohydrate and nitrogen for the resprouting ability of *Quercus crispula* seedlings. *Annals of Botany* 96:47–88.

Kaelke, C. M., E. L. Kruger, and P. B. Reich. 2001. Trade-offs in seedling survival, growth, and physiology among hardwood species of contrasting successional status along a light-availability gradient. *Canadian Journal of Forest Research* 31:1602–16.

Kembel, S. W., and J. F. Cahill. 2005. Plant phenotypic plasticity belowground: A phylogenetic perspective on root foraging trade-offs. *American Naturalist* 166:216–30.

Kessler, A., and I. T. Baldwin. 2002. Plant responses to insect herbivory: The emerging molecular analysis. *Annual Review of Plant Biology* 53:299–328.

Killingbeck, K. T. 1996. Nutrients in senesced leaves: Keys to the search for potential resorption and resorption proficiency. *Ecology* 77:1716–27.

Killingbeck, K. T., and W. G. Whitford. 1996. High foliar nitrogen in desert shrubs: An important ecosystem trait or defective desert doctrine? *Ecology* 77:1728–37.

King, D. A. 1994. Influence of light level on the growth and morphology of saplings in a Panamanian forest. *American Journal of Botany* 81:948–57.

Kitajima, K. 1994. Relative importance of photosynthetic traits and allocation patterns as correlates of seedling shade tolerance of 13 tropical trees. *Oecologia* 98:419–28.

Kitajima, K., and B. M. Bolker. 2003. Testing performance rank reversals among coexisting species: Crossover point irradiance analysis by Sack & Grubb (2001) and alternatives. *Functional Ecology* 17:276–81.

Kitajima, K., S. S. Mulkey, M. Samaniego, and S. J. Wright. 2002. Decline of photosynthetic capacity with leaf age and position in two tropical pioneer tree species. *American Journal of Botany* 89:1925–32.

Klak, C., G. Reeves, and T. Hedderson. 2004. Unmatched tempo of evolution in Southern African semi-desert ice plants. *Nature* 427:63–65.

Knops, J. M. H., W. D. Koenig, and T. H. I. Nash. 1997. On the relationship between nutrient use efficiency and fertility in forest ecosystems. *Oecologia* 110:550–56.

Knops, J. M. H., M. E. Ritchie, and D. Tilman. 2000. Selective herbivory on a nitrogen fixing legume (*Lathyrus venosus*) influences productivity and ecosystem nitrogen pools in an oak savanna. *Ecoscience* 7:166–174.

Kobe, R. K., C. A. Lepczyk, and M. Iyer. 2005. Resorption efficiency decreases with increasing green leaf nutrients in a global data set. *Ecology* 86:2780–92.

Koerselman, W., and A. F. M. Meuleman. 1996. The vegetation N:P ratio: A new tool to detect the nature of nutrient limitation. *Journal of Applied Ecology* 33:1441–50.

Kraus, T. E. C., R. A. Dahlgren, and R. J. Zasoski. 2003. Tannins in nutrient dynamics of forest ecosystems: A review. *Plant and Soil* 256:41–66.

Kraus, T. E. C., R. J. Zasoski, and R. A. Dahlgren. 2004. Fertility and pH effects on polyphenol and condensed tannin concentrations in foliage and roots. *Plant and Soil* 262:95–109.

Krause, G. H., and E. Weis. 1991. Chlorophyll fluorescence and photosynthesis: The basics. *Annual Review of Plant Physiology and Plant Molecular Biology* 42:313–49.

Kronzucker, H. J., M. Y. Siddiqi, A. D. M. Glass, and D. T. Britto. 2003. Root ammonium transport efficiency as a determinant in forest colonization patterns: An hypothesis. *Physiologia Plantarum* 117:164–70.

Kruckeberg, A. R. 1954. The ecology of serpentine soils. 3. Plant species in relation to serpentine soils. *Ecology* 35:267–74.

Kursar, T. A., and P. D. Coley. 1999. Contrasting modes of light acclimation in two species of the rainforest understory. *Oecologia* 121:489–98.

———. 2003. Convergence in defense syndromes of young leaves in tropical rainforests. *Biochemical Systematics and Ecology* 31:929–49.

Lacointe, A., E. Deleens, T. Ameglio, B. Saint-Joanis, C. Lelarge, M. Vandame, G. C. Song, and F. A. Daudet. 2004. Testing the branch autonomy theory: A C-13/C-14 double-labelling experiment on differentially shaded branches. *Plant Cell and Environment* 27:1159–68.

Lambers, H., F. S. Chapin, and T. L. Pons. 1998. *Plant Physiological Ecology.* New York: Springer-Verlag.

Lambers, H., and H. Poorter. 1992. Inherent variation in growth-rate between higher-plants: A search for physiological causes and ecological consequences. *Advances in Ecological Research* 23:187–261.

Lambrecht, S., and T. Dawson. 2007. Correlated variation of floral and leaf traits along a moisture availability gradient. *Oecologia* 151:574–83.

Leadley, P. W., J. F. Reynolds, and F. S. Chapin III. 1997. A model of nitrogen uptake by *Eriophorum vaginatum* roots in the field: Ecological implications. *Ecological Monographs* 67:1–22.

Lee, D. W., J. B. Lowry, and B. C. Stone. 1979. Abaxial anthocyanin layer in leaves of tropical rain-forest plants: Enhancer of light capture in deep shade. *Biotropica* 11:70–77.

Lee, E. J., and T. Booth. 2003. Macronutrient input from pollen in two regenerating pine stands in southeast Korea. *Ecological Research* 18:423–30.

Lee, W. G., M. Fenner, A. Loughnan, and K. M. Lloyd. 2000. Long-term effects of defoliation: Incomplete recovery of a New Zealand alpine tussock grass, *Chionochloa pallens*, after 20 years. *Journal of Applied Ecology* 37:348–55.

Lessmann, J. M., H. Brix, V. Bauer, O. A. Clevering, and F. A. Comin. 2001. Effect of climatic gradients on the photosynthetic responses of four *Phragmites australis* populations. *Aquatic Botany* 69:109–26.

Levin, D. A. 1976. Chemical defenses of plants to pathogens and herbivores. *Annual Review of Ecology and Systematics* 7:121–59.

Liang, Y., and J. M. Harris. 2005. Response of root branching to abscisic acid is correlated with nodule formation both in legumes and nonlegumes. *American Journal of Botany* 92:1675–83.

Liang, Y. C., J. Si, and V. Romheld. 2005. Silicon uptake and transport is an active process in *Cucumis sativus*. *New Phytologist* 167:797–804.

Liebig, J. 1843. Chemistry in its application to agriculture and physiology, London.

Lovelock, C. E., M. Jebb, and C. B. Osmond. 1994. Photoinhibition and recovery in tropical plant-species: Response to disturbance. *Oecologia* 97:297–307.

Lucas, P. W., I. M. Turner, N. J. Dominy, and N. Yamashita. 2000. Mechanical defences to herbivory. *Annals of Botany* 86:913–20.

Ludlow, M. M., and O. Bjorkman. 1984. Paraheliotropic leaf movement in siratro as a protective mechanism against drought-induced damage to primary photosynthetic reactions: Damage by excessive light and heat. *Planta* 161:505–18.

Lunt, O. R., J. Letey, and S. B. Clark. 1973. Oxygen requirements for root growth in 3 species of desert shrubs. *Ecology* 54:1356–62.

MacArthur, R. H., and E. O. Wilson. 1967. *The Theory of Island Biogeography*. Princeton, NJ: Princeton University Press.

Macgillivray, C. W., J. P. Grime, S. R. Band, R. E. Booth, B. Campbell, G. A. F. Hendry, S. H. Hillier, et al. 1995. Testing predictions of the resistance and resilience of vegetation subjected to extreme events. *Functional Ecology* 9:640–49.

Mahmoud, A., and J. P. Grime. 1976. Analysis of competitive ability in 3 perennial grasses. *New Phytologist* 77:431–35.

Marks, P. L., and C. L. Mohler. 1985. Succession after elimination of buried seeds from a recently plowed field. *Bulletin of the Torrey Botanical Club* 112:376–82.

Marschner, H. 1986. *Mineral Nutrition of Higher Plants*. New York: Academic Press.

Mauseth, J. D. 1993. Water-storing and cavitation-preventing adaptations in wood of cacti. *Annals of Botany* 72:81–89.

———. 1995. Collapsible water-storage cells in cacti. *Bulletin of the Torrey Botanical Club* 122:145–51.

Maxwell, K., and G. N. Johnson. 2000. Chlorophyll fluorescence: A practical guide. *Journal of Experimental Botany* 51:659–68.

McCosh, F. W. J. 1975. Boussingault versus Ville: The social, political, and scientific aspects of their disputes. *Annals of Science* 32:475–90.

McKane, R. B., D. F. Grigal, and M. P. Russelle. 1990. Spatiotemporal differences in nitrogen-15 uptake and the organization of an old-field plant community. *Ecology* 71:1126–32.

McManus, W. R., V. N. E. Robinson, and L. L. Grout. 1977. Physical distribution of mineral material on forage plant-cell walls. *Australian Journal of Agricultural Research* 28:651–62.

McNaughton, S. J., M. Oesterheld, D. A. Frank, and K. J. Williams. 1989. Ecosystem-level patterns of primary productivity and herbivory in terrestrial habitats. *Nature* 341:142–44.

McNaughton, S. J., J. L. Tarrants, M. M. McNaughton, and R. D. Davis. 1985. Silica as a defense against herbivory and a growth promotor in African grasses. *Ecology* 66:528–35.

Midgley, J. J. 2003. Is bigger better in plants? The hydraulic costs of increasing size in trees. *Trends in Ecology & Evolution* 18:5–6.

Millard, P. 1988. The accumulation and storage of nitrogen by herbaceous plants. *Plant Cell and Environment* 11:1–8.

Miller, A. J., and M. D. Cramer. 2005. Root nitrogen acquisition and assimilation. *Plant and Soil* 274:1–36.

Mills, J. N. 1986. Herbivores and early postfire succession in Southern-California chaparral. *Ecology* 67:1637–49.

Mitchell, C. E. 2003. Trophic control of grassland production and biomass by pathogens. *Ecology Letters* 6:147–55.

Mitchell, D. T., P. G. F. Coley, S. Webb, and N. Allsopp. 1986. Litterfall and decomposition Processes in the coastal fynbos vegetation, Southwestern Cape, South-Africa. *Journal of Ecology* 74:977–93.

Mohammed, G. H., and W. C. Parker. 1999. Photosynthetic acclimation in eastern hemlock [*Tsuga canadensis* (L.) Carr.] seedlings following transfer of shade-grown seedlings to high light. *Trees—Structure and Function* 13:117–24.

Moles, A., M. Gruber, and S. Bonser. 2008. A new framework for predicting invasive plant species. *Journal of Ecology* 96:13–17.

Moles, A. T., D. D. Ackerly, C. O. Webb, J. C. Tweddle, J. B. Dickie, and M. Westoby. 2005. A brief history of seed size. *Science* 307:576–80.

Monod, J. 1950. La technique de culture continue: Théorie et applications. *Annales Institut Pasteur* 79:390–410.

Monson, R. K., T. N. Rosenstiel, T. A. Forbis, D. A. Lipson, and C. H. Jaeger. 2006. Nitrogen and carbon storage in alpine plants. *Integrative and Comparative Biology* 46:35–48.

Muller-Landau, H. C. 2004. Interspecific and inter-site variation in wood specific gravity of tropical trees. *Biotropica* 36:20–32.

Nambiar, E. K. S. 1987. Do nutrients retranslocate from fine roots? Iufro (International Union of Forestry Research Organization) Working Party Meeting on Roots in Forest Soils: Biology and Symbioses, Victoria, British Columbia, Canada, August 4–8, 1986. *Canadian Journal of Forestry Research* 17:913–18.

Naumburg, E., and D. S. Ellsworth. 2000. Photosynthetic sunfleck utilization potential of understory saplings growing under elevated CO_2 in FACE. *Oecologia* 122:163–74.

Niinemets, U. 2001. Global-scale climatic controls of leaf dry mass per area, density, and thickness in tress and shrubs. *Ecology* 82:453–69.

———. 2006. The controversy over traits conferring shade-tolerance in trees: Ontogenetic changes revisited. *Journal of Ecology* 94:464–70.

Niinemets, U., and J. D. Tenhunen. 1997. A model separating leaf structural and physiological effects on carbon gain along light gradients for the shade-tolerant species *Acer saccharum. Plant Cell and Environment* 20:845–66.

Nobel, P. S. 1991. Achievable productivities of certain CAM plants: Basis for high values compared with C3 and C4 plants. *New Phytologist* 119:183–205.

Nobel, P. S. 1999. *Physicochemical and Environmental Plant Physiology*. New York: Academic Press.

Nordin, A., and T. Nasholm. 1997. Nitrogen storage forms in nine boreal understorey plant species. *Oecologia* 110:487–92.

Noret, N., P. Meerts, M. Vanhaelen, A. Dos Santos, and J. Escarre. 2007. Do metal-rich plants deter herbivores? A field test of the defence hypothesis. *Oecologia* 152:92–100.

Noy-Meir, I. 1973. Desert ecosystems: Environment and producers. *Annual Review of Ecology and Systematics* 4:25–51.

Nutman, P. S. 1987. Centenary Lecture. *Philosophical Transactions of the Royal Society of London, Series B, Biological Sciences* 317:69.

Ohnmeiss, T. E., and I. T. Baldwin. 1994. The allometry of nitrogen allocation to growth and an inducible defense under nitrogen-limited growth. *Ecology* 75:995–1002.

Olofsson, J. 2006. Short- and long-term effects of changes in reindeer grazing pressure on tundra heath vegetation. *Journal of Ecology* 94:431–40.

Orians, C. M., M. M. I. van Vuuren, N. L. Harris, B. A. Babst, and G. S. Ellmore. 2004. Differential sectoriality in long-distance transport in temperate tree species: evidence from dye flow, N-15 transport, and vessel element pitting. *Trees—Structure and Function* 18:501–9.

Pacheco, M. A., M. A. Garcia-Amado, C. Bosque, and M. G. Dominguez-Bello. 2004. Bacteria in the crop of the seed-eating Green-rumped Parrotlet. *Condor* 106:139–43.

Parker, K. G. 1957. "Water-belly" (urolithiasis) in range steers in relation to some characteristics of rangeland. *Journal of Range Management* 10:105–11.

Pastor. 1984. Aboveground production and N and P cycling along a nitrogen mineralization gradient on Blackhawk Island, Wisconsin. *Ecology* 65:256–68.

Pauw, A., S. A. Van Bael, H. A. Peters, S. D. Allison, J. L. C. Camargo, M. Cifuentes-Jara, A. Conserva, et al. 2004. Physical damage in relation to carbon allocation strategies of tropical forest tree saplings. *Biotropica* 36:410–13.

Pearce, R. S. 2001. Plant freezing and damage. *Annals of Botany* 87:417–24.

Pearcy, R. W. 1990. Sunflecks and photosynthesis in plant canopies. *Annual Review of Plant Physiology and Plant Molecular Biology* 41:421–53.

Pearcy, R. W., F. Valladares, S. J. Wright, and E. L. de Paulis. 2004. A functional analysis of the crown architecture of tropical forest *Psychotria* species: Do species vary in light capture efficiency and consequently in carbon gain and growth? *Oecologia* 139:163–77.

Peat, H., and A. Fitter. 2008. *Ecological Flora of the British Isles*. http://www.york.ac.uk/res/ecoflora/cfm/ecofl/index.cfm (accessed March 1, 2008).

Peters, H. A., A. Pauw, M. R. Silman, and J. W. Terborgh. 2004. Failing palm fronds structure Amazonian rainforest sapling communities. *Proceedings of the Royal Society of London, Series B, Biological Sciences* 271:S367–69.

Polley, H. W., H. B. Johnson, B. D. Marino, and H. S. Mayeux. 1993. Increase in C3 plant water-use efficiency and biomass over glacial to present CO_2 concentrations. *Nature* 361:61–64.

Polley, H. W., H. B. Johnson, H. S. Mayeux, and S. R. Malone. 1993. Physiology and growth of wheat across a subambient carbon-dioxide gradient. *Annals of Botany* 71:347–56.

Poorter, H. 1989. Interspecific variation in relative growth rate: on ecological causes and physiological consequences. In *Causes and Consequences of Variation in Growth Rate and Productivity of Higher Plants*, ed. H. Lambers, M. L. Cambridge, H. Konigs, and T. L. Pons, 45–68. The Hague: SPB Academic Publishing.

———. 1994. Construction costs and payback time of biomass: A whole plant perspective. In *A Whole-Plant Perspective on Carbon-Nitrogen Interactions*, ed. J. Roy and E. Garnier, 111–27. The Hague: SPB Academic Publishing.

Poorter, H., A. Vanderwerf, O. K. Atkin, and H. Lambers. 1991. Respiratory energy-requirements of roots vary with the potential growth-rate of a plant-species. *Physiologia Plantarum* 83:469–75.

Poorter, L. 1999. Growth responses of 15 rain-forest tree species to a light gradient: The relative importance of morphological and physiological traits. *Functional Ecology* 13:396–410.

Poorter, L., M. V. de Plassche, S. Willems, and R. G. A. Boot. 2004. Leaf traits and herbivory rates of tropical tree species differing in successional status. *Plant Biology* 6:746–54.

Pregitzer, K. S., R. L. Hendrick, and R. T. Fogel. 1993. The demography of fine roots in response to patches of water and nitrogen. *New Phytologist* 125:575–80.

Pringle, E. G., P. Alvarez-Loayza, and J. Terborgh. 2007. Seed characteristics and susceptibility to pathogen attack in tree seeds of the Peruvian Amazon. *Plant Ecology* 193:211–22.

Putz, F. E., and C. D. Canham. 1992. Mechanisms of arrested succession in shrublands: Root and shoot competition between shrubs and tree seedlings. *Forest Ecology and Management* 49:267–75.

Quammen, D. 2006. *The Reluctant Mr. Darwin: An Intimate Portrait of Charles Darwin and the Making of His Theory of Evolution*. New York: W. W. Norton.

Raaimakers, D., and H. Lambers. 1996. Response to phosphorus supply of tropical tree seedlings: A comparison between a pioneer species *Tapirira obtusa* and a climax species *Lecythis corrugata*. *New Phytologist* 132:97–102.

Rastetter, E. B., and G. R. Shaver. 1992. A model of multiple-element limitation for acclimating vegetation. *Ecology* 73:1157–74.

Raubenheimer, D., and S. J. Simpson. 2004. Organismal stoichiometry: Quantifying non-independence among food components. *Ecology* 85:1203–16.

Raven, J. A. 2003. Cycling silicon: The role of accumulation in plants. *New Phytologist* 158:419–21.

Raynaud, X., and P. W. Leadley. 2004. Soil characteristics play a key role in modeling nutrient competition in plant communities. *Ecology* 85:2200–14.

Read, D. J. 1991. Mycorrhizas in ecosystems. *Experientia* 47:376–91.

Rebele, F. 2000. Competition and coexistence of rhizomatous perennial plants along a nutrient gradient. *Plant Ecology* 147:77–94.

Reed, J. D. 1995. Nutritional toxicology of tannins and related polyphenols in forage legumes. *Journal of Animal Science* 73:1516–28.

Reich, P., I. Wright, J. Cavender-Bares, J. Craine, J. Oleksyn, M. Westoby, and M. Walters. 2003. The evolution of plant functional variation: Traits, spectra, and strategies. *International Journal of Plant Sciences* 164:S143–64.

Reich, P. B. 2000. Do tall trees scale physiological heights? *Trends in Ecology & Evolution* 15:41–42.

Reich, P. B., C. Buschena, M. G. Tjoelker, K. Wrage, J. Knops, D. Tilman, and J. L. Machado. 2003. Variation in growth rate and ecophysiology among 34 grassland and savanna species under contrasting N supply: A test of functional group differences. *New Phytologist* 157:617–31.

Reich, P. B., D. S. Ellsworth, M. B. Walters, J. M. Vose, C. Gresham, J. C. Volin, and W. D. Bowman. 1999. Generality of leaf trait relationships: A test across six biomes. *Ecology* 80:1955–69.

Reynolds, H. L., and S. W. Pacala. 1993. An analytical treatment of root-to-shoot ratio and plant competition for soil nutrient and light. *American Naturalist* 141:51–70.

Reynolds, J. F., P. R. Kemp, K. Ogle, and R. J. Fernandez. 2004. Modifying the "pulse-reserve" paradigm for deserts of North America: Precipitation pulses, soil water, and plant responses. *Oecologia* 141:194–210.

Reynolds, J. F., R. A. Virginia, P. R. Kemp, A. G. de Soyza, and D. C. Tremmel. 1999. Impact of drought on desert shrubs: Effects of seasonality and degree of resource island development. *Ecological Monographs* 69:69–106.

Richardson, D. M., P. A. Williams, and R. J. Hobbs. 1994. Pine invasions in the southern-hemisphere: Determinants of spread and invadability. *Journal of Biogeography* 21:511–27.

Ritchie, M. E., and D. Tilman. 1995. Responses of legumes to herbivores and nutrients during succession on a nitrogen-poor soil. *Ecology* 76:2648–55.

Robbins, C. T., A. E. Hagerman, P. J. Austin, C. McArthur, and T. A. Hanley. 1991. Variation in mammalian physiological responses to a condensed tannin and its ecological implications. *Journal of Mammalogy* 72:480–86.Robertson, G. P., and K. L. Gross. 1994. Assessing the heterogeneity of belowground resources: Quantifying pattern and scale. In *Plant Exploitation of Environmental Heterogeneity*, ed. M.M. Caldwell and R. Pearcy, 237–53. New York: Academic Press.

Robinson, D., A. Hodge, B. S. Griffiths, and A. H. Fitter. 1999. Plant root proliferation in nitrogen-rich patches confers competitive advantage. *Proceedings of the Royal Society of London, Series B, Biological Sciences* 266:431–35.

Robinson, N., R. J. Harper, and K. R. J. Smettem. 2006. Soil water depletion by *Eucalyptus* spp. integrated into dryland agricultural systems. *Plant and Soil* 286:141–51.

Roda, A. L., and I. T. Baldwin. 2003. Molecular technology reveals how the induced direct defenses of plants work. *Basic and Applied Ecology* 4:15–26.

Rogers, R. W., and H. T. Clifford. 1993. The taxonomic and evolutionary significance of leaf longevity. *New Phytologist* 123:811–21.

Rose, S., and L. Poorter. 2003. The importance of seed mass for early regeneration in tropical forest: a review. In *Long-term changes in composition and diversity: case studies from the Guiana Shield, Africa, Borneo, and Melanesia*, ed. H. Ter Steege, 19–35. Wageningen, The Netherlands: Tropenbos Foundation.

Rosenthal, G. A. 1977. Biological effects and mode of action of L-canavanine, a structural analog of L-arginine. *Quarterly Review of Biology* 52:155–78.

Rothstein, D. E., and D. R. Zak. 2001. Photosynthetic adaptation and acclimation to exploit seasonal periods of direct irradiance in three temperate, deciduous-forest herbs. *Functional Ecology* 15:722–31.

Ruess, R. R., R. L. Hendrick, and J. P. Bryant. 1998. Regulation of fine root dynamics by mammalian browsers in early successional Alaskan taiga forests. *Ecology* 79:2706–20.

Ruimy, A., P. G. Jarvis, D. D. Baldocchi, and B. Saugier. 1997. CO_2 fluxes over plant canopies and solar radiation. *Advances in Ecological Research* 26:1–63.

Runyon, J., R. H. Waring, S. N. Goward, and J. M. Welles. 1994. Environmental limits on net primary production and light-use efficiency across the Oregon transect. *Ecological Applications* 4:226–37.

Ryan, M. G., R. M. Hubbard, S. Pongracic, R. J. Raison, and R. E. McMurtrie. 1996. Foliage, fine-root, woody-tissue and stand respiration in *Pinus radiata* in relation to nitrogen status. *Tree Physiology* 16:333–43.

Ryser, P., and L. Eek. 2000. Consequences of phenotypic plasticity vs. interspecific differences in leaf and root traits for acquisition of aboveground and be-lowground resources. *American Journal of Botany* 87:402–11.

Ryser, R., and S. Wahl. 2001. Interspecific variation in RGR and the underlying traits among 24 grass species grown in full daylight. *Plant Biology* 3:426–36.

Sack, L., and P. J. Grubb. 2001. Why do species of woody seedlings change rank in relative growth rate between low and high irradiance? *Functional Ecology* 15:145–54.

———. 2003. Crossovers in seedling relative growth rates between low and high irradiance: Analyses and ecological potential (reply to Kitajima & Bolker 2003). *Functional Ecology* 17:281–87.

Sage, R. F. 2004. The evolution of C-4 photosynthesis. *New Phytologist* 161: 341–70.

Sala, O. E., R. A. Golluscio, W. K. Lauenroth, and A. Soriano. 1989. Resource partitioning between shrubs and grasses in the Patagonian steppe. *Oecologia* 81:501–5.

Sameshima, R. 1996. Analysis and modeling of dry matter production rate by soybean community: Curvilinear response to radiation intensity. *Journal of Agricultural Meteorology* 52:99–106.

Sammul, M., K. Kull, L. Oksanen, and P. Veromann. 2000. Competition intensity and its importance: Results of field experiments with *Anthoxanthum odoratum*. *Oecologia* 125:18–25.

Sanson, G. 2006. The biomechanics of browsing and grazing. *American Journal of Botany* 93:1531–45.

Scanlon, B. R., D. G. Levitt, R. C. Reedy, K. E. Keese, and M. J. Sully. 2005. Ecological controls on water-cycle response to climate variability in deserts. *Proceedings of the National Academy of Sciences of the United States of America* 102:6033–38.

Schimel, J. P., and J. Bennett. 2004. Nitrogen mineralization: Challenges of a changing paradigm. *Ecology* 85:591–602.

Schoettle, A. W. 1990. The interaction between leaf longevity and shoot growth and foliar biomass per shoot in *Pinus-contorta* at two elevations. *Tree Physiology* 7:209–14.

Schulze, E. D., M. M. Caldwell, J. Canadell, H. A. Mooney, R. B. Jackson, D. Parson, R. Scholes, O. E. Sala, and P. Trimborn. 1998. Downward flux of water through roots (ie inverse hydraulic lift) in dry Kalahari sands. *Oecologia* 115:460–62.

Seyfried, M. S., S. Schwinning, M. A. Walvoord, W. T. Pockman, B. D. Newman, R. B. Jackson, and E. M. Phillips. 2005. Ecohydrological control of deep drainage in arid and semiarid regions. *Ecology* 86:277–87.

Shane, M. W., K. W. Dixon, and H. Lambers. 2005. The occurrence of dauciform roots amongst Western Australian reeds, rushes and sedges, and the impact of phosphorus supply on dauciform-root development in *Schoenus unispiculatus* (Cyperaceae). *New Phytologist* 165:887–98.

Shane, M. W., and H. Lambers. 2005. Cluster roots: A curiosity in context. *Plant and Soil* 274:101–25.

———. 2006. Systemic suppression of cluster-root formation and net P-uptake rates in *Grevillea crithmifolia* at elevated P supply: A proteacean with resistance for developing symptoms of "P toxicity." *Journal of Experimental Botany* 57:413–23.

Shane, M. W., C. Szota, and H. Lambers. 2004. A root trait accounting for the extreme phosphorus sensitivity of *Hakea prostrata* (Proteaceae). *Plant Cell and Environment* 27:991–1004.

Shipley, B., M. J. Lechoweicz, I. Wright, and P. B. Reich. 2006. Fundamental trade-offs generating the worldwide leaf economics spectrum. *Ecology* 87: 535–41.

Shipley, B., and R. H. Peters. 1990. A test of the tilman model of plant strategies: Relative growth-rate and biomass partitioning. *American Naturalist* 136: 139–53.

Sinclair, T. R., and W. I. Park. 1993. Inadequacy of the Liebig limiting-factor paradigm for explaining varying crop yields. *Agronomy Journal* 85:742–46.

Sinsabaugh, R. L., M. E. Gallo, C. Lauber, M. P. Waldrop, and D. R. Zak. 2005. Extracellular enzyme activities and soil organic matter dynamics for northern hardwood forests receiving simulated nitrogen deposition. *Biogeochemistry* 75:201–15.

Sinsabaugh, R. L., and D. L. Moorhead. 1994. Resource-allocation to extracellular enzyme-production: A model for nitrogen and phosphorus control of litter decomposition. *Soil Biology & Biochemistry* 26:1305–11.

Smethurst, P. J., and N. B. Comerford. 1993. Simulating nutrient uptake by single or competing and contrasting root systems. *Soil Science Society of America Journal* 57:1361–67.

Smith, C. K., A. D. Munson, and M. R. Coyea. 1998. Nitrogen and phosphorus release from humus and mineral soil under black spruce forests in central Quebec. *Soil Biology & Biochemistry* 30:1491–500.

Smith, M. D., J. C. Wilcox, T. Kelly, and A. K. Knapp. 2004. Dominance not richness determines invasibility of tallgrass prairie. *Oikos* 106:253–62.

Smith, S. D., T. E. Huxman, S. F. Zitzer, T. N. Charlet, D. C. Housman, J. S. Coleman, L. K. Fenstermaker, J. R. Seemann, and R. S. Nowak. 2000. Elevated CO_2 increases productivity and invasive species success in an arid ecosystem. *Nature* 408:79–82.

Soltis, D. E., and P. S. Soltis. 2003. The role of phylogenetics in comparative genetics. *Plant Physiology* 132:1790–800.

Sperry, J. S., and U. G. Hacke. 2002. Desert shrub water relations with respect to soil characteristics and plant functional type. *Functional Ecology* 16:367–78.

Sperry, J. S., U. G. Hacke, and J. K. Wheeler. 2005. Comparative analysis of end wall resistivity in xylem conduits. *Plant Cell and Environment* 28:456–65.

Sperry, J. S., N. Z. Saliendra, W. T. Pockman, H. Cochard, P. Cruiziat, S. D. Davis, F. W. Ewers, and M. T. Tyree. 1996. New evidence for large negative xylem pressures and their measurement by the pressure chamber method. *Plant Cell and Environment* 19:427–36.

Sperry, J. S., V. Stiller, and U. G. Hacke. 2002. Soil water uptake and water transport through root systems. In *Plant Roots: The Hidden Half*, ed. Y. Waisel, A. Eshel, and U. Kafkafi, 663–82. New York: Marcel Dekker.

———. 2003. Xylem hydraulics and the soil-plant-atmosphere continuum: Opportunities and unresolved issues. *Agronomy Journal* 95:1362–70.

Sprent, J. I. 2007. Evolving ideas of legume evolution and diversity: A taxonomic perspective on the occurrence of nodulation. *New Phytologist* 174:11–25.

Sprugel, D. G., T. M. Hinckley, and W. Schaap. 1991. The theory and practice of branch autonomy. *Annual Review of Ecology and Systematics* 22:309–34.

Stamp, N. 2003. Theory of plant defensive level: Example of process and pitfalls in development of ecological theory. *Oikos* 102:672–78.

Stephenson, N. L. 1990. Climatic control of vegetation distribution: The role of the water balance. *American Naturalist* 135:649–70.

Sterner, R. W., and J. Elser. 2002. *Ecological Stoichiometry*. Princeton, NJ: Princeton University Press.

Suding, K. N., J. R. Larson, E. Thorsos, H. Steltzer, and W. D. Bowman. 2004. Species effects on resource supply rates: Do they influence competitive interactions? *Plant Ecology* 175:47–58.

Tessier, J. T., and D. J. Raynal. 2003. Use of nitrogen to phosphorus ratios in plant tissue as an indicator of nutrient limitation and nitrogen saturation. *Journal of Applied Ecology* 40:523–34.

Thomas, S. C., and F. A. Bazzaz. 1999. Asymptotic height as a predictor of photosynthetic characteristics in Malaysian rain forest trees. *Ecology* 80:1607–22.

Thompson, K. 1987. The resource ratio hypothesis and the meaning of competition. *Functional Ecology* 1:297–303.

Thorne, R. F. 1992. Classification and geography of the flowering plants. *Botanical Review* 58:225–348.

Tilman, D. 1977. Resource competition between planktonic algae: Experimental and theoretical approach. *Ecology* 58:338–48.

———. 1982. *Resource Competition and Community Structure*. Princeton, NJ: Princeton University Press.

Tilman, D. 1985. The resource-ratio hypothesis of plant succession. *American Naturalist* 125:827–52.

———. 1986. Nitrogen-limited growth in plants from different successional stages. *Ecology* 67:555–63.

———. 1987a. On the meaning of competition and the mechanisms of competitive superiority. *Functional Ecology* 1:304–15.

———. 1987b. Secondary succession and the pattern of plant dominance along experimental nitrogen gradients. *Ecological Monographs* 57:189–214.

———. 1988. *Plant Strategies and the Dynamics and Function of Plant Communities*. Princeton, NJ: Princeton University Press.

———. 1990. Mechanisms of plant competition for nutrients: The elements of a predictive theory of competition. In *Perspectives on Plant Competition*, ed. J. B. Grace and D. Tilman, 484–00? New York: Academic Press.

———. 1991. Relative growth-rates and plant allocation patterns. *American Naturalist* 138:1269–75.

———. 2006. Resource competition and plant traits: A response to Craine et al. 2005. *Journal of Ecology* 95:231–34.

Tilman, D., and M. L. Cowan. 1989. Growth of old field herbs on a nitrogen gradient. *Functional Ecology* 3:425–38.

Tilman, D., and D. Wedin. 1991. Dynamics of nitrogen competition between successional grasses. *Ecology* 72:1038–49.

Ting, I. P. 1985. Crassulacean acid metabolism. *Annual Review of Plant Physiology and Plant Molecular Biology* 36:595–622.

Tinker, P. B., and P. H. Nye. 2000. *Solute Movement in the Rhizosphere*. Oxford: Oxford University Press.

Titman, D. 1976. Ecological competition between algae: Experimental confirmation of resource-based competition theory. *Science* 192:463–65.

Tjoelker, M. G., J. M. Craine, D. Wedin, P. B. Reich, and D. Tilman. 2005. Linking leaf and root trait syndromes among 39 grassland and savannah species. *New Phytologist* 167:493–508.

Turner, I. M. 1994. Sclerophylly: Primarily protective. *Functional Ecology* 8: 669–75.

Tuskan, G. A., S. DiFazio, S. Jansson, J. Bohlmann, I. Grigoriev, U. Hellsten, N. Putnam, et al. 2006. The genome of black cottonwood, *Populus trichocarpa* (Torr. & Gray). *Science* 313:1596–604.

Tyree, M. T., S. D. Davis, and H. Cochard. 1994. Biophysical perspectives of xylem evolution: Is there a tradeoff of hydraulic efficiency for vulnerability to dysfunction. *IAWA Journal* 15:335–60.

van der Ploeg, R. R., W. Bohm, and M. B. Kirkham. 1999. On the origin of the theory of mineral nutrition of plants and the law of the minimum. *Soil Science Society of America Journal* 63:1055–62.

Van Soest, P. J. 1982. *Nutritional Ecology of the Ruminant*. Corvallis, OR: O & B Books.

van Wijk, M. T., and W. Bouten. 2001. Towards understanding tree root profiles: Simulating hydrologically optimal strategies for root distribution. *Hydrology and Earth System Sciences* 5:629–44.

Van Zandt, P. A. 2007. Plant defense, growth, and habitat: A comparative assessment of constitutive and induced resistance. *Ecology* 88:1984–93.

Vedel, H. 1961. Natural regeneration in *Juniper*. *Proceedings of the Botanical Society of the British Isles* 4:146–48.

Veneklaas, E. J., and L. Poorter. 1998. Growth and carbon partitioning of tropical tree seedlings in contrasting light environments. In *Inherent Variation in Plant Growth: Physiological Mechanisms and Ecological Consequences*, ed. H. Lambers, H. Poorter, and M.M.I. Van Vuuren, 337–62. Leiden: Backhuys.

Vesk, P. A., and M. Westoby. 2004. Funding the bud bank: A review of the costs of buds. *Oikos* 106:200–208.

Violle, C., M.-L. Navas, D. Vile, E. Kazakou, C. Fortunel, I. Hummel, and E. Garnier. 2007. Let the concept of trait be functional! *Oikos* 116:882–92.

Vitousek, P. 2004. *Nutrient Cycling and Limitation*. Princeton, NJ: Princeton University Press.

Wahl, S., and P. Ryser. 2000. Root tissue structure is linked to ecological strategies of grasses. *New Phytologist* 148:459–71.

Waldrop, M. P., D. R. Zak, and R. L. Sinsabaugh. 2004. Microbial community response to nitrogen deposition in northern forest ecosystems. *Soil Biology & Biochemistry* 36:1443–51.

Walters, M. B., and P. B. Reich. 1999. Low-light carbon balance and shade tolerance in the seedlings of woody plants: Do winter deciduous and broad-leaved evergreen species differ? *New Phytologist* 143:143–54.

———. 2000. Seed size, nitrogen supply, and growth rate affect tree seedling survival in deep shade. *Ecology* 81:1887–901.

Ward, J. K., J. M. Harris, T. E. Cerling, A. Wiedenhoeft, M. J. Lott, M. D. Dearing, J. B. Coltrain, and J. R. Ehleringer. 2005. Carbon starvation in glacial trees recovered from the La Brea tar pits, Southern California. *Proceedings of the National Academy of Sciences of the United States of America* 102:690–94.

Warming, E. 1909. *The Oecology of Plants*. Oxford: Clarendon Press.

Warren, C. R., and M. A. Adams. 2004. Evergreen trees do not maximize instantaneous photosynthesis. *Trends in Plant Science* 9:270–74.

Wassen, M. J., H. Veterink, and E. Deswart. 1995. Nutrient concentrations in mire vegetation as a measure of nutrient limitation in mire ecosystems. *Journal of Vegetation Science* 6:5–16.

Weaver, J. E., and F. Clements. 1938. *Plant Ecology*, 2nd ed. New York: McGraw-Hill.

Wedin, D. A., and D. Tilman. 1990. Species effects on nitrogen cycling: A test with perennial grasses. *Oecologia* 84:433–41.

———. 1993. Competition among grasses along a nitrogen gradient: Initial conditions and mechanisms of competition. *Ecological Monographs* 63:199–229.

———. 1996. Influence of nitrogen loading and species composition on the carbon balance of grasslands. *Science* 274:1720–23.

Weintraub, M. N., and J. P. Schimel. 2005. The seasonal dynamics of amino acids and other nutrients in Alaskan Arctic tundra soils. *Biogeochemistry* 73:359–80.

Welden, C. W., and W. L. Slauson. 1986. The intensity of competition versus its importance: An overlooked distinction and some implications. *Quarterly Review of Biology* 61:23–44.

West, N. E. 1981. Nutrient cycling in desert ecosystems. In *Arid-Land Ecosystems: Structure, Functioning and Management*, ed. D. W. Goodall and R. A. Piercy, 301–24. Cambridge: Cambridge University Press.

Wheeler, J. K., J. S. Sperry, U. G. Hacke, and N. Hoang. 2005. Inter-vessel pitting and cavitation in woody Rosaceae and other vesselled plants: A basis for a safety versus efficiency trade-off in xylem transport. *Plant Cell and Environment* 28:800–812.

White, T. C. R. 1993. *The Inadequate Environment.* New York: Springer-Verlag.

Whittaker, R. H. 1975. *Communities and Ecosystems.* New York: Macmillan.

Williams, P. A. 1977. Growth, biomass, and net productivity of tall-tussock (*Chionochloa*) grasslands, Canterbury, New Zealand. *New Zealand Journal of Botany* 15:399–442.

Williams, R. J., B. A. Myers, W. J. Muller, G. A. Duff, and D. Eamus. 1997. Leaf phenology of woody species in a North Australian tropical savanna. *Ecology* 78:2542–58.

Willis, K. J., and J. C. McElwain. 2002. *The Evolution of Plants.* Oxford: Oxford University Press.

Wilson, P. J., K.E.N. Thompson, and J. G. Hodgson. 1999. Specific leaf area and leaf dry matter content as alternative predictors of plant strategies. *New Phytologist* 143:155–62.

Wilson, S. D., and D. Tilman. 1993. Plant competition and resource availability in response to disturbance and fertilization. *Ecology* 74:599–611.

Wilson, S. L., and G.I.H. Kerley. 2003. The effect of plant spinescence on the foraging efficiency of bushbuck and boergoats: Browsers of similar body size. *Journal of Arid Environments* 55:150–58.

Withington, J. M., P. B. Reich, J. Oleksyn, and D. M. Eissenstat. 2006. Comparisons of structure and life span in roots and leaves among temperate trees. *Ecological Monographs* 76:381–97.

Wright, I. J., D. S. Falster, M. Pickup, and M. Westoby. 2006. Cross-species patterns in the coordination between leaf and stem traits, and their implications for plant hydraulics. *Physiologia Plantarum* 127:445–56.

Wright, I. J., P. B. Reich, J.H.C. Cornelissen, D. S. Falster, P. K. Groom, K. Hikosaka, W. Lee, et al. 2005. Modulation of leaf economic traits and trait relationships by climate. *Global Ecology and Biogeography* 14:411–21.

Wright, I. J., P. B. Reich, and M. Westoby. 2001. Strategy shifts in leaf physiology, structure and nutrient content between species of high- and low-rainfall and high- and low-nutrient habitats. *Functional Ecology* 15:423–34.

Wright, I. J., P. B. Reich, M. Westoby, D. D. Ackerly, Z. Baruch, F. Bongers, J. Cavender-Bares, et al. 2004. The worldwide leaf economics spectrum. *Nature* 428:821–27.

Yang, Y. L., and A. Joern. 1994. Compensatory feeding in response to variable food quality by *Melanoplus-differentialis. Physiological Entomology* 19:75–82.

Zalucki, M. P., L. P. Brower, and A. Alonso. 2001. Detrimental effects of latex and cardiac glycosides on survival and growth of first-instar monarch butterfly larvae *Danaus plexippus* feeding on the sandhill milkweed *Asclepias humistrata*. *Ecological Entomology* 26:212–24.

Zimmermann, M. 1983. *Xylem Structure and the Ascent of Sap*. New York: Springer-Verlag.

Index

Milton Keynes UK
Ingram Content Group UK Ltd.
UKHW020643290824
447545UK00008B/240

9 780691 139128